GERMAN SECRET
WEAPONS
OF THE SECOND WORLD WAR

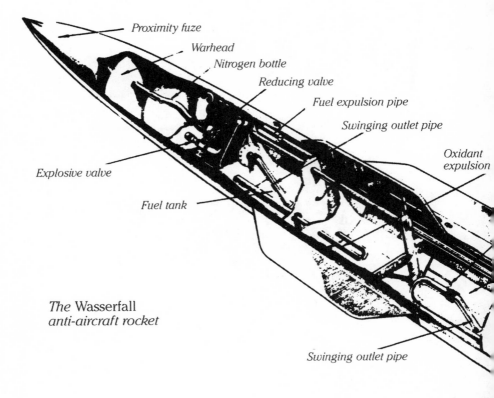

Proximity fuze

Warhead

Nitrogen bottle

Reducing valve

Fuel expulsion pipe

Swinging outlet pipe

Oxidant
expulsion

Explosive valve

Fuel tank

The Wasserfall
anti-aircraft rocket

Swinging outlet pipe

Radio recei

GERMAN SECRET WEAPONS
OF THE SECOND WORLD WAR

THE MISSILES, ROCKETS, WEAPONS AND NEW TECHNOLOGY OF THE THIRD REICH

IAN V. HOGG

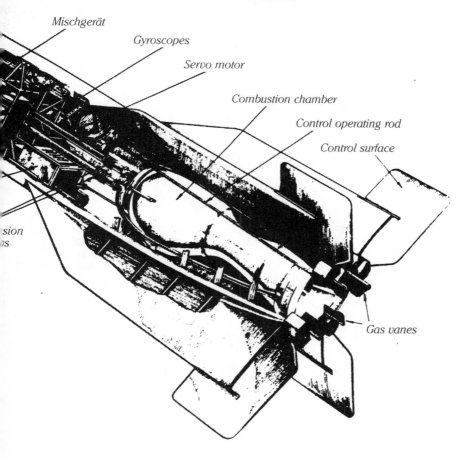

pe

xidant tank

Mischgerät

Gyroscopes

Servo motor

Combustion chamber

Control operating rod

Control surface

sion
s

Gas vanes

FALL RIVER PRESS

Fall River Press
122 Fifth Avenue
New York, NY 10011

ISBN-13: 978-1-4351-0444-0
ISBN-10: 1-4351-0444-7

Printed and bound in the United States of America

1 3 5 7 9 10 8 6 4 2

Contents

Photographs

Line drawings

Introduction

On 19 September 1939 Adolf Hitler visited Danzig, lately a free city, now incorporated into the German *Reich* as a result of the Polish campaign. In a speech to a rally of Nazi party members he said,

> 'Es könnte sehr schnell der Augenblick kommen, da wir eine Waffe zur Anwendung bringen in der wir nicht angegriffen werden können.'

Like so many of Hitler's utterances this can be interpreted in various ways; strictly, the literal translation runs,

> 'The moment might very quickly come for us to use a weapon with which we could not be attacked.'

Because of mis-hearing or mis-reporting this was widely quoted in the British press as a reference to some unknown, un-named, secret weapon about which Hitler was hinting in order to terrify his opponents. But no such weapon appeared, and within a year or so 'Hitler's Secret Weapon' became the subject of music-hall jokes. To the man in the street, or the soldier on the conscript recruit's basic training course, the term came to be applied to any military device of dubious worth or any soldier of more-than-average clumsiness; anything, in other words, which tended to hinder the smooth progress of the Allies and thus give aid and solace to the enemy.

Since the war Hitler's phrase has been mulled over and, in retrospect, applied to just about everything from the *Panzer* division to the nuclear bomb, and sometimes on the flimsiest of assumptions, liberally laced with 'perhaps', 'possibly' and 'it may be assumed'. What many of these interpretations overlook is that Adolf Hitler was addressing a Nazi Party rally; and in those circumstances he might be expected to draw the long bow, hint at greater things to come, and generally assume the air of omnipotence which political leaders of all shades tend to assume on the platform. And the faithful were expected to take the whole thing with a pinch of salt. After all, when Churchill said to Roosevelt, 'Give us the tools and we will finish the job', he did not literally mean that if America sent Britain a shipload of rifles the British would immediately dash off and defeat the entire German Army, and nor did anyone believe he meant that for a minute. It was stimulating rhetoric, no more and no less, and Hitler's speech deserves to be classed in the same category.

Nevertheless, even stimulating rhetoric needs some basis upon which to be built, and by September 1939 Hitler knew very well that his scientists and engineers were busy developing new weapons. He may not have known very much about their details, but he knew of their general intent and possibilities, and he doubtless felt that to suggest that, one day, the German nation might use weapons which the other side did not have was a fairly sound prophecy which was unlikely to rebound on him. But I think it unrealistic to assume, as has been done, that in this relatively throw-away line, Hitler was specifically referring to nuclear bombs, nerve gas, biological warfare or any other of the more exotic devices favoured by conspiracy theorists. He was much more likely to have been thinking about the 80cm *Gustav* railway gun, jet-propelled aircraft, various rocket projects and recoilless guns, all of which were then well advanced in their development, all of which were well within Hitler's technical comprehension, and none of which, to Germany's knowledge, were under development or suspected by the British or French.

Allied responses

However, on the British side of the North Sea there were, behind the scenes, people who listened to Hitler's words and, whilst still eyeing the salt-cellar, knew enough to realise that there might, just, be something behind them worth investigating. They, too, believed that such a statement implied that there was a foundation which, though possibly not earth-shaking, was at least worth closer study. In the course of the war they gradually accumulated knowledge of weapon projects within Germany which were obviously a serious threat to the Allies, and in many cases they were able to instigate action to counter these weapons. As they uncovered this information, piece by piece, it suggested a depth of scientific and engineering research which held promise of even more discoveries, and as the war began to draw to its close, both the British and American authorities made plans for a thorough investigation of every German research station, test ground, firing range, munitions factory and laboratory, so that all these potential secrets might be uncovered and investigated, possibly to the Allies' advantage in the continuation of the war against Japan, possibly for their commercial advantage in the post-war world.

As a result, there came into being a number of agencies charged with this investigation: the British Intelligence Objectives Sub-Committee (BIOS), which gradually became subsumed into the Combined Intelligence Objectives Sub-Committee (CIOS) and which were both prepared to investigate anything they came across; the Alsos Mission, specifically directed to investigate German nuclear research; Operation Paperclip, an American investigation of the German missile industry, primarily aimed at gathering up everything involved, from notebooks to research scientists, and shipping them back to the USA for interrogation and employment, before the British or French or Russians could do the same; and several other bodies of more-or-less official standing. As the Allied armies advanced in 1944 and 1945 so these various parties, frequently more concerned with keeping their activities secret from competing agencies than of uncovering German secrets, advanced close behind them.

What they uncovered proved to be startling in its breadth of subjects and depth of endeavour, since there were scores of weapon projects afoot in Germany of which the Allies had known nothing. The CIOS alone, for example, produced over 13,000 reports on its investigations; some were the results of careful analysis by Allied scientists and engineers, others were voluminous narratives of wartime research produced by simply taking the German most closely concerned with the project, sitting him down with a pencil and paper, and telling him 'Write down all you know about Project X and then you can go home.'

Some of what was uncovered forms the subject of the following pages; some of it is fairly well known, much of it less well-known. But perhaps the most important thing which the Allies discovered was that luck had been on their side; the potential for dangerous German weapons was enormous, but the practical effect was diminished by the chaotic administration and organisation which should have been directing it.

In Britain, and to a slightly lesser degree in the USA, there was usually one central agency overseeing each aspect of weapon technology, through which any proposal would be routed; in Britain it was the Ordnance Board in the case of conventional weapons, the Maud Committee for nuclear affairs, the Mechanization Board for tanks and vehicles and so forth. Gruesome tales are told, usually by disgruntled inventors, of the obstinacy and conservatism of these various bodies, particularly the Ordnance Board. Perhaps one of the best tales about the Ordnance Board, and one which well illustrates the opinion held of it by its detractors, comes from Victorian days. A member of the Board was asked why inventions were invariably turned down. He replied,

> 'If we only make one mistake out of every hundred decisions that we give, it will be acknowledged that we do remarkably well. Ninety-nine inventions out of every hundred submitted to the committee are worthless. We shall, therefore, do "remarkably well" if we condemn them all.'

Whether or not their reputations for obstruction were deserved, these various bodies had behind them an enormous bulk of expertise and experience, and they also held records, going back into the mid-19th century, of experiments and trials with every sort of weapon. When an inventor appeared with an idea for a new and powerful device, the Board could often produce the same idea which had been tested in the past, and ask the inventor how he proposed to improve upon it? Or they could refer to earlier

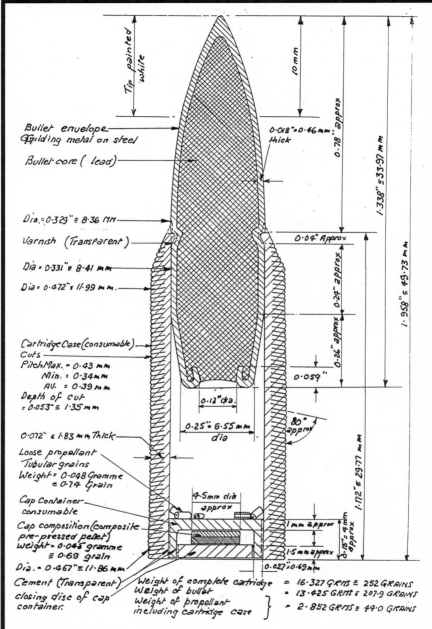

Bullet envelope.
Gilding metal on steel

Bullet core (lead)

Dia = 0.329" ≡ 8.36 MM

Varnish (Transparent)

Dia = 0.331" ≡ 8.41 mm

Dia = 0.472" ≡ 11.99 mm.

Cartridge Case (consumable)
Cuts
Pitch Max. = 0.43 mm
Min. = 0.34 mm
AV. = 0.39 mm
Depth of cut
= 0.053" ≡ 1.35 mm

0.072" ≡ 1.83 mm Thick

Loose propellant
Tubular grains
Weight = 0.048 Gramme
= 0.74 Grain

Cap Container
consumable

Cap composition (composite
pre-pressed pellet)
weight = 0.045 gramme
≡ 0.69 grain

Dia. = 0.467" ≡ 11.86 mm

Cement (Transparent)
closing disc of cap
container.

Tip pointed white

10 mm

0.018" = 0.46 mm. thick

0.78 approx

1.338" ≡ 33.97 mm

0.04" Approx

0.24" approx

0.26 approx

0.059"

0.12" dia.

0.25" = 6.55 mm
dia

80° approx

1.958" ≡ 49.73 mm

1.172" ≡ 29.77 mm

4.5 mm dia approx

1 mm approx

0.15" = 4 mm approx

1.5 mm approx

0.027" ≡ 0.69 mm

Weight of complete cartridge = 16.327 GRMS ≡ 252 GRAINS
Weight of bullet = 13.425 GRMS ≡ 207.9 GRAINS
Weight of propellant
including cartridge case } = 2.852 GRMS ≡ 44.0 GRAINS

Some German research was far ahead of its time; this remarkable drawing of a caseless cartridge – one using a solid block of propellant to support the bullet instead of a brass cartridge case – was discovered in 1945, but it was to be another 40 years before the idea was successfully incorporated into a practical weapon system.

experiments on similar devices and show that there was some fundamental flaw.

Where no such precedent existed, then the combined expertise of the various members would be used to assess the idea and pass it to the appropriate research establishment for comment and, if that was favourable, allow development to commence. But, except for relatively insignificant things like small arms, it was virtually impossible for any manufacturer, laboratory or design office to take upon itself the design and promotion of some major weapon unless it was sanctioned by the appropriate body. And it was a waste of time to write to your Member of Parliament or Congressman about your idea, since he would merely pass it to the authority you were trying to by-pass.

The German system

They did things differently in Germany. I quote from one of the CIOS reports:

> 'This device was made by a set of irresponsible inventors with no manufacturing connections. They would have been shut down but for their political connections.'

Or this, from an American report:

> 'Very definitely we believe that no other German proximity fuze is worth following up; there were more crackpot notions getting political support than we would have imagined.'

Or this, from the interrogation report of a senior German general

> 'The Army ordered a new anti-tank gun; the Air Force ordered an anti-aircraft gun; the Navy ordered a gun for attacking naval and air targets. All three branches worked entirely independently of one another, and generally in opposition to one another, and so it happened that orders for the same thing might come from three different sources. As every engineer has a different conception of the same thing, it came to pass that three different equipments were introduced where one might have done.'

There, in three nutshells, lies the clue to the failure of the German secret weapons programme. There was no central authority with the ability to assess ideas, reject bad ones, allocate research facilities to good ones, and organise production. Almost every field of activity could muster five or six authorities all competing to be the supreme arbiter in that particular branch of expertise. So, if an inventor failed to get a hearing from the first, he could try the second or third and continue to play one off against the other until he managed to get a foot into one door. Alternatively, if an inventor could interest a manufacturer, and if the manufacturer had the ear of a party official, then all the official bodies could be by-passed by a direct appeal to the *Führer* or to *Reichsmarschal* Goering or Himmler or some other similarly powerful figure. And even the most august figures were not averse to extending their empires, increasing their influence and thus binding themselves closer to Hitler. As an example of this, once Himmler discovered the existence of the V-2 rocket programme he never rested until he had the entire control of it in his own hands and his nominees in all the positions of responsibility.

Thus, instead of fastening on an idea and throwing the entire weight of the national effort behind it, weapon programmes were competing among themselves for priorities in materials, workmen, research facilities and production resources, with the result that similar weapons and devices were being pursued by different organisations, generally in complete ignorance of what anyone else was doing in the same field. Each group held tightly to its secrets, fearful that another group might steal the idea and get a better priority for it. A further complication was that different organisations had their own secrecy rules; a project being followed up a researcher politically bound to the SS, for example, would be kept secret from researchers working for the army or navy, and vice-versa.

On top of this organisational confusion, there was strategic confusion. In the summer of 1940 the war seemed to be progressing very well from the Nazi point of view, and Hitler decided that 'defensive' weapons were not necessary. He ordered that, unless a research programme could guarantee producing a service weapon within twelve months, it would not be allowed to continue. This decree took effect in 1941 and several promising lines of development were axed; perhaps the most important of these was in various aspects of radar research. Many scientists and research workers were drafted into the armed forces and irreplaceable research teams broken up.

When, in 1943, the Allied superiority in air weapons and electronics was beginning to make itself felt in increasingly heavy air raids on Germany, Hitler called a conference of scientists and engineers and decreed that Germany had to catch up; special commissions were set up to oversee crash programmes of research, the surviving scientists were recalled to their laboratories and money and materials were placed at their disposal. The one thing that could not be regained was time; the two years during which German radar technology had virtually stood still could never be recovered.

By late 1944 the situation was so bad that a *Führer* directive said,

> 'It is important to strengthen the firepower of the anti-aircraft defence in every conceivable way in order to make use of this psychological and tactical moment. I therefore command immediate increases in the anti-aircraft weapons and ammunition programme, although the notice

given is short. At the same time, all current development projects designed to increase the efficiency of guns and shells, and any other developments in anti-aircraft defence, are to be carried out energetically and with accelerated effort.'

It was this directive which accounted for the sudden rush of ground-to-air missile designs in 1944–45, most of which were begun too late to have any effect upon the war. It is easy to issue directives, less easy to design and produce effective weapons.

Author's note

The information presented in the following pages has been accumulated over a long period from a wide variety of sources. Much of it comes from CIOS and BIOS reports and interrogations, and from intelligence reports on weapon development programmes which were produced at the war's end. More information has come to light over the years, which in some cases modifies the immediate post-war information. It would be pointless to list every source, even if, after all these years, it were possible. But it can be taken that everything in these pages has been based upon a stated fact or opinion in the historical record, or on actual examination of the weapon in question, and nothing is assumed or imagined.

Ian V. Hogg, 1999

The V Weapons

At about four o'clock in the morning of 13 June 1944, two elderly men sat in a sandbagged hole in the ground somewhere on the Kentish coast of England and listened. A week had gone by since the Allies had invaded France and there was always the chance that the Germans might try some sort of retaliation. And because these two men were members of the Observer Corps, and their task was to watch or listen for enemy aircraft, they were especially alert. Moreover they had just read a warning order which suggested that Hitler had something up his sleeve with which to bombard England, and the intelligence people had managed to put together enough information to suggest what form this retaliation might take.

Thus, when one of them heard what might have been a two-stroke motorcycle, but high in the sky, he alerted his companion. They looked up and there was a pulsing flame moving across the sky in the general direction of London, and this stuttering rattle of some peculiar engine. The observer took a quick sight through his plotting instrument, the teller reached for the telephone, and The Word was given 'Diver! 98 degrees, 4000 feet, 300 miles an hour, course towards London!' Diver was the code word to be used to warn of the new weapon. The Battle of the Buzz-Bombs was about to begin.

Vergeltungswaffe 1

The origin of the V-1 might be said to be the development of a suitable engine, because, if this had not been available, it is doubtful if the idea of a flying bomb would ever have occurred to anyone or, if it had, would have been taken seriously. It was the existence of a cheap and simple engine of sufficient power which clinched the argument. The engine development began in 1927–28 when an aerodynamicist called Paul Schmidt had the idea of a pulse-jet device. The theory was fairly simple once you had the inspiration: a tube was fitted with a screen of spring-loaded flaps at its front end, a petrol injection system and a spark plug. As it flew through the air, the air pressure forced open the flaps and air flowed into the tube. The flaps operated a valve and petrol was sprayed into the tube so as to make an explosive petrol/air mist. This mixture was then ignited by the spark plug.

The explosion blew the flaps shut, and the blast then shot out of the rear end of the tube, driving it forwards. As the pressure inside died down so the air forced the flaps open and refilled the tube, more petrol was sprayed in and was ignited by either the hot interior of the tube or by residual hot gas from the previous blast, giving another pulse of power. And so it went on, several times a second.

There were one or two drawbacks to this device. In the first place it was incapable of sustaining itself at speeds under about 190mph, so that it was not possible to start the engine and take off in the normal way. It could not be throttled down or speeded up; it had its own natural speed and worked up to it from its initial 190+mph; once it achieved the optimum speed, it stuck closely to it. It was very inefficient above about 7,000 feet, where the density of the air began to fall off and the engine began to run out of breath. And after 30 to 45 minutes of operation the flap-valves were burned and damaged and the engine liable to fail. Therefore, although it was an ingenious method of propulsion, it had, it appeared, limited practical value in conventional aviation design. However, in 1934 Professor Schmidt suggested that it might be a useful method of driving an aerial torpedo, but nobody appears to have taken much notice of that idea.

In 1938 the *Reichsluftministerium* (Air Ministry, or *RLM*) had begun examining the jet engine concept, and in an endeavour to satisfy itself that all the likely avenues were being explored, it commissioned the Argus Motor Works to build a 'Schmidt engine'. Argus went ahead with this and produced an engine developing some 300kg of thrust, and delivered it to the *RLM*. They played around with it for some time, gave the matter some thought, then observed what the army was up to in Peenemünde and concluded that if the army was poking its boots into flying missiles, the air force ought to be doing the same, only more so. The *RLM* therefore called upon the Fieseler aircraft works for some ideas, and late in 1941 its chief engineer Lusser came up with some sketches. These were pondered, and finally, on 19 June 1942, development of the flying bomb was officially authorised. To conceal its purpose it was officially called the *Flakzielgerät 76*, a title which would suggest some sort of target for training AA gunners to anyone who heard it. The Fieseler company called it the Fi 103, in accordance with its usual system, but it is unlikely that anyone else ever called it that. To the people of south-east England and other places who suffered from it, it became 'the Doodlebug'. At the same time the Argus company was given a contract for the engine unit and the Walter company, specialists in rockets and fuels, was handed the problem of getting the device into the air at something over the critical 190mph speed so that it would sustain flight.

Work moved ahead quite rapidly; the first successful launch of the *FZG 76* was made on 24 December 1942 at Peenemünde. It was, though, followed by numbers of unsuccessful launches as various problems were encountered and solved.

The *FZG 76*, as it was eventually perfected, was a mid-wing monoplane with the Schmidt engine mounted above the rear of the fuselage and tail fin. Inside the body, from front to rear, were an air log (a propeller-driven counter which measured the distance flown); the warhead containing 1,870 lb of high explosive and three different types of fuze; a fuel tank containing 150 gallons of low-grade 75-octane petrol; two compressed air tanks pressurising the fuel system and supplying air to various servos controlling the rudder and tail elevators; a 42-cell 30-volt battery; a master gyroscope; and the various servos and other controls.

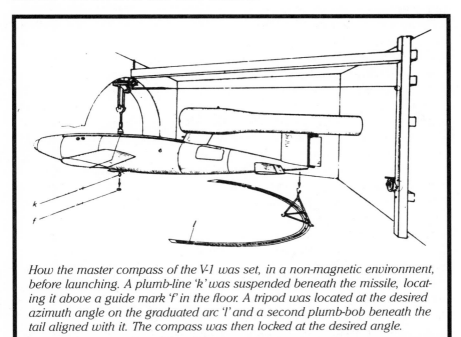

How the master compass of the V-1 was set, in a non-magnetic environment, before launching. A plumb-line 'k' was suspended beneath the missile, locating it above a guide mark 'f' in the floor. A tripod was located at the desired azimuth angle on the graduated arc 'l' and a second plumb-bob beneath the tail aligned with it. The compass was then locked at the desired angle.

The weapon was prepared by firstly filling the fuel tank, fitting a fully-charged battery and charging up the compressed air tanks. It was then taken to a non-magnetic area where the magnetic master compass was checked for deviation and set at the correct bearing from the launch site to the target, after which it was trollied to the launching ramp.

The launching ramp was essentially a slotted tube about 150 feet long, in eight sections which could be bolted together, supported on concrete and steel at a suitable launching angle. Both ends of the tube were open, and the rear had a form of bayonet joint. A large dumb-bell shaped piston, with a fin on one side, was loaded into the rear of the tube like an artillery shell, the fin protruding through the slot, and a flexible sealing tube was inserted into the firing tube and held with wires close to the slot. On top of the firing tube was the launching trolley, a simple framework on to which the actual missile was placed, and behind which the fin on top of the firing piston bore.

The 'combustion chamber trolley' was now wheeled up behind the rear end of the firing tube and locked to it by means of the bayonet joint. This trolley carried containers of potassium permanganate (known to the Germans as *Z-Stoff*) and hydrogen peroxide (*T-Stoff*), three bottles of compressed air, and the combustion chamber itself, a heavy steel forging.

Just off to the left side of the ramp was the 'distributor unit', mounted on a steel platform. This carried more compressed air tanks, pressure gauges and distribution valves supplying compressed air to the missile, firstly to blow air into the front of the duct and simulate flight, and secondly to switch on the fuel valve (and switch it off again should there be any malfunction). There was also a transformer and trembler coil which supplied power to the engine spark plug by a flexible lead.

With the missile placed on the trolley and the trolley hard back against the fin on the firing piston, the various operators took cover in a specially prepared pillbox some distance from the ramp and the launch procedure was started. Air was blown in to the engine and the spark plug fired so that the engine started and ran at full power. After about 7 seconds of this warm-up, the valves on the combustion chamber trolley were opened by remote control; this injected *T-Stoff* and *Z-Stoff* into the combustion chamber under pressure, where their reaction produced a massive volume of super-heated steam. The firing piston was restrained by a shearable bolt, and as soon as the pressure was high enough to shear this the piston began moving up the firing tube, pushing the firing trolley and the missile ahead of it. The gas pressure behind the piston forced the sealing tube into the slot, forming a crude and not very effective gas seal.

The volume of steam and its pressure was enough to ensure that the missile was flying at about 250mph when it left the end of the launching tube. At the end of the tube the huge piston simply shot out of the tube, and as it fell away from the trolley, so the trolley fell from the missile, leaving it climbing at the same angle as the launching ramp and gradually accelerating.

Each site was equipped with several pistons and two combustion chamber trolleys. While one trolley was in use the other was being recharged with compressed air and fuel. After launching, the base of the ramp, which was stained by permanganate, had to be washed down by personnel in rubber boots and protective clothing.

The missile was now climbing steadily at about 500 feet per minute, and the various control systems began to function. The master magnetic compass compared the missile's heading with the azimuth set into the compass. If it discovered a deviation it would send a blast of compressed air down a duct to the master gyroscope, nudging it in the required direction. Movement of the gyro was then converted into another movement of compressed air to the relevant servo motor controlling the tail fin, steering the machine into the correct track. A similar barometric sensor sampled the air pressure and once it decided that the operation altitude of 3,000 feet had been reached, the elevator controls were operated to bring the machine into level flight. It generally took about six minutes for the *FZG 76* to reach this altitude, after which it settled down at its optimum speed. This could be anything between 300mph and 420mph, depending upon the natural frequency of the engine and various other factors. An unusual point was that once the machine had reached its optimum speed it tended to stay at it because, although it was using up fuel and therefore getting lighter, any advantage this might have given was offset by the mechanical deterioration of the engine as the fuel flaps burned away.

Before firing the air-log had been set at the range to the target. As the missile flew so the air-log propeller turned and, through a gearing system, gradually counted up the air miles flown. When the set distance had been covered, two detonators were fired which locked the rudder and elevators and drove two sets of spoilers down from the tail, so forcing the machine into a steep dive. This usually caused the fuel supply, which by this time would be low, to fail and the engine thus stopped; though on some occasions the machine went into a fully powered dive, the engine cutting out just before impact. A fairly high percentage of machines failed to go into a steep dive immediately and instead made a long glide before turning into a final dive. It appears that the nature of the final dive was largely governed by the amount of fuel left in the tank and its effect upon the machine's balance; the more fuel, the steeper the dive.

As soon as the missile struck the ground, or any other solid object, the warhead detonated. And the fuzing system of the warhead was so efficient that of the first 2,700 incidents monitored in Britain, only four missiles failed to detonate. The system consisted of one electrical impact fuze (ElAZ 106), one mechanical all-ways fuze (AZ 80A) and one mechanical clockwork delay fuze (ZZ 17B). The impact fuze, which was powered from the 30-volt battery and armed by the air log about 40 miles after launch, had three switches; a pressure plate in the missile nose for cases of direct impact; a pressure switch on the underside of the fuselage for a belly landing; and an inertia switch inside the fuze itself which would operate on rapid deceleration if the other two should fail to function. There was even a resistor-condenser circuit, charged up by the battery, which contained enough electricity to fire the detonators of the fuze should the battery connection be damaged on impact.

The AZ 80A fuze was a fairly simple trembler switch type of fuze which would make an electrical contact and detonate the warhead no matter what angle the missile hit the ground. It was armed by a clockwork device which was set off by a wire being pulled out during the launch and which armed the fuse some 10 minutes after leaving the ramp. The fuze was there simply as an insurance if the ElAZ 106 failed to work.

And finally the ZZ 17B delay fuze was a clockwork delay adjustable up to two hours. This, too, was started at launch, and should the other fuzes fail and the missile land in one piece then, after the delay had run its time, the warhead would be detonated.

Once all this technology had been mastered and proved to work, the *FZG 76* went into production. It was designed with simple mass-production in mind from the very start of the project, a distinctly different approach to that taken by the designers of the V-2 rocket. It was constructed almost entirely of mild steel plate (later versions used wooden wings) and each of the component parts was of the simplest form, even if it meant additional weight.

Manufacture of the components was dispersed widely through Germany, and assembly of the components into complete missiles was also dispersed in various places. The largest assembly plants were in Nordhausen, in the Harz Mountains about 50 miles west of Halle; Dannenberg, some 50 miles southeast of Hamburg; Fallersleben, a few miles north of Brunswick, where the Volkswagenwerke at KDF-Stadt was taken over; and Stettin (now Szczecin in Poland), the Baltic port close to Peenemünde. The early missiles, used for tests and training, were, of course, built entirely within the Peenemünde complex, and it was here that a newly-formed anti-aircraft regiment, Flakregiment 155(W), was mustered and set to training on the *FZG 76* in 1943.

The Nordhausen *Mittelwerke* was a massive subterranean factory run almost entirely on slave labour; political and other prisoners who were, quite literally, worked to death. It was also charged with the assembly of the V-2 missiles and of aero-engines and all manner of munitions. Less is known of the other assembly plants, since they were not such a remarkable construction as the *Mittelwerke* but were fairly conventional factories dispersed into areas of little apparent importance so as to minimise their chance of being attacked from the air.

The operational use of the *FZG 76* was originally planned to begin in December 1943, but two main schools of thought emerged on the actual method of use. The first, championed by Field Marshal Milch of the *Luftwaffe* was to construct a limited number of immense underground bunkers which would combine the functions of storage, preparation and launching. By amply stocking these well before the operational date, and keeping them well-supplied with missiles, it would thus be possible to bring a continuous stream of missiles to bear against England, saturating the defences and causing enormous damage.

The other view, held by General von Axthelm and others, was that such enormous constructions would undoubtedly come to the notice of aerial reconnaissance and would thereafter be bombed unremittingly, preventing them from functioning at all. He preferred a large number of simple sites which could be quickly constructed and as quickly abandoned if they were bombed. With a large number of sites it would be probable that half of them would never be discovered and thus the offensive would be able to continue; not, perhaps at such an intensity, but at least at a sufficient rate to cause the same amount of damage, though over a longer time.

A third alternative was also suggested; carry the bombs into the air beneath larger aircraft, fly them close to the English coast, and then release them. This would allow a much deeper penetration into Britain within the limited flight time of the missile. Experiments with this idea duly began, using the Heinkel 111 as the parent machine.

Flakregiment 155 (W) had been set up in August 1943 and had begun training, but production problems now appeared and caused a series of delays. The production of wings and bodies by the Volkswagen factory proved to be faulty and several hundred components had to be scrapped and re-made; the Fieseler factory was bombed, more production was destroyed and the manufacturing plant had to be rebuilt; there was a shortage of labour among sub-contractors and deliveries became later and later.

After modifications had been made and the various hold-ups and bottlenecks cleared, mass production started early in 1944, with a target of 8,000 missiles per month to be reached by October of that year. It is generally estimated that about 24,000 missiles were built in 1944, of which 12,000 were ready for use when their offensive employment began in June. The first months of 1945 saw another 9,500–10,000 made before production came to a halt in April. It has been estimated that production of one *FZG 76* took 900 man-hours of work, 550 of these being by the assembly works and the balance by sub-contractors.

In December 1943 Flakregiment 155(W) moved into its operational positions in France, with the intention of beginning the offensive on 13 February 1944. No missiles appeared and the date was put back to April. April became May, May became June, and on 6 June the Allies invaded Normandy. That concentrated German minds wonderfully, and Hitler decreed that the bombardment of England would commence on the evening of 12 June.

By this time the question of the firing sites had been settled, largely by the Allies. Rumours of mysterious weapons gradually turned into information and by the summer of 1943 Allied photo-reconnaissance aircraft were systematically photographing every square kilometre of northern France. The major civil engineering works which were caused by the large combined storage, service and launch bunkers were soon discovered and systematically bombed into ruins, and in their place came a widely dispersed collection of sites, carefully blended into their surroundings, in which the principal service and preparation buildings were either erected or made over from existing buildings, and the most prominent feature, the launching ramp, was left unassembled. Many of these sites were noted, if not precisely identified as to their purpose, in the early months of 1944.

It appeared that nothing very much was happening at them, and they were merely watched, being rephotographed periodically to see what might turn up. But in the aftermath of D-Day these sites suddenly sprang into life. Launching ramps were erected, soldiers appeared, test equipment was brought in, followed by fuel, compressed air, and finally missiles. By the 12th few of the sites were ready; most had not been tested to prove that the launcher worked, and most had no missiles. But Colonel Wachtel, commanding Flak Regiment 155(W), was a regular soldier who knew very well that argument would do no good; he saluted and got on with producing some sort of effort for the 12th so that it could duly be reported back up the chain of command that the offensive had begun on schedule.

At 3.30 a.m. on 13 June 1944 the first operational V-1 was launched. It was followed by nine more; five of them crashed almost immediately they took to the air, one flew off into the night and was never seen again, and four made their way across the Channel to England. Of this four, one landed in the Sussex countryside, one near Sevenoaks in Kent, one on the outskirts of London at Swanscombe, and one reached north of the Thames to land at Bethnal Green. The last two appear to have been well guided, bearing in mind that the aiming point was the Tower of London, though the other two appear to have strayed seriously off-course.

Having duly fired these ten missiles and thereby complied with his orders, Colonel Wachtel wisely closed down his operation and sent his men back to the task of preparing sites, testing launchers, training and building up a stock of missiles. Two days later, on 15 June, the campaign opened in earnest. At about 10 p.m. launching commenced from 55 sites, with a total of 244 missiles being fired against London and about 50 against Southampton. Of these, 144 crossed the English coast, 14 were shot down by anti-aircraft guns, seven shot down by fighter aircraft and one was credited as being shared by guns and fighters before they reached any significant targets; 73 crossed the boundary of Greater London, and of these 11 more were shot down by the London defences. Of those which functioned correctly, most landed south of the Thames. A handful reached Southampton and one went grossly astray and ended up in Norfolk.

Intelligence had provided the British with a reasonable estimate of what they were facing; the abortive attempt of 13 June alerted them to what was about to arrive, and the two days of grace enabled them to assemble their defences. Once the scale of the attack became apparent, more guns and aircraft were allocated, by reducing the defences in other parts of Britain, and by 28 June there were 376 heavy and 576 light anti-aircraft guns manned by the army, plus a further 560 light guns manned by the RAF Regiment, spread around the south-east of London. Four squadrons of Mosquitos and eight of Tempests, Typhoons and Spitfires were also in action.

By mid-July Wachtel's men had fired over 4,000 missiles towards London, of which about 3,000 had come within reach of the defences.

Fighter aircraft had claimed 924, guns 261, and another 55 had collided with barrage balloon cables. One missile was fired on by a fighter, ran into a shell burst and then collided with a balloon, and one-third was duly credited to each service. This scoring rate, about 42 per cent, was considered poor against a target which flew a straight and level course at a regular speed, but this problem was partly due to the tactical deployment of the British defences which prevented guns firing when fighters were operating in their area, and, of course, partly because of the carefully selected speed and height of the missiles which were just too fast and low for heavy anti-aircraft guns to track smoothly, and too high for light guns for most of their firing arc.

These problems were eventually solved by redeploying the defences so that the guns were clustered around the coast, an area denied to fighters, with the fighters allowed to roam behind the guns and catch the ones which got past, and then by bringing in more static-mounted guns, which could track more smoothly, and allying them to new auto-tracking radars and giving them ammunition fitted with proximity fuzes. Eventually there were 800 heavy and 1,200 light guns plus 700 rocket launchers deployed around the English coast from Sussex to Suffolk, with a further 144 heavy guns waiting in reserve, backed up by fighter squadrons of the RAF operating in mid-Channel to catch the missiles before they reached the coast, and behind the guns to catch those which had got through the cordon.

The German response to this was firstly to keep up the pressure, since a proportion of the bombs always got through, and secondly to outflank the defences by using the air-launching system mentioned earlier. Heinkel bombers began flying the missiles to more or less undefended areas and then launching them against London, Southampton and Bristol in directions which, it was hoped, would evade the defences. By the end of August 1944 the total of air-launched bombs included 300 against London, 90 for Southampton and about 20 against Bristol and Gloucester.

By the end of August the Allied advance from the Normandy beaches was drawing close to the launching sites in the Pas de Calais, and Flakregiment 155(W) dismantled its equipment and withdrew to the Netherlands. The air-launching squadrons also ceased their operations and withdrew to northern Germany. During this 'first phase' 9,017 missiles had been launched, of which 6,725 had been seen over England. Of this 6,725, 1,771 (26 per cent) were shot down by fighter aircraft, 1,459 (22 per cent) by guns, and 231 (4 per cent) fell victim to barrage balloons. Of the remainder, 2,340 (35 per cent) actually landed in the Greater London area.

The 'second phase' began on 16 September, when the air-launching squadrons, now reinforced to a strength of 90 aircraft, began operations once more. On the first day nine missiles were launched; the Royal Navy shot down two at sea, fighters got three, two crashed in Suffolk and two reached London. Anti-aircraft artillery failed to score because this new attack had outflanked the gun defences by approaching from the northeast, and in view of the lack of threat from the Pas de Calais area the southern end of the gun defence line (or 'Diver Belt' as it was known to the British) was now uprooted and shifted north to extend the line past Great Yarmouth.

The second phase continued until mid-January 1945, by which time an estimated 1,200 missiles had been launched, of which 638 were seen by the defences. Guns got 331½, fighters 71½, 66 reached London and the remaining 169 were spread around the Home Counties. During this period there had also been a very serious attempt to by-pass the defences by flying the missiles to the Yorkshire coast before releasing them against Manchester. Only one actually reached its target, but the very threat was sufficient to cause another redeployment of guns to the north-east coast of England.

There was now a lull in V-1 activity, because the Germans were concentrating on operations with the V-2, before the 'third phase' of the V-1 campaign opened on 3 March 1945. The *FZG 76* was given increased fuel capacity, thus increasing its range to about 200 miles and Wachtel's men in the Netherlands were now able to activate three sites and recommence their bombardment of London. In the following four weeks they managed to fire 275 missiles of which 125 crossed the North Sea. Guns got 87 of them, fighters four, and only 13 reached London. The last V-1 to be recorded was in flight to London at 12.43 p.m. on 28 March when it was destroyed by gunfire over Orfordness, Suffolk.

The V-1 campaign against Britain was over. But during the second and third phases another campaign had been waged with perhaps even greater ferocity, against Antwerp and Liège. In late 1944 and early 1945 Antwerp was probably the most important port in the world, for through it were to pass most of the munitions and supplies to sustain the Allied armies on their advance into Germany. Allied intelligence warned of probable attacks in early September and British and American anti-aircraft guns were emplaced all round the city in good time to be ready when, on 27 October, the first V-1 was launched against Antwerp from sites in the area of Bocholt, north-east of Essen, and Koblenz. On 28 November the River Scheldt was finally cleared of mines and supply ships began arriving in Antwerp docks; as a result the V-1 attacks were stepped up until some 50 per day were being launched. This increased until on 16 February the maximum was reached with 160 bombs launched in one day.

When the Antwerp attacks ended on 30 March a total of 4,883 missiles had been launched, of which only 211 landed within an eight-mile radius of Antwerp docks; and of those 211, 55 got through because at the moment of their appearance the guns were unable to fire because Allied aircraft were operating in the area. A further 1,096 missiles had been launched against Liège, with a similar rate of success. The final 'kill rate' of the guns defending the two cities was 97 per cent; no balloons or fighter aircraft were used in the defences at all.

As might be imagined, the accuracy of the *FZG 76* was a variable factor. As originally designed it was primarily intended for use against large targets such as the London, Southampton and Bristol areas, from launching sites near the French coast. For this purpose a range of 150 miles or so was sufficient, and 160 miles probably represented the maximum achieved. When the Germans lost control of the French coast they continued their attacks by air-launching the *FZG 76* from He 111 aircraft, and later increased the fuel capacity to give a range of 200 miles from the ground-launched missiles. Broadly, it appears that the average accuracy of missiles launched at a range of 125–130 miles was such that 50 per cent would fall within an eight-mile radius of their target. For air-launched missiles the circle within which 50 per cent of missiles fell grew to have a radius of 24 miles around their intended target, and this inaccuracy was the principal reason for the eventual abandonment of air launching. Missiles ground-launched with a range of 200 miles had a 50 per cent radius of error of about 12 miles. The other fifty per cent could fall more or less anywhere along the line of flight.

Reichenberg

A codicil to the *FZG 76* story is the brief history of the Fi 103 (Re) or *Reichenberg*, an *FZG 76* with a cockpit and manual flying controls. A number of these were discovered by the Allies when they entered Germany, whereupon they leapt to the conclusion that there was a plan for suicide missions afoot, in which dedicated Nazi fanatics would deliberately fly the bombs to selected targets in London and other places, sacrificing their lives to ensure success. At this time, of course, *kamikaze* aircraft were regularly making suicide attacks on American aircraft carriers in the Pacific, and it seemed logical to suppose that the Nazis were no less fanatic. The truth appeared to be rather more prosaic. Germans interrogated at the time insisted that these machines had been built solely in order to investigate the flying capabilities of the *FZG 76* and thus make refinements to the design which might otherwise never have been apparent. This was a reasonable argument, and gradually the *kamikaze* idea was forgotten.

More recent research, however, has unearthed more information on the *Reichenberg* project. There is no doubt that the first conversion to manual operation was, indeed, for aerodynamic investigation. But once it had been shown that it was possible to fly the *FZG 76* like a conventional aircraft, the idea arose of removing the warhead and fitting a battery of guns or rockets into the space, then towing the manned aircraft up into the sky until it had sufficient flying speed to start the engine and fly independently. It would then fly off towards the nearest enemy bomber formation and shoot down as many as it could before its estimated engine life of 30–45 minutes was up. Then the pilot would glide back to his base and take to his parachute, leaving the expended aircraft to crash.

Nothing very much seems to have come out of that idea, but the next suggestion brought up the *kamikaze* proposal once more. This time the pilots, all fanatical Nazi party members, would fly the missile, with its standard warhead, to selected targets of vital importance and there deliberately dive into the target, sacrificing themselves in the process. It was assumed, one supposes, that the queue of potential pilots would be enthusiastic and long, but this seems not to have been the case. Volunteers did appear when the scheme was first proposed, and about 150 V-1 missiles were converted into piloted vehicles. But by the time the machines were ready, the intended targets – the Allied invasion fleet – were history, and when the pilots were requested to immolate themselves on lesser targets such as railway stations and bridges, their enthusiasm waned and the *Reichenberg* project was quietly terminated.

Vergeltungswaffe 2

Staveley Road in Chiswick, a suburb of London, is today a pleasantly quiet residential street; it must have been even more peaceful on the evening of 8 September 1944. The peace, though, was abruptly disturbed just after 6.30 p.m. when, with a thunderous explosion, half-a-dozen houses were wrecked, three people killed and six injured. Witnesses told afterwards of how, as the sound of the explosion died away, they heard a rushing noise as if something huge was flying through the air. The experts were quick to explain; the weapon which had caused the devastation was a German rocket; and it was supersonic – it flew faster than sound – so the first thing you heard was the detonation as it struck, after which you heard the noise of its approach catching up with it. Supersonic it may have been, but it had taken that first rocket almost thirteen years to reach Staveley Road.

The second vengeance weapon, the V-2 or A4 rocket, can, in the long run, be attributed to the Versailles Treaty. The treaty restricted the German army to 100,000 men and placed strict limitations upon its artillery; it also placed strict limitations upon the great German gunmakers as to what they could and could not produce. Under the guidance of General von Seekt the slimmed-down army became an army of professionals, with every man trained for a rank three or four grades higher than the one he held. Every possible technical improvement or innovation was closely examined to see what it might hold for the future of the army. Under the Weimar Republic the adherence to the terms of the Treaty was performed to the letter, if not necessarily to the spirit. If the treaty said 'no tanks in Germany' then there would be no tanks in Germany; but there were tanks in Russia, and a German training ground in Russia, to which German soldiers were surreptitiously sent for instruction and German tracked 'tractors' built for assessment. And if heavy artillery was banned, then look for a way round it; what about rockets? There was nothing in the treaty forbidding rockets.

Rockets, for some reason, had captured the public imagination in Germany in the 1920s. There were rocket-propelled cars, rocket-boosted gliders, mail delivery by rockets, and a spate of futuristic science-fiction films depicting rockets exploring space. In June 1927 the Society for Space Travel (*Verein für Raumschiffart* or *VfR*) was founded by a number of rocket enthusiasts and acquired an old artillery practice ground in the Jungfernheide near Reinickendorf, a suburb of Berlin (roughly where Tegel airport is today), where they were able to conduct experiments with various small rockets. By 1930 the *VfR* was experimenting with liquid-fuelled rockets, using oxygen and petrol as the fuel, and in March 1931 actually managed to make a successful one which flew.

At more or less the same time the army had begun looking into the rocket. The chief of the *Heereswaffenamt* (Army Weapons Bureau, or *HWA*) at that time was Colonel Karl Becker, a notable ballistician, who had inserted a brief monograph on rockets into the army's 1926 Textbook of Ballistics, and in 1929 he ordered one of his staff to study the available technical journals and visit the various amateur rocket societies to find out if there was anything there worth pursuing. The resulting report showed that there were, indeed, some ideas of military value in the rocket field, and after some debate it was decided to try to develop a simple solid-fuelled rocket which could be used as a field artillery weapon up to ranges of about seven or eight kilometres. Early in 1930 a Captain Walter Dornberger was posted into Becker's department to start planning and design studies for this weapon. He began by secretly funding some of the *VfR* experiments, in an attempt to keep the army's interest in rockets hidden, but it soon became apparent that the *VfR* was more interested in space flight than in rockets as rockets, and by 1931 Dornberger had established a small research centre, operated entirely by the army, at Kummersdorf, a training area some 19 miles south of Berlin.

Colonel Becker's original thoughts had been on long-range rocket weapons to supplant heavy artillery; the short-range weapon was merely intended as a starting exercise. As a result, work on solid fuel rockets at Kummersdorf was soon elbowed aside by work on liquid-fuel types, since these appeared to be the only method of achieving the long range which Becker wanted. But in 1931 there were very few people in the world who had any knowledge, even theoretical knowledge, of liquid-fuelled rockets, and progress at Kummersdorf was slow. Dornberger frequently went back to the *VfR* to tap the enthusiasts' knowledge, and even permitted the *VfR* to come down and use the Kummersdorf range for some of its experiments (for the neighbours around Reinickendorf were getting a little apprehensive of the activities there).

Eventually, in 1932, Dornberger persuaded a young graduate and member of the *VfR* called Werner von Braun to come and work at Kummersdorf. By the end of the year Braun, and two other *VfR* members who had also joined him as civil employees of the army, were working on a liquid oxygen/alcohol rocket motor. And in 1933 the objections of the local population, and the objections of the authorities to what appeared to be a somewhat international approach to something which they felt ought to be strictly for the national good, caused the *VfR* to be evicted from its test ground at Reinickendorf and disbanded.

Later in 1933, after a long series of experiments which had taught them a great deal about the design and construction of liquid-fuelled rockets, Dornberger and his team began work on a complete rocket, *Aggregat 1* or A1, which would prove that rocket flight was possible. After static tests, the design was abandoned and A2 was started. In December 1934 this was taken to the island of Borkum in the Baltic, and successfully fired to an altitude of 2,200 metres. With this to their credit the team now moved on to A3, which would show an increase in power and range and thus convince the army that the idea was feasible and worth some major investment.

By this time, of course, the potential power of the rockets was reaching a point where firing them from Kummersdorf was no longer practical. A more isolated location with an ample firing area was vitally needed, and in 1935 Dornberger's men explored various parts of Germany to find some suitable site. Werner von Braun happened to spend the Christmas of 1935 with friends at Anklam, near the Baltic coast between Stettin and Stralsund. Close by was the estuary of the Peene river and a sparsely inhabited island called Usedom; further out in the Baltic was a smaller island, Greifswalder Oie, and after that the Baltic Sea stretched away to the horizon. On his return to Kummersdorf von Braun reported this to Dornberger, who promptly visited the area and immediately saw the advantages. It was well away from industrial areas and it would be a comparatively easy task to isolate it from the mainland and thus preserve the utmost security.

The discovery of Usedom could scarcely have been made at a more propitious time. In March 1936 General von Fritsch, the Army Commander-in-Chief, was to make an inspection visit to Kummersdorf and pronounce on the fate of the rocket project. Dornberger and von Braun worked hard to prepare a demonstration of three rocket engines, which went off perfectly and von Fritsch was duly impressed. If the team could come up with a viable weapon design, then the necessary financial support would be provided. The A3 design was now re-worked into the A4, the first serious attempt at a workable weapon; this was to have a range of 260km with a warhead weighing 1,000kg, and this came out of their calculations as a rocket some 13 metres long demanding a thrust of over 25,000kg. At the same time planning was going ahead on the facility they would like to build on the island of Usedom, should they get permission to move.

By now, Dornberger had also interested the *Luftwaffe* in his work, particularly by offering solid-fuel assisted take-off rockets to help heavy bombers into the air, and at a meeting with army and air force chiefs later in 1936 he finally received the necessary approval, and the army went ahead with purchasing the land. At this point a technical set-back occurred; models of the A3 had been sent to a wind-tunnel for testing and it was discovered that the fins needed to be re-designed. The delay of re-design, re-model, send to the wind-tunnel, await results and analyse them infuriated the Kummersdorf team and von Braun pressed Dornberger to go back to the army and ask for a wind tunnel to be built in their new establishment. Again he enlisted the aid of the *Luftwaffe*, who could see good reasons for having access to an up-to-date facility of this nature, and approval was obtained. It was to prove a vital part of the new organisation.

Construction on Usedom began in the spring of 1937, and the Peenemünde test centre slowly took shape. At Kummersdorf the A3, which was to act as the test vehicle for the next model, the A4, also took shape, and in December 1937 the first A3 was launched from Peenemünde. It failed; so did the next, and the next. The conclusion reached was that progress had been too swift; many individual components would have to be flight tested before they were incorporated into any design, instead of relying on purely theoretical ideas being built into a rocket and expected to work. This, of course, meant that progress on the A4 was suspended since, until the test vehicle had shown reliable results, there was no point in incorporating anything into the A4 design.

After much study, most of the problems were resolved, and now the next test vehicle was developed, the A5. This was similar to the A3 but somewhat larger and was provided with radio control to switch off the rocket fuel and deploy a parachute for recovery of the rocket after the necessary part of its flight had been performed.

Late in 1938 four A5 rockets were successfully launched, and work now turned to such matters as gyroscope control, fuel pumps and similar mundane but vital components. By October 1939 the A5 had been fitted with full control systems and every item which was proposed for the service A4 weapon. Three such rockets were successfully fired, proving the guidance system and various other improvements, and Dornberger now decided that work should go ahead on the development of the A4, incorporating all that had been learned from the A3 and A5, with the aim of placing the A4 into production some time in mid-1943.

Then, in the summer of 1940, just as things were beginning to come right, Hitler decided that everything was going his way, the war would be over within the coming year, and therefore no project that could not be completed in that time should be continued. In fact the directive was evaded in various ways and Peenemünde kept itself occupied on various research projects, but any prospect of putting the A4 into production was firmly halted. The 25-ton thrust engine for the A4 was perfected, more test flights with the A3 and A5 took place, the A4 design was completed and assembly of the first hand-built specimens began.

On the 7 February 1942 Dr Fritz Todt, head of the German munitions production programme, died in an aircraft accident; Hitler, to avoid his underlings squabbling over who should succeed to the job, appointed Albert Speer, who happened to be in his headquarters at the time, in Todt's place. This was a fortunate turn of events for the A4 project, since Speer was very willing to listen to what Dornberger had to say, whereas Todt had not been particularly impressed with the prospects of a rocket weapon. But the first flight test of the A4, on 13 June 1942, was a failure. The second, on 16 August was another. Finally, on 3 October came the first successful flight, when the missile performed perfectly, took off, flew 201km up the length of the Baltic and landed within 4km of its target. More successful tests followed, modifications were made and tried, and at last it was time to go back to the purseholders and ask for production facilities for a proven weapon.

Early in 1943 politics and power-play came on the scene. Himmler, head of the SS, discovered that the rocket project had Hitler's eye and, anxious to consolidate his position, he manoeuvred to have the SS take over the running of the project and installed his own man as chief production engineer. The political ramifications of this need not detain us; what was important was that Degenkolb, the engineer, took command of the question of A4 production, gave everyone a good shaking, and eventually got mass production under way. Had it been left to the Peenemünde staff, it is doubtful whether production would ever have been achieved; like all advanced engineers and scientists, what they had in front of them was never quite good enough, it merely needed a small modification...

It is commonly said that the A4 design required 65,000 modifications during its progress from drawing board to service, but this figure, I suspect, comes from myth rather than from a more firm source. Assuming that the design began in the middle of 1940 and that production ended in March 1945, we have about 1750 working days, meaning that about 20 modifications were produced per day for four and a half years. I think not; no doubt the number was large, but not that large.

In July 1943 Dornberger and von Braun, accompanied by Speer, visited Hitler and showed him film of a successful launch; Hitler was finally convinced that this was actually a working weapon, and gave Speer the priorities needed to obtain materials and organise production. This, finally, got the production under way, although Hitler over-reached himself by demanding 2,000 a month.

By 1943, though, the Allies had a watchful eye on Peenemünde and once evidence of missile development had been detected the watch was intensified. Finally, in August 1943, the British mounted a massive air raid which damaged the site and killed a number of the specialists. It unfortunately killed far more of the civilian labourers (many of them foreigners conscripted to work for the Germans) and did more damage to their housing than to the actual research laboratories, but it was enough to disrupt development for some weeks and indicate that their activities there had been discovered. It was therefore decided that test firings should be removed from Peenemünde and conducted deep inside Poland, in an SS training area near Blizna, located in the triangle formed by the Krakow–Lvov railway line and the Rivers Vistula and San as they converge. Rockets were moved by rail from Peenemünde to Blizna, tests were fired, and the remains and experimental results shipped back.

Late in 1942 General (as he now was) Dornberger had sent survey parties into France to determine locations for the launching facilities; two sites, at Watten, between St Omer and Calais, and a quarry at Wizernes nearby, were selected and plans drawn up for an enormous bunker at Watten to which rockets would be shipped, there to be fuelled, checked, and then taken outside and fired. This was in accordance with the plan laid down by Field Marshal Milch covering both the V-1 and V-2 projects; concentrating the weapons into a small number of complex centres so that a constant barrage could be kept up. Dornberger himself preferred the view of General von Axthelm, of having mobile and easily-concealed firing sites, and the Peenemünde team had designed the entire A4 system so that it required only a small piece of flat ground upon which to plant the 'firing table' and room to park and hide the various supporting vehicles.

Which was just as well. Work began at Watten in the spring of 1943, and in May it was spotted by a British photo-reconnaissance flight. All that could be seen was an enormous excavation and foundations for what was obviously going to be a huge piece of construction. The photo-interpreters of the RAF did not know what it was, but since everything in northern France was suspect in those days, it was assumed to have some connection with the German secret weapon programme.

A prominent civil engineer was asked what would be the most critical phase of the construction, when it would be most vulnerable to attack; his answer was to wait until the concrete was poured, but before it had set. And a few days after the RAF had bombed Peenemünde, the time seemed ripe and the US Eighth Air Force sent 185 B-17 Flying Fortresses to bomb the site at Watten. The result was a heap of reinforcing steel and wet concrete which rapidly hardened into an enormous mass. The civil engineer was consulted again; 'It would be easier to start again somewhere else.' he said. They did, moving their operations a few hundred yards away and adopting a different technique; now the engineers would excavate a shallow pit, fill it with concrete and then, when it had hardened, excavate the earth away beneath it to make the necessary chambers. But this, too, was attacked.

Meanwhile the alternative site at Wizernes, originally intended only as a store, was now selected as a store-cum-firing point and work began there in November 1943. A similar principle was to be used; encase the top of a hill in an enormous and bomb-proof concrete dome, then excavate away underneath it. This would result in a series of caverns in which the V-2s could be assembled, tested, erected and fuelled under cover, then trundled out on a railway and launched from the floor of the quarry. Such an ambitious construction was, of course, soon spotted by the RAF and they visited the site in March 1944. In a demonstration of precision bombing the bombs were placed around the edge of the concrete dome and so undermined it that it took on a tilt and was considered hazardous. Several parts of the underground workings were also damaged, and the whole thing was so unsafe that it had to be abandoned.

This threw the system back on to the mobile launching routine which Colonel Wachtel had supported and which General Dornberger had now perfected, and therefore we can now pass on to look at the missile system which had evolved from all this work.

The A4 design

The A4 was a long fin-stabilised rocket which weighed approximately 13.6 tons at firing and carried a warhead containing about one ton of explosive. The body shape is said to have been based upon Germany's standard 7.92mm pointed and boat-tailed rifle bullet, since this was the best ballistic shape known to the designers.

The missile contained, from front to rear, a pointed warhead with pointed nose fuze; control gyroscopes, amplifiers and other electrical equipment; an alcohol fuel tank; a liquid oxygen fuel tank; a turbine and fuel pumps; hydrogen peroxide and calcium permanganate tanks; a burner and heat exchanger to provide power for the turbine; and the main combustion chamber, venturi and jet steering carbon vanes.

The rocket was controlled by four internal carbon vanes, two for azimuth and two for pitch, and four external vanes. The internal vanes were located at the rear of the venturi so that they projected into the gas stream, while the external vanes were located at the rear of each large fin. The two carbon vanes associated with the azimuth control were connected by means of a shaft to the related external vanes, so that the internal and the external azimuth vanes moved at the same time and in the same direction. However, the internal and external pitch control vanes were connected so as to permit separate control.

The methods used for setting the control surfaces and for controlling the burning period varied considerably among rockets. All rockets employed a gyroscope to prevent roll and control azimuth. At times the azimuth control was supplemented by radio signals from the launch site. A pitch control gyroscope was included to control the trajectory during the rocket's burning period. The azimuth and pitch gyroscopes controlled electro-hydraulic servomotors to position the control surfaces. Early missiles used radio for control of burning time, but later a gyro-integrating accelerometer was used. Still later both radio and accelerometer were used in some missiles.

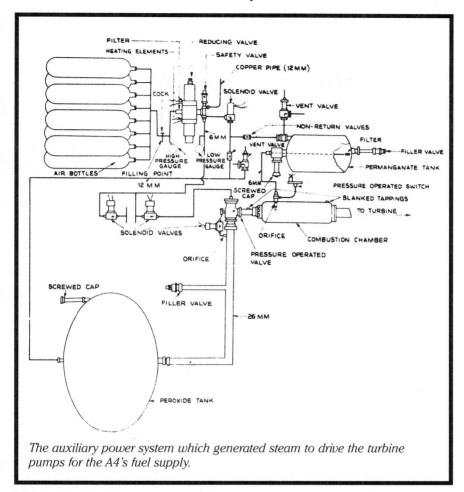

FILTER
HEATING ELEMENTS
REDUCING VALVE
SAFETY VALVE
COPPER PIPE (12MM)
COCK
SOLENOID VALVE
VENT VALVE
NON-RETURN VALVES
6MM
FILTER
VENT VALVE
FILLER VALVE
HIGH PRESSURE GAUGE
LOW PRESSURE GAUGE
PERMANGANATE TANK
AIR BOTTLES
FILLING POINT
12 MM
6MM
SCREWED CAP
PRESSURE OPERATED SWITCH
BLANKED TAPPINGS
TO TURBINE
SOLENOID VALVES
ORIFICE
COMBUSTION CHAMBER
ORIFICE
PRESSURE OPERATED VALVE
SCREWED CAP
FILLER VALVE
26 MM
PEROXIDE TANK

The auxiliary power system which generated steam to drive the turbine pumps for the A4's fuel supply.

The pitch gyroscope assembly included a controller driven by a constant-speed motor and a precessing coil which caused the axis of the gyroscope to be changed, thus changing the pitch angle of the missile in flight. The rotation of the controller operated electrical switches which precessed the gyroscope in pitch at a predetermined rate, so that the missile travelled on a predetermined trajectory for the first 51 seconds of its flight.

Propulsion was by means of a 25-ton thrust liquid-fuelled rocket motor. The fuel was alcohol and liquid oxygen which were delivered to the combustion chamber by means of high-speed pumps driven by a steam turbine. The steam generator system that furnished power to drive the turbine consisted of a hydrogen peroxide tank, a calcium permanganate tank, air supply, control valves and a combustion chamber. Air was stored in eight 7-litre bottles connected by a manifold and passed via a porcelain filter, a reducing valve, and a safety valve to the peroxide and permanganate tanks.

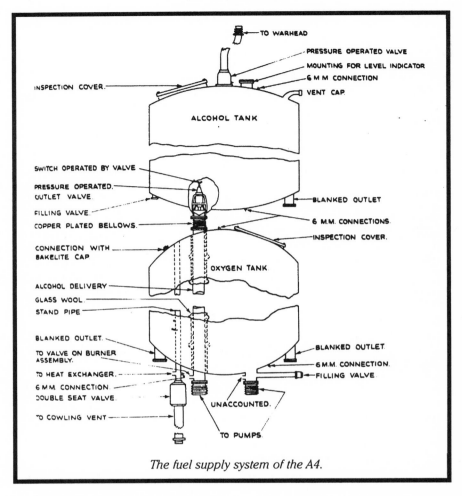

The fuel supply system of the A4.

Permanganate passed directly to the reaction chamber as a jet, after which the peroxide was injected. Reaction produced super-heated steam and oxygen gases which drove the turbine. The turbine exhausted through two louvres behind the venturi.

The liquid oxygen was sprayed through 18 rose jets into the forward end of the combustion chamber. The alcohol was circulated through the hollow wall of the venturi before being injected into the combustion chamber; this served to pre-heat the alcohol and also cool down the combustion chamber. Ignition was by means of a pyrotechnic candle wedged into the venturi by a wooden plank and fired electrically.

The warhead carried 1,605lb of cast amatol (60 per cent ammonium nitrate, 40 per cent TNT). This, at first sight, seems peculiar. Amatol is one of the least powerful blast explosives known; had the Germans chosen to use an aluminised explosive (which they certainly understood and used in

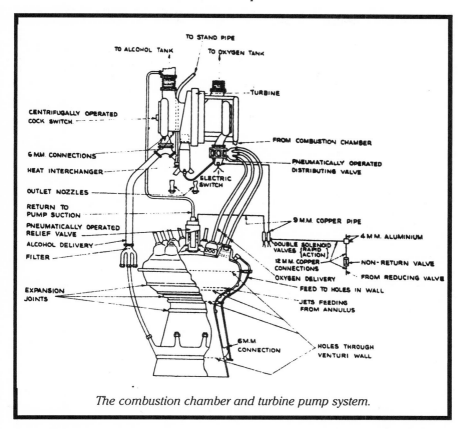

TO STAND PIPE

TO ALCOHOL TANK

TO OXYGEN TANK

TURBINE

CENTRIFUGALLY OPERATED COCK SWITCH

FROM COMBUSTION CHAMBER

6 MM. CONNECTIONS

PNEUMATICALLY OPERATED DISTRIBUTING VALVE

HEAT INTERCHANGER

ELECTRIC SWITCH

OUTLET NOZZLES

RETURN TO PUMP SUCTION

9 M.M. COPPER PIPE

PNEUMATICALLY OPERATED RELIEF VALVE

4 M M. ALUMINIUM

ALCOHOL DELIVERY

DOUBLE SOLENOID VALVES (RAPID ACTION)

FILTER

12 M M. COPPER CONNECTIONS

NON-RETURN VALVE

OXYGEN DELIVERY

FROM REDUCING VALVE

FEED TO HOLES IN WALL

EXPANSION JOINTS

JETS FEEDING FROM ANNULUS

6 M.M. CONNECTION

HOLES THROUGH VENTURI WALL

The combustion chamber and turbine pump system.

other munitions) the blast and damage radius around the point of impact could have been considerably increased. But amatol was apparently chosen because it was less likely to detonate from the heating effect as the missile passed back into the atmosphere at supersonic speeds. There is no evidence available of the local temperature necessary to cause detonation of the amatol, but since the time during which high temperatures were involved was small, it seems probable that a little melting of the filling occurred close to the casing. The liquid and the steel casing itself then probably distributed the heat, preventing the local temperature becoming high enough to cause detonation. A steel central tube running through the warhead carried a number of pellets of TNT to act as boosters to transmit the detonation of the fuze to the main filling, another standard requirement of amatol fillings.

The fuzing system was so efficient that only two incidents of unexploded warheads are known between 8 September 1944 and 9 January 1945 in which time 1,150 rockets had landed in England. The fuzing arrangement employed sensitive electrical fuzes of a new design so as to give instantaneous detonation with maximum blast effect. The system employed two electrical fuzes, one at the rear of the central exploder tube and the other in a conical steel housing at the forward end. The two fuzes were similar and consisted of a Bakelite moulding containing two inertia switches and an igniter. The igniter projected through a hole in the fuze casing and engaged the end of an adjacent TNT booster. In addition to the inertia switches the forward fuze was provided with a nose switch on the end of a steel tube which projected through the front end of the nose housing. This nose switch comprised a central electrode and a dome shaped collapsible outer electrode, insulated from each other by glass insulation. The switch was connected in parallel with the inertia switches. The fuses received a 32-volt electrical supply from a nickel-iron battery.

Once electrical connection to the fuzes had been made, operation of any inertia switch of either fuze, or crushing of the nose switch, caused the igniter of that fuze to fire and so detonate the warhead. The arrangement of the tremblers ensured detonation irrespective of the angle or attitude the missile impacted at.

To achieve a safety factor in the fuzing, the supply of current to the fuzes was controlled by means of two relay switches, A and B, in series. A was controlled by the timing switch in the control compartment and operated 40 seconds after propulsion commenced. B operated when the engine was cut off, normally after 60 seconds; operation of A followed by B, which was normal, resulted in normal operation of the fuzes on striking the ground. If the rocket propulsion operated irregularly and cut before 40 seconds, switch B closed before A; this sequence caused fusible bridges in the supply circuit to break and isolate the fuzes preventing normal detonation on impact. The battery circuit also contained a resistor-condenser circuit which charged up during flight and which was so connected as to provide an emergency source of sufficient power to fire the detonators should the direct battery connection have been broken by some malfunction.

Launching was performed from a firing table placed on firm ground or on a platform of logs smoothed on the upper surface. The equipment was all mobile, therefore the launching site could be changed as often as desired. The erection, servicing and testing of the rocket before launch required 32 vehicles or trailers

After the site was cleared and access tracks made, the rocket was transported on the trailer truck *FR-Anhänger-S*, more generally called the *Meillerwagen* from the maker's name. The launching table was brought on its trailer, lifted off and placed directly behind the rocket trailer, and the launcher trailer removed. Then the table, which was simply a flat steel plate with an upstanding blast deflector rather like a convex lemon-squeezer, was levelled and attached to the trailer by holding brackets. Cable trailers and power supply trucks were then brought on site and the cable squad and electricians reeled out the cables and placed them in position. The tarpaulin cover was removed from the rocket. The tail and centre rocket-retaining bands were removed, leaving the top band secured. The nose fuze was attached. The elevating motor of the trailer was started, driving the hydraulic pumps which lifted the platform and rocket to the vertical. About 12 minutes were required from starting the motor until the rocket was hanging vertically above the launching table. The table legs were now jacked up until the table took the weight of the rocket, after which the top retaining band was removed.

A contact on the end of the number one fin of the rocket fitted into a hole on the launch table. Now a plate was screwed up under this hole which pushed up the contact and switched on the internal circuits for acceptance of power from the ground cables. The radio test apparatus was plugged into the base of Fin No. 4. The rocket trailer drew off and the three working platforms were extended. The crew now used these platforms to carry out electrical tests and then fill the turbine fuel tanks. The rocket fuel trucks were then brought up and the alcohol and oxygen tanks were filled. Finally the table was revolved so as to orient the rocket in the required direction of flight and the pyrotechnic igniter wedged into the venturi and its electrical connection made.

All vehicles and men were then withdrawn and the firing crew went to its firing station, usually an armoured personnel carrier provided with the necessary switches and radio connections. Operation of the firing switch caused the valves to open to release fuel to the steam generator and start the turbine pumps. Once these were run up, the main fuel valves were opened and fuel delivered to the combustion chamber, and the pyrotechnic igniter was fired. The fuel mixture ignited, thrust built up, and the rocket left the firing table.

The initial stage of flight, when the speed of the rocket was insufficient for the airflow over the fins to allow any directional control to take effect, was controlled by the carbon fins inside the venturi. As the rocket rose, so the gyroscopes caused it to tilt over in the direction of the target and assume the angle calculated to place it on the proper trajectory for the desired range. A calculation had been made of the velocity which must be reached on this trajectory to produce this range, and this velocity was determined originally by radio measurement and later by use of the integrating gyro-accelerometer system. At the selected point the fuel valves were closed, shutting off the supply of fuel to the rocket motor. From this point onwards the rocket was no longer capable of being controlled from the ground and was now following a normal ballistic trajectory, having reached supersonic speed. At the end of that trajectory it simply struck the ground and detonated.

To get to this state of perfection the designers had gone through a series of modifications. They also had gone through a series of potential designs, and it would be as well to tabulate all these, since a mere narrative listing can be confusing.

The A Series

A1 This was von Braun's first attempt, developed at Kummersdorf. Accounts and details tend to be conflicting; about the only thing which can be said with certainty is that it never left the ground.

A2 His second try. Two were successfully launched from the island of Borkum, in the Baltic, in December 1934 and were the first encouragement for the liquid-fuel enthusiasts.

A3 Developed at Peenemünde, this was the first model to use a control system to maintain its flight attitude by using a gyroscope. It was intended as the prototype and test vehicle for the next in the series, A4, the future military rocket. One was successfully fired in 1938, but others were not so successful and the A3 was therefore abandoned, the A5 replacing it as the test vehicle

A4 This was the service weapon, the V-2 missile, described above.

A4b Very similar to the A4 but with the addition of wings intended to increase the range to 250 miles by giving the weapon the ability to glide. Several wing and tail configurations were tested in the wind tunnel, and two rockets were actually built and fired at Peenemünde, but both failed – one due to a structural failure and the other due to a control fault – and the war ended before the project could be followed up. It was hoped that the A4b would eventually supersede the A4 as the production and service model in due course.

A5 The later test vehicle for the A4 system. It was about 16 feet long and two feet in diameter and was powered by a Walter hydrogen peroxide rocket motor. Several were used in trials, both ground-launched and launched from aircraft. Some confusion can be caused by this rocket because there were a number of sub-models with changes in design which were called A5 V-1, V-2 etc., up to V-16. In this case 'V' stood for *Versuchs* or research.

A6 A project only, this was to have been similar to the A4 but propelled by a bi-fuel rocket using 90 per cent sulphuric acid and 10 per cent hydrocarbons for propulsion.

A7 A winged version of the A5, used as the test vehicle for the A9 project. It was air launched from about 40,000 feet altitude in order to study the aerodynamic aspects of the glide component of the A9's trajectory.

A8 A design study contemporary with the A6, with which it was almost identical. The difference lay in the fuel system which was to be a liquid oxygen/alcohol system, like the A4 but using a pressurised delivery system instead of turbines.

A9 Similar to A4b but lighter and fitted with the A6 fuel system so as to achieve a range of 400 miles. Control was to have been by accelerometer during the early part of the trajectory, and then by radio during the glide portion. The missile was to be continuously monitored by two radar stations to obtain a constant fix of its location, and when directly above the target it would be commanded into a vertical dive. It was hoped that this trajectory would make detection and defence more difficult.

This design was scheduled for production until, in 1943, the military situation demanded a quicker and more easily manufactured solution and it was therefore abandoned in favour of the A4. Some reports speak vaguely of a piloted version with pressurised cabin, retractable landing gear and controls to allow it to be landed manually at the end of its flight, but there was no military value in such a project and such ideas probably relate to musings about post-war possibilities rather than suggestions for a definite project. It may be this which has caused the occasional flight of fancy regarding a piloted missile which was to have crossed the Atlantic and aim at New York, after which the pilot would take to his parachute for a rendezvous with a convenient U-Boat.

A10 This was the project for a two-stage rocket for use as a trans-Atlantic bombardment missile. It was conceived in 1940 (before America entered the war, one notes) and the A10 was to be the first stage with the A4 or A9 – proposals varied – as the second stage.

The range was expected to be in the (continued on p. 42)

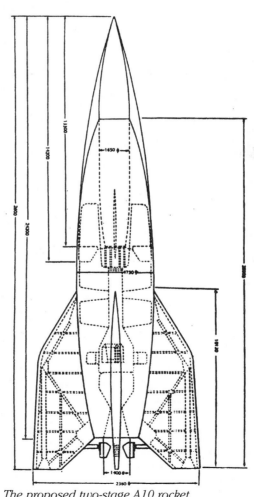

The proposed two-stage A10 rocket.

(continued from p. 41) region of 2,800 miles, but although preliminary calculations were carried out, no detailed design was ever prepared.

It is also worth remembering that an A4 was fired from a submerged U-Boat in the Baltic in late 1942. This was in the course of studying a proposal to send a suitably equipped U-Boat to the Atlantic coast of the USA and then fire a few missiles at selected targets. As the proposal was examined more closely, however, and as the build quality of the production A4 became apparent, it was obvious that this idea was never practical. It was impossible to fuel a rocket inside a U-Boat, and the conditions that would have to be endured by a fuelled and primed rocket during an ocean voyage would more or less guarantee that it would be completely unserviceable and highly unstable by the time it got there. The idea got no further.

By the middle of 1944, A4 rockets were coming off the production line in increasing numbers. It has been estimated that possibly 3,000 were used up in experiments, testing and training and that about a quarter of these were failures on account either of errors on the part of the launching troops or because of structural defects. The *Mittelwerke* factory was intended to have a capacity of 900 A4 missiles per month by autumn 1944 and maintain this rate throughout 1945. The total produced in 1944 was approximately 7,500, and in the first three months of 1945 a further 2,500 were made. When the operation against England began in September 1944 an estimated 1,800 missiles were ready for use. It is believed that production of one A4 required 4,000 man-hours, of which 2,600 were in the *Mittelwerke* and the rest by sub-contractors. At *Mittelwerke* two 10-hour shifts of 2,300 men worked each day. Production was affected by supply difficulties arising from Allied bombing of the German transport system which reduced output by 10–15 per cent. The scale of launchings was also affected by 25 per cent by the loss of fuel manufacturing plants in the west and a further 15 per cent when similar plants in the east were captured by the Russians.

But, in spite of all these problems, the project went forward and in the summer of 1944 the service troops, who had trained on the missiles at Blizna and Peenemünde, were deployed to France. As with the V-1 programme, the enormous bunkers proposed for storage, servicing and firing, were all destroyed or rendered unusable by Allied bombing, and it was the mobile units which did the business. The sites which were originally selected for the mobile launchers, in the Cherbourg peninsula and the vicinity of Calais, were all over-run by the Allies before the V-2 could be put into service. Plans were then made for firing from Belgium, between Tournai and Ghent, then from Antwerp, but the speed of the British advance into Belgium soon out-paced these proposals and the final choice was the Hague in the Netherlands. Two launch groups were formed, Gruppe Nord to fire against London, and Gruppe Sud to fire against targets in France and Belgium.

Gruppe Sud was first to fire operationally, at 8.30 a.m. on 8 September, when it launched a V-2 aimed at Paris which failed to reach its target. Later that day, just after 6.30 p.m., Gruppe Nord set up two rockets aimed at London and fired them in quick succession. The first landed at 6.40 p.m. at Staveley Road in Chiswick as we have seen, some eight miles away from the aiming point in Southwark. A few seconds later the second rocket fell in a field near Epping, Essex, a good 18 miles from the aiming point.

Firing continued from the Hague; the Allies soon discovered the area from which the launching was being done, but since the vehicles simply drove off as soon as they had fired the rocket, there was never anything to hit when bombing raids were made on the area and except for damaging the local houses and killing the local population, raiding had no effect.

The last rocket was fired from the Hague, landing at 7.21 p.m. on 27 March 1945 on a block of flats in Whitechapel and killing 134 people. Altogether a total of 1,359 V-2 rockets was aimed at England, of which 517 arrived in London, and 27 in Norwich, killing 2,754 people and injuring 6,523 more.

As to defence, there was none. There was no way that such a weapon could be countered by the technology of 1945. The only conceivable solution was to mass anti-aircraft guns and put up a barrage when a missile was expected in the hope that fragments from bursting shells would detonate the warhead in the sky. Given the near-impossibility of forecasting when and where a rocket might arrive, this idea was given very short shrift. Artillery flash-spotting troops were deployed in Belgium to observe the skies over the Hague and spot the track of an ascending missile, so that some warning, however scant, could be given to England by radio. A special RAF unit, 108 Mobile Air Reporting Unit, took radars to Belgium to try and achieve radar detection of the launches, but the system produced as many false alarms as real ones and frequently failed to spot the rocket at all. The only thing which stopped the V-2 bombardment of London was the advance of Allied soldiers into the Netherlands. On 29 March 1945 Gruppe Nord fell back into Germany, taking 60 unfired missiles with it.

Gruppe Sud had also made its mark; a total of 1,341 V-2s was fired against Antwerp, 98 against Liège, 65 against Brussels, 15 against Paris, five against Luxembourg, and 11 against the Rhine bridges at Remagen.

The High Pressure Pump

In about 1885 two Americans named Lyman and Haskell appeared at the door of the Chief of Ordnance, US Army, with a proposal for a new and powerful cannon. At that time, it should be recalled, the only cannon propellant was gunpowder, which was impossible to control. You could make the grains larger or smaller, but beyond that there seemed no way to modify its speed of burning, and as a result there were limits to what you could do in the way of cannon construction. Build the barrel too short, and a portion of the powder was ejected before it had completely burned, so wasting propellant; make the barrel too long and the powder burned out and the subsequent friction in the bore tended to restrict velocity. Put a bigger charge in and you ruptured the gun.

Lyman and Haskell's alternative proposition sounded logical. You built a breech-loading cannon, and then, at intervals up the barrel, you placed branching secondary chambers with breech-blocks, swept back at an angle so that, in plan, it looked like a herring-bone. You now loaded the shell into the gun chamber and followed it up with a cartridge, and you also loaded more cartridges, one into each side-branching chamber. You then fired the charge behind the shell. As the shell moved up the bore with the hot gas behind it, it came to the entrance to the first side chamber, and as it passed, the hot gases ignited the charge therein. This exploded and added more propelling gas and power to the shell, giving it more acceleration. The same thing would happen as it passed each chamber, so that eventually it would have the combined explosion gases of perhaps five or six cartridges behind it. Since the chambers were spaced out, the size of the cartridges could be calculated so that just as the force from one had reached its maximum, the next would come into play, and because of the expanding space behind the shell the pressure would never rise to a dangerous figure which might break the gun. And so the shell would leave the muzzle at some fearful velocity, never previously attained, and would reach to an unheard-of range.

Well, all this was too good to miss, and the Lyman and Haskell gun was forthwith ordered to be built, in 6-inch calibre. And in 1885–86 it was given a series of tests with results that were quite astonishing. The velocity attained was rather less than that which a common 6-inch gun with no additional chambers could achieve. Something was obviously wrong with Lyman and Haskell's theory. Careful study revealed the flaw; the sealing of the shell inside the rifling was faulty, so that the flames of the first explosion leaked past the shell and ignited the second chamber before the shell had reached it., so setting up a pressure in front of the shell which, of course, nullified some of the energy behind it and thus reduced the velocity. The same effect fired all the other chambers ahead of the shell. The Lyman and Haskell gun was forthwith consigned to the history books.

About thirty years later, with a major war in progress in Europe, somebody – the name is lost – proposed the multiple-chambered gun to the British Ordnance Board. But the Ordnance Board had been around for a long time and it had the reports of the Chief of Ordnance, US Army on its shelves, and somebody remembered the 1885 attempt and its result. So the idea was politely turned down.

Rather less than thirty years went by before the next appearance, which was in early 1943 when a German engineer named Cönders, working for the Röchling Eisen- und Stahlwerke of Leipzig proposed the idea to Albert Speer, Hitler's minister of munitions. Whether Cönders knew of the Lyman and Haskell gun is not known; it would seem that he did not, or else he was so confident of his engineering ability that he felt that all the problems could be overcome. Through his contact with Speer he was able to obtain Hitler's ear and was able to convince the *Führer* that this was indeed a war-winning weapon, since it promised a piece of artillery which would span the English Channel with ease. Moreover, he was also able to extract a condition: that the development would rest in his hands alone and that there would be no involvement (he probably meant interference) from the Army Weapons Office or any other official body. It should be said that Cönders and the Röchling Eisen- und Stahlwerke were not exactly strangers to Hitler; they had developed the Röchling anti-concrete shell, dealt with elsewhere in these pages, which had deeply impressed Hitler with its performance, and the *Führer* probably thought that if they could come up with one winner, their chances of coming up with another were quite good.

Cönders went off and made a scale model of his gun to fire 20mm cannon shells. This worked satisfactorily, and since this appeared to augur well for the future of the project, Hitler now made one of his typical grandiose enhancements. Instead of a simple gun or two, a battery of 50 barrels would be emplaced on concrete behind Calais, aligned upon London. The emplacement would be built into a hill and there would be underground chambers for storing ammunition and loading, so that a constant barrage of fire could be kept up by night and day. The 150-metre barrels would be 15cm calibre (6-inch) and would have an indeterminate number of side-chambers – whatever might prove necessary to achieve the desired range. Indeed, the postulated figure went as high as 28 chambers per barrel at one stage of the planning. Loading such a weapon would be a slow business, but if we assume one shot every 15 minutes, which could probably have been reached, the battery would thus have been able to drop 200 shells an hour on London. Presumably the barrels would have been slightly splayed so as to spread the fall of shot, and with that and the inevitable degree of natural dispersal of the shells in the target zone, a fair amount of havoc could have been unleashed on central London with such a bombardment continuing over a period of several days.

By the later summer of 1943 work had begun at Marquise-Mimoyecques, between Calais and Boulogne and 95 miles in a direct line from London, where two suitable spots were selected and excavation commenced. The plan was to build two banks of 25 barrels each, protected by enormous steel plates slotted to allow only the muzzles to protrude. Below this an army of miners and engineers laboured to build the supporting system. Meanwhile Cönders worked on his full-sized gun, 15cm calibre, and on the design of the shell, a long dart-like projectile weighing about 300lb and with a set of flexible metal fins which were wrapped around the shell in the barrel but which sprang out into the air stream once the shell had left the muzzle of the gun.

The development of the full-sized gun was undertaken at the Hillersleben Proving Ground, a military establishment of considerable size devoted entirely to weapon development. An area some 19 miles long and up to 8 miles wide, it was located 15 miles northwest of Magdeburg, and about 80 miles west of Berlin. About 15 miles down the range from the administration buildings, in an isolated area forbidden to all except those connected with the development, the 'High Pressure Pump' as the gun was code-named, was assembled and tested. The gun was mounted on a concrete ramp so as to give an elevation of about 6 degrees, sufficient to achieve a range of about 8km with special proof projectiles which resembled dumb-bells.

All did not go well. The side-chambers were to be fired electrically in sequence, but this gave problems, and the shells became unstable at high velocities. These, in addition, were not high enough to produce the trajectory which had been forecast. Calculations showed that a muzzle velocity of something approaching 5,000 feet per second would be required to pitch a shell from Mimoyecques to London, and the best that the test gun achieved was 3,300 ft/sec, nowhere near good enough but, even so, too high for the shell's stability in flight. In addition, the shell failures were compounded by irregular opening of the fins or, in several cases, failure to open at all. And, to add to the problems, periodically the gun would suffer an internal explosion and a section or two would be blown to pieces and have to be replaced.

Even so, construction of a full-sized single-barrel gun was now under way at Misdroy, on the Baltic coast close to Peenemünde. An artillery battalion had been formed to fire it and was, by the end of 1943, undergoing training in the use of the gun. Construction was also forging ahead in the Pas de Calais, so Cönders had to make his gun work.

Matters came to a head in March 1944 when General von Leeb of the *Heereswaffenamt* decided to go and inspect this mysterious gun at Misdroy and watch it put through its paces. The demonstration shoot was a total disaster, with shells flying haphazardly through the air, and it was obvious that the Cönders gun was nowhere near being a viable weapon – and by that time something like 20,000 projectiles were either made or in process of being made. General Leeb convened a conference on the spot and called in various *HWA* experts; far too much time and money had been sunk into this project simply to walk away from it, and, in any case, whoever decided to cancel it would have to make his explanations to Hitler in person, never an attractive prospect. There was no time now for pandering to Cönders' insistence upon total autonomy in the design and production of the weapon. As General Schneider of the *HWA* commented, had the *HWA* been called in at the start of the project they would doubtless have thrown it out forthwith, but had they been ordered to make it work, they might very well have succeeded; now they would be lucky if they could salvage something from the wreckage.

Three problem areas were identified; firstly the shape of the shells; secondly the old problem of flash passing round the shell to ignite the side chambers in advance of the shell and thus generate excessive local pressures; and thirdly the problem of igniting the side chambers at precisely the right moment.

The shell question was addressed simply by calling in six different design and manufacturing companies and asking for their best effort. Skoda, Krupp, Wittkowitz Eisen- und Stahlwerke, Röchling, Fasterstoff and Bochumer Verein all produced workable designs and prototypes were made. The question of pre-ignition was more or less solved by the use of a large cylindrical piston which fitted behind the base of the projectile and acted as a pusher and a gas seal, being discarded as the projectile left the gun muzzle. The question of the ignition of the charges was more difficult. Electric ignition of a charge is not instantaneous, but lies within a tolerance of about 0.015 of a second which, with a shell travelling at a velocity of, say, 2000 metres per second means that in the time taken to ignite the propellant the shell will have moved about 30 metres along the barrel. Precise ignition was therefore impossible, and the only solution was simply to do away with the electric ignition system and revert to the original proposal of the 1880s – allow the flash behind the projectile to ignite each chamber as it came to it.

Even with all these points attended to, there were still some weaknesses in the concept. Wear on the junction of the main bore and the side-chambers could give rise to some odd pressure effects, and since the chambers were relatively close together (3.20 metres) it was possible for one chamber to ignite while the previous one was still building up its pressure, and the resultant meeting of forces would set up sporadic peaks of high pressure in the barrel.

Experiments had also shown that the idea of 20 or more side-chambers was not practical. After about six of the side-chambers had functioned the projectile was moving so fast that the subsequent explosions had no time to develop a useful pressure; space was evolving behind the moving projectile faster than the gases could fill it.

By May 1944 sufficient projectiles from the various manufacturers had been assembled and the Misdroy gun was to be put through its paces once more. However, by this time, other factors had entered the equation. As related elsewhere, the *FZG 76* or V-1 missile was about to be brought into service, and the Allies suspected that launching sites for it were being prepared all over northern France. This led the Allies to carry out an exhaustive photographic survey, searching for such launch sites, and in the process the activity at Mimoyecques was discovered. As early as September 1943 RAF photo-interpreters had seen loops from the main Calais–Boulogne rail line which ran into tunnels beneath the two battery sites. In October another reconnaissance flight showed excavations being driven down into the area of these tunnels and being concealed by false haystacks. Whatever it was – and the estimates of its purpose were varied – it obviously boded no good for the British Isles and in November the US Ninth Air Force delivered a raid which bombed the area around both tunnels.

By this time the Germans were wise in the ways of deceiving aerial reconnaissance. They knew from experience that if they immediately cleared up the damage and made everything good, the RAF or the USAAF would simply come back for another try. So they abandoned work on the western site, and, carefully leaving a useful amount of debris untouched, continued work surreptitiously on the eastern battery. Tunnelling and other underground activities continued throughout the winter.

Towards the end of May 1944 the Misdroy tests were run, firing the different models of shell into the Baltic. Ranges of about 55 miles were occasionally reached, and the considered opinion was that if the muzzle velocity could be increased to about 5,000 ft/sec then the desired range would be possible. Unfortunately this rosy prospect was immediately dimmed when the gun blew itself apart, two sections being demolished. Bad workmanship was blamed, replacements ordered, and more trials scheduled for July 1944.

By this time, though, the Allied air forces were scrutinising every inch of northern France for signs of weapon activity, and Mimoyecques again came under the stereoscopes. Careful study of photographs showed that there had been a considerable amount of activity since the previous October. On 6 July, therefore, 617 Squadron of the Royal Air Force made its contribution. In the course of a series of raids on suspected flying bomb sites, a 12,000 lb 'Tallboy' penetrating bomb landed on the top of the eastern Mimoyecques battery, bored into the earth and detonated, leaving an enormous crater and severely damaging much of the installation; four other Tallboys near-missed but delivered such a ground shock that one of the sloping shafts intended to take the gun barrels, and some of the underground tunnels collapsed. Indeed one German engineer opined that the place was wrecked beyond possible repair.

By coincidence, the renewed trials at Misdroy took place on 4 and 5 July; eight shells were fired, one reaching 58 miles into the Baltic, and then the gun burst once more. After the usual post-mortem it was decided to call in some experts to re-design the side-chambers and strengthen the barrel. But in June the Allies had invaded France and in August they over-ran the Mimoyecques site and brought the saga of the V-3 to an end.

Well, an end as far as the threat to London was concerned; but at Misdroy the work went forward, testing new shells, new configurations of barrel, new propelling charges. There seemed little point in it; by that time recriminations were flying quite freely; Cönders blamed the *HWA*, the *HWA* blamed Cönders and Röchling, and so it went round. In November General Dornberger (whom we have already met in connection with the V-1 and V-2) was ordered by SS-General Kammler to be ready to take over two 'High Pressure Pumps' for field service, an order which might well have caused Dornberger some wonder. How did one put a 150-metre long concrete-bound gun into 'field service'?

The answer to this lies shrouded in hearsay and mystery. It is said that two short-barrel versions were made and put into action in support of the December 1944 Battle of the Bulge in the Ardennes. One was allegedly mounted on either a converted railway gun mounting or on a number of railway flat cars coupled together – accounts vary – and the other was simply laid out on a convenient hillside, presumably anchored by concrete blocks or steel girders driven into the ground. The railway equipment is said to have been fired against the US Third Army some time in December from an unspecified position, the ground mount from a site near Hermeskeil at targets in Luxembourg. Both weapons were supposedly blown up when the American counter-attack drove the German forces back. Another report claims that one shortened gun was mounted 'near Trier'.

This, frankly, is hard to believe. The initial German advance swept the Allies out of Luxembourg at such a speed that any pre-arranged targets in the state would have been out of date within the first day of fighting. The weather was so bad that air observation would have been impossible and shooting fin-stabilised projectiles into the teeth of a blizzard would have resulted in shells going anywhere but where they were aimed. And the eventual German retreat was a slow, well-ordered fall-back which would have given ample time to remove both guns without the need to blow them up to avoid capture. Indeed the Hermeskeil area was not even reached in the retreat. No combat reports or accounts of the battle have ever referred to mysterious shells landing where no shells ought to have landed, and had they done so they could scarcely have been assumed to be aerial bombing in weather conditions which kept both sides out of the sky for most of the battle. And there are no reports anywhere of any Allied unit finding the remains of any multiple-chambered guns. The whole business has a distinct smell of ripe Limburger; I doubt if it will ever be satisfactorily resolved.

What information the Allies gained of the Cönders gun came firstly from accounts given by the few people captured in the Mimoyecques area with any comprehensive knowledge of the site and its purpose. This was enough to alarm the higher command and an investigative mission was dispatched to the site to find out what it could. All it found out was that it appeared to be a deadly weapon aimed at the heart of London, and after some degree of argument between Winston Churchill and the Foreign Office, the two battery sites were demolished by piling surplus bombs and explosives inside and detonating them, wrecking the installation so well that a civil engineer, after examining the wreckage, opined that it would be easier and cheaper to build a new installation than to repair the damage.

The second, and more revealing discovery was when Allied troops finally captured the Hillersleben Proving Ground and found two guns in situ, though somewhat damaged. The reports of the examining commission observed that,

> 'It is not known for certain whether the damage was due to demolition or accident, but it seems probable, from rumours that had been heard by the staff in other parts of the establishment, that at least one had suffered self-destruction. This theory would be consistent with the presence of a linnet's nest, containing warm eggs, found in an opening of the tube less than 14 days after the place was captured.
>
> 'Apart from the rumour referred to above, no information was obtained from the Germans, the guns having been sited some 25km down-range and accessible only to the chosen few, who had of course disappeared from Hillersleben.'

Two guns were found, both 15cm smooth-bore, one with 10 pairs of subsidiary chambers, the other with five pairs. The length from breech face to muzzle was 75 metres (246ft). A noticeable difference between the two guns was that on the first gun the chambers were at right-angles to the bore, whilst on the second they were inclined at 45 degrees towards the rear. On

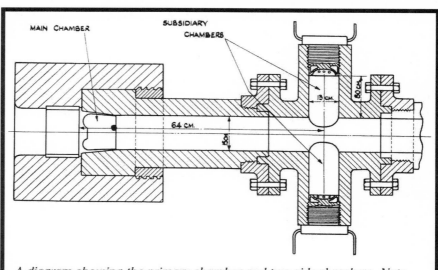

A diagram showing the primary chamber and two side-chambers. Note that in this case, the chambers join the bore at 90 degrees instead of 45 degrees as in the first gun. This appears to have made little difference to the performance.

examination it was found that the first gun used a screw breech system for its main breech, while the second used a sliding block and the cartridge case of the standard 10.5cm leFH 18 field howitzer. Both guns used screw breeches on the side chambers, loaded with bag charges.

The report (CIOS XXVIII-2) of the investigative team from the Combined Intelligence Objectives Sub-Committee which visited Hillersleben between 5 and 18 May 1945 sums everything up,

'In spite of an intensive search for records, and persistent interrogation of the German staff, no direct evidence of the method of ballistic calculation, nor of the results obtained, were unearthed.'

Nor has any emerged since then. We know no more about the V-3 today than we did fifty years ago.

V-4?

The expression 'V-4' appears here and there, but it rarely seems to apply to the same thing twice. It has been applied to the A9/A10 rocket combination, to the German nuclear bomb, to the piloted V-1 and to a postulated German radioactive bomb, among other things. According to one reporter, Hitler had the last word on the subject. Upon being informed, early in 1945, that a mysterious man in Sweden was telling various foreign diplomats that he was a German agent who knew all about the V-4 project, Hitler laughed and said 'He's no V-man, he's an S-man!' a play on words, since the German expression *V-Mann* meant *Vertrauens-mann* or confidential agent, while *S-Mann (Schwindel-mann)* was in common use for confidence tricksters and fraudsters in general.

It would seem likely that if V-4 had any application, then it would have been to the German nuclear programme, but since this virtually ended in 1942, long before the concept of the V-weapons appeared, this has to be discounted. The term was certainly used in an official US publication of 1946 on German missile development, where it was applied to the piloted V-1, but as we have seen later information showed that this project was officially known as *Reichenberg*, never as V-4.

The radioactive bomb is dealt with elsewhere, with the rest of the nuclear threat, which leaves us with the A9/A10 combination missile for the bombardment of America. Since this is allied to the V-2, and since it appeared after the adoption of the V-weapons terminology, it has to be admitted that there is a reasonable argument for applying it to this development. But, again, there is no German authority for it.

Aircraft

The *Luftwaffe* was, in many respects, created as an extension of the German Army's fighting ability, insofar as it was intended principally as a supporting arm for the ground troops and as a defence of the *Reich*, and rather less as a long-range strategic weapon. As a result, fighter aircraft had a high priority and many remarkable developments were therefore produced in this field.

Messerschmitt 163

One of the early ideas in this line was to produce a fighter propelled by a rocket motor, in order to get up to operational height very quickly, after which it could cruise down, dealing with enemy aircraft on the way. The first practical rocket fighter was the Messerschmitt 163A, a stubby and awkward-looking single-seat machine powered by a liquid-fuel Walter rocket. After being towed around in order to prove that it could fly – for its appearance was against it on that score – the Me 163A was finally given its first powered flight in August 1941, when it was timed at speeds of over 600mph. If one remembers that the average speed of a fighter aircraft at that time was about 350mph, the Me 163A held out great promise. A second version, the Me 163B, was built, with a more powerful bi-fuel rocket motor. Then another variant was developed by the Junkers company, the Ju 263, but the project remained firmly in Messerschmitt hands and this model was renamed the Me 263.

However, there is a lot more to producing a viable fighter aircraft than simply making it fly. It has to be armed, it has to be controllable, and it has to be put into production, and all these things take time. Although the Me 163 flew in 1941, it was not perfected until the middle of 1944. About 370 were built and armed in the last months of the war and were sent to various airfields around Germany in order to be used against Allied air raiders. From accounts of RAF and USAAF fliers who met these machines, they were highly impressive and very dangerous, moving so fast that the air gunners had little or no chance to deal with them. But their combat endurance was very short – little more than 25 minutes, most of which was unpowered – and they were too few in number to make much impression.

The *Luftwaffe's* Viper

By the beginning of 1944 Allied air raids were beginning to put a considerable strain on the *Luftwaffe's* fighter arm, and in February the *RLM* sent out a letter to aircraft manufacturers asking for proposals for a 'small, fast fighter' which would not demand scarce raw materials in its construction. Among the recipients of this letter was Dr. Ing. Erich Bachem, one-time technical director of the Fieseler aircraft company who had set himself up in business in Bad Waldsee, south of Ulm, as a consultant and supplier of components to the aircraft industry.

Bachem was an experienced glider pilot, and from his contacts with Fieselerwerke knew of the development of the Fi 103 (or *FZG 76* or V-1); he also knew about jet propulsion and rocket-assisted take-off experiments. And putting one thing and another together he came up with the idea of a small, cheap, flying machine (you can scarcely call it an aeroplane) which would be fired straight up into the air by a rocket. It would be manned, but in deference to the pilot, who would scarcely be in a position to control anything for the first few seconds of flight, the initial climb would be conducted by an auto-pilot. When the machine reached operational altitude – about 30,000 feet – the rocket motor would have burned out, the pilot would have regained his senses and would then switch off the auto-pilot, turn the machine into a glide posture, and glide down into the formation of enemy bombers against which he had been launched. Once among them he would fire off his armament of rockets, glide away from the formation, head for his base and, once there, would parachute clear, leaving the machine to crash. It was hoped that sufficient of the motor and other parts might be salvaged from the wreckage to allow them to be used again. The whole affair, from launch to parachute, would last no more than three minutes and would take place within sight of the launching pad.

Bachem worked out the design of the 'BP20' in detail and in August 1944 submitted it to the *RLM*, where it received some support. Somehow the SS got wind of the project, and they gave it vigorous support in September 1944 as the Ba 349, allocated it the code-name *Natter* ('Viper'), gave it the topmost priority under the SS gradings, and classified the entire project as *Geheime Reichs Sache*, a more serious category of security than the usual *Geheim Kommando Sache*. Only the designers and construction personnel concerned had any knowledge of this project, and even that was compartmentalised.

The first *Natter* was produced in October 1944, a small (5.7m long, 3.2m wing-span), mid-wing monoplane made almost entirely of wood, using shapes which could be easily made in any carpenter's workshop and thus not interfere with other aircraft production programmes. Propulsion was two-stage. The primary or sustainer motor was a Walter 109-509A-2 bi-fuel rocket using *T-Stoff* (hydrogen peroxide) and *C-Stoff* (a 50/50 mixture of hydrazine hydrate and methanol). Some 1,320lb of fuel were carried, which gave the motor a full power thrust of 3,700lb-ft for about 80 seconds. The initial take-off impulse was provided by two or possibly four SR34 solid-fuel rockets, each delivering about 2,200lb-ft for 12 seconds, because for the first few seconds the sustainer motor was not delivering full power

Natter was to be launched almost vertically, from a simple framework. At first this consisted of two 50-foot vertical poles embedded in the ground. Lugs on the wings of *Natter* ran in guides on the poles. The final version consisted of a single pole 52.5 feet high in a concrete foundation 6.5 feet deep. Lugs on the fuselage and fin ran in a channel on this pole and additional support was provided by two flat strips parallel to the pole which were in contact with a slide under the wings. The whole ramp could be rotated about its foundation so that the cockpit of the aircraft was pointed towards any point of the compass. A simple winch and hoist were used to place the aircraft on the launcher.

Natter left the launcher accelerating at 2.2*g*, and the take-off rockets burned for 12 seconds, by which time the machine had reached about 3,500 feet and the sustainer motor was delivering full power. The take-off rocket cases now fell away and *Natter* continued to climb, accelerating at about 0.7*g*, until it reached a speed of about 435mph. The pilot then took over from the auto-pilot, throttled the engine back and continued climbing at the same speed until he reached his intended altitude; the maximum he could achieve was calculated to be 39,400 feet. Once at his operational height he would again throttle back the engine to set a cruising speed of 406mph, although by this time the fuel would be almost entirely consumed.

Now the pilot would glide down to the enemy formation. *Natter* was to be provided with 20 R4M rockets in a cluster of barrels in the nose. According to the records these were to be fired in a single salvo at a range of 50–100 metres from the target, which seems to be somewhat close. (It might be noted that alternative armament was suggested; either 33 R4M rockets, or 24 75-mm *Föhn* rockets, or a bank of 30-mm cannons; the final choice was never made.) Once the rockets had been fired, the pilot was to go into an evasive glide, in the direction of his base, until he reached an altitude of about 10,000 feet. He would then jettison the nose of the fuselage, release his safety harness and fold the control column forward. This action automatically threw out the braking parachute packed in the rear of *Natter*. The sudden deceleration caused by the parachute opening would throw the pilot forward and clear of the aircraft so that he could then open his own parachute and land safely in due course. It was originally thought that the braking parachute would allow the *Natter* to be landed on its nose at a relatively low falling speed, so that the sustainer rocket motor could be salvaged, refurbished and used once more, but after a few experimental flights it became obvious that this was not practical; the landing speed was too great and the damage to the motor too serious for it to be easily or economically repaired.

It can be seen from this description that *Natter* was potentially the most versatile and invulnerable weapon in the whole German secret armoury. Its high speed and rapid rates of manoeuvre would make it an extremely difficult target to intercept. But the route from drawing board to service is always fraught with problems, and *Natter* was no exception.

Experimental aircraft were built by Bachem at Waldsee; models were made and tested in wind-tunnels at Berlin and Brunswick. Secrecy was so compartmented that the firm never saw the results of these tests other than information that the aircraft should have satisfactory flying characteristics at speeds up to 685mph. Flight tests began when the first aircraft was completed in November 1944. The flight test programme was to consist of unmanned take-offs, some with an auto-pilot, gliding tests, powered flight tests at altitude, and finally manned take-offs. Initially take-offs were made at Heuberg near Sigmaringen. The assisted take-off rockets were used, two extra being installed as a substitute for the Walter rocket engine. The towed gliding tests were made to explore stability and stalling characteristics, *Natter* being towed behind or vertically below a Heinkel 111 bomber.

Once the wind tunnel tests had been completed, construction of full-sized *Natters* took place and by mid-October 1944 unmanned vertical launches were being made, the machine being fitted with a braking parachute to bring it back to earth fairly close to the launch site. Each launch taught the designers something new, and of the fifteen 'Mark 1' models built virtually every one had minor changes. A Mark 2 version was then made, the fuselage being about one foot longer, and three or four of these were launched in tests.

In February 1945 the SS higher authorities decided the programme was not going fast enough, and ordered a manned take-off with rocket motor and take-off rockets, even though the flight testing programme was some distance away from that stage. The pilot, Oberleutnant Lothar Siebert, climbed into the machine, the rockets fired and the *Natter* went straight up to about 300 feet, whereupon the cockpit cover fell off. The *Natter* turned onto its back and continued ascending to about 1,500 feet, then turned over and power-dived straight into the ground, killing the unfortunate Siebert instantly.

The initial assessment was that the cockpit cover hinge had failed, and since the cover also carried the pilot's headrest, its sudden removal during the initial acceleration allowed the pilot's head to fly back and strike the fuselage, rendering him unconscious. This suggests that the auto-pilot either failed or was not in use. A later examination suggested that either a spoiler in the tail had functioned wrongly, causing a sudden change in the flight path, or that the auxiliary take-off rockets had been wrongly installed so that their thrust axis was not correctly aligned with the *Natter*.

Unmanned launches were resumed and development continued. A Mark 3 version was designed, the principal feature being that the wing was

a separate component which could be inserted through a hole in the fuselage and secured in place, thus allowing easier transportation of the
machine.

Approximately 30 aircraft were built at Waldsee, of which 15 were Mark 1
and the remainder Mark 2. Of these 18 were expended in unmanned take-
offs, one was allowed to crash after glide tests and one destroyed in the
manned flight. Shortly before Waldsee was occupied by American troops
part of the Bachem organisation moved to Bad Werdershofen and after a
short stay part moved to St Leonard, a nearby village, with four Mark 2 aircraft and various parts that were found there by the occupying forces. Six
machines were burned to avoid their capture when Bachem left Waldsee.
A further order for Mark 2 *Natters* had been placed with Wolf Hirth
Flugzeugbau at Naber-unter-Teck but only one was ever completed and
delivered to Waldsee.

In the final analysis, it has to be admitted that in spite of its various
tactical attractions, there were some drawbacks to *Natter*. The range was
restricted to within visible distance of the launch site. Its high speed limited
manoeuvrability, which would have been a handicap in combat against
fighter aircraft. It could be used only once to fire a single burst of rockets. The
expense made it an extremely wasteful weapon. And two serious human
limitations existed: firstly the problem of finding safe conditions for training
pilots, for whom a full course in flying rocket aircraft would have been a
necessary preliminary; and secondly the strain on human physique which
would have resulted from the rapid changes in speed and air pressure.

Natter leads us to *Julia* a piloted, rocket-propelled machine of much the
same type, built to answer the same demand, but built so that it would
survive a few take-offs and landings instead of being a one-shot project. It
was designed by Heinkel as the He P-1077 and two machines were under
construction when the war ended. They were never completed, so we cannot really say whether the concept was sound or not.

Dornier's Arrow

Natter and *Julia* might be considered at the far end of the fighter spectrum,
a half-breed between the aeroplane and the pure missile. Not all designers
were quite so bold, and many were content to take more conventional engineering to what appeared to be its furthest limits. In 1937 the Dornier company had contemplated a twin-engined fighter; there was nothing very new
in this idea, but experience showed that twin-engined fighters were bigger
and less easily manoeuvred than single-engines machines. So Dornier came
up with the idea of an aeroplane which had the usual outline of a single-
engined fighter but with two engines buried in the fuselage, one driving the
normal propeller on the front, and the second driving a similar propeller at
the rear end. During 1939–40 a flying test-bed was built and proved that the

idea could be made to work, and in 1941 design of a fully-fledged fighter, the Dornier 231, later re-numbered the Do 335, began. The 335, code-named *Pfeil* ('Arrow'), made its first flight in the autumn of 1943 and was so successful that Dornier was given an order for some 20 machines for service tests and training. It also broke new ground in being the first production machine to use an ejector seat, an essential feature in view of the two propellers. By the end of the war about 90 had been built, of which 20 had been supplied to service squadrons. It could reach a speed of 765km/hr (475mph), was armed with a 30mm cannon and two machine guns, carried a single 500kg bomb and had a range of just over 2,000km, which could be increased by fitting a drop fuel tank in place of the single bomb. Little is known, though, of its combat performance, since by the time it got into the hands of operational units the fuel situation had grounded most of the *Luftwaffe*.

New bombers

With the arrival over Germany of the RAF's four-engined bombers, the proposal to develop an equivalent German machine was put forward and the Heinkel company undertook the development. Their Heinkel 111 was the standard German twin-engined bomber and a highly effective one at that. Numerous variations were developed as the war called for improvements, and taking this well-tried design as a starting point Heinkel designed the He 177 four-engined bomber. Known as the *Greif* ('Griffin'), it was capable of carrying almost eight tons of bombs. In their enthusiasm, however, the designers called for engines which were too powerful.

Though at first glance the *Greif* looked like a twin-engined design, each 'engine' was, in fact, two Daimler-Benz V-12 motors geared together to a single propeller in each wing. While they pulled the machine through the air at a respectable speed, they overheated badly, causing a series of catastrophic accidents. The heat was conducted through the air-frame to the adjacent petrol tanks in the wings, where the fuel was brought rapidly to boiling point and vapourised. The vapour then seeped to the engines, met the flame from the exhaust, and in seconds the plane had exploded. This did its reputation no good at all and did much to set back the development programme. Eventually, with re-positioned engines, the problem was solved, but now the speed had gone down to the point where it became questionable whether the machine was worth it. More trouble arose over armament, the high command demanding a weight of guns and equipment which reduced the performance even further, and eventually the whole programme fell to pieces.

Almost a thousand of these machines were built to one specification or another, and about 700 went to the Eastern Front, many being armed with 5cm and 7.5cm guns for the anti-tank role, but except for one or two raids over England in late 1944 they were never used in their originally-planned strategic role and finished up on the scrap heap.

Another bomber idea was the Focke-Wulf design somewhat grandiosely known as the 1,000 x 1,000 x 1,000, because it was predicted that it would carry 1,000 kilograms of bombs at 1,000 kilometres per hour to a range of 1,000 kilometres. It was a highly-streamlined, delta-winged machine, but since it never got out of the drawing office we have no idea of how close it might have got to the magic figures.

Equally blue-sky was another Focke-Wulf design called the Fw 03-10225. This number does not seem to have any special significance and was probably the drawing office number. The 10225 was a design for a long-range bomber capable of flying 5,000 miles to attack the USA with a bomb-load of 3,000 kilograms. It was intended to fly at extreme altitudes, 35,000 feet and above, at 350mph or more, but, again, never reached even the trial stage.

Jet engines

Far more fundamental than all these peculiar designs was the aircraft feature which, of all those which were developed during the war, has affected design in post-war years the most: the jet engine. Like radar, infra-red, and a lot of other ideas, warlike or peaceful, the jet engine appears to have occurred to different people in different places at more or less the same time, and the subsequent development was solely a matter of how much faith they had in the idea and how well they could 'sell' their idea to higher authority.

In Germany the bulk of the work was done by the Heinkel company; the idea had occurred to its researchers in the early 1930s and in the following years they quietly worked on the theory. A suitable aircraft was designed, and, in order to prove it, was flown using a rocket motor at the Peenemünde research establishment in the early summer of 1939. After a successful flight, the rocket motor was replaced by the first Heinkel jet engine and the aircraft, known as the He 178, flew under jet power at the end of August 1939, the world's first jet-powered flight.

Now came the 'selling' part, and here Heinkel was unsuccessful; nobody was interested. Not the *Luftministerium*, not even Hitler himself. Then, to make matters worse, in the summer of 1940, when everything seemed to be going Germany's way, Hitler was so convinced that it would all be over quickly that he forbade the development of any project which could not be guaranteed to be brought into service within twelve months. The Heinkel company went home with its jet aircraft and, officially, put it to one side. In fact, it kept up its research work, though at a reduced priority.

By that time somebody else was looking at the same idea. The Junkers designers had also thought of jet propulsion, but instead of trying for an aircraft straight away, they contented themselves with perfecting an engine. In the latter part of 1941 they finally fitted one into a converted Messerschmitt Bf 110 for flying tests, and as a result of these managed to raise some interest from the *Luftwaffe*, whose leaders realised by 1942 that the 'one-year' ban was a dead number and were casting around for new ideas. Unfortunately the *Luftwaffe* had the disastrous habit of asking for too much; whenever a designer went before them with a proposition, the *Luftwaffe* chiefs would invariably agree, but would ask for twice the speed, treble the ceiling, double the fire-power, five times the muzzle velocity, or some equally unlikely figures. In the case of jet fighters they demanded a production rate of a thousand machines a month, and with this made clear they authorised production of the Messerschmitt 262 fitted with Junkers engines in the autumn of 1943.

Messerschmitt 262

The history of the Me 262 is one of the great 'might-have-been' stories of the war. Design had begun in late 1938, but Messerschmitt could raise very little interest from the *Luftministerium*, and at one stage of its progress Hitler directed that it should be rebuilt as a bomber. It eventually flew, with a conventional piston engine shoe-horned into its nose, in April 1941. In June 1942 it made its first flight with the planned two Junkers jet engines beneath the wings, and in July 1943 the fifth development model, with tricycle undercarriage and the final configuration, made its first flight. More delays followed, but production duly began and the first deliveries were made in June 1944.

By late 1944 production had reached one hundred a month, whereupon the *Luftwaffe* demanded 2,500 a month. In spite of this slight disagreement, the jet fighter managed to get into production in respectable figures, over 1,300 being built before the war ended, and the 100 or so which got into the hands of service pilots and could find fuel gave the Allied air forces a nasty shock, over 100 bombers falling victim to this fast and agile machine. Armed with four 30mm cannon and 24 R4M rockets, it had a top speed of 755km/hr (470mph) when fully loaded and an operational range of over 1,000km. Had this machine appeared a year earlier, the consequences for the Allies would have been grave indeed.

Arado 234

Another firm which went into the jet engine business was the well-known motor company of BMW. It had begun its development in 1934 in conditions of extreme secrecy, and its first engine ran in the summer of 1940. When the Junkers engine was approved by the *Luftwaffe*, BMW was brought in as a contractor to Junkers, but the BMW company later managed to interest the *Luftwaffe* in its own designs and eventually the BMW engine was used in the four-engined Arado 234 *Blitz* bomber, a machine which could travel at over 550mph at an altitude of 33,000 ft. Arado had begun design of this machine as early as 1941, when the jet engine was by no means fully proven, to meet a *Luftwaffe* specification which called for a jet-engined reconnaissance machine with a range of 2,000km (1,250 miles). As originally designed, the Ar 234 was a high-winged monoplane with two Junkers engines, and the first prototype flew in June 1943. Some 20 or more pre-production machines followed before the design was finalised as the Ar 234 B-1, and operational deliveries began in September 1944. This twin-engined machine was virtually unstoppable, with a top speed of 750km/hr (465mph) and a 1500kg bomb load, and made a considerable impression on both the Eastern and Western Fronts, including bombing the famous Remagen bridge. Arado felt that it could stand another two engines, which would boost the top speed and probably allow a greater bomb-load into the bargain, but time was running out by then and beyond a couple of prototypes, the four-engined *Blitz* got no further.

The People's Fighter

By late 1944 things were looking black in Germany and in September the *Luftministerium* issued a demand for a cheap and expendable jet fighter capable of 750km/hr and armed with two 30mm cannon, to be ready for production by 1 January 1945. Today such a demand would be laughed out of existence, but in September 1944 people were prepared to work miracles if necessary, and Heinkel replied with the He 162 *Salamander*, sometimes referred to as the *Volksjäger* or 'People's Fighter'.

This remarkable machine was constructed largely of wood, with the jet engine housed on top of the fuselage exhausting between two tail fins. Design was completed by 30 October, the prototype flew on 6 December, and the first production model appeared in the first week of January. Nine metres long, with a 7.2-metre (23.6ft) wing-span, it flew at 835km/hr (518mph) at 29,000 feet, and by the time the war ended no less than 300 had been built and a further 800 were in various stages of manufacture. One *Luftwaffe* squadron, based at Leck, close to the Danish border, had been issued with a number of He 162s but, like most other *Luftwaffe* squadrons by that time, it had no fuel with which to fly them.

There seems little doubt that the *Luftwaffe* suffered more than its sister services from the indecision and tribal warfare which went on between different factions. In the first year of the war it had undoubted air superiority wherever it appeared, but this was gradually whittled away, and the greatest damage was done by the 'one year ban' and the decision, by Hitler, to restrict the development of weapons which he considered 'defensive' and, by inference, pessimistic or even defeatist. Had the various jet aircraft which were on the drawing board in September 1939 been pushed with the urgency which saw them go from lines on paper to production in just over three months in 1944–45, the Allies might well have found that mounting bombing raids on Germany in 1943–44 would have been so costly in crews and equipment as to have been unsustainable.

Air-Launched Weapons

Getting an aircraft into the air is only part of the problem in war. Once it is there it has to have some form of offensive armament in order to do some damage, and possibly some defensive armament as well. And the armament ideas of the *Luftwaffe* ranged from the brilliant to the absolutely crazy, though it must be admitted there was a bias to the former.

Recoilless guns

In the 1920s the American aviator 'Billy' Mitchell gave some startling demonstrations of the ability of aircraft to bomb, disable and even sink a battleship; so convincing, indeed, that he got himself court-martialled for his temerity in challenging the natural order of things and suggesting that the battleship might not, after all, be the supreme and invincible weapon. The German Air Force, with its modern outlook and absolute conviction of the worth of air power in a future war, was intensely interested in this problem of attacking heavy ships from the air, but its planners were realists enough to appreciate that dropping a bomb on a tethered and unmanned hulk was a different matter from trying to drop one onto a real live moving battleship which was shooting back at them. They therefore looked for solutions which would allow a heavy weight of explosive to be delivered from a distance with some degree of accuracy and some chance of success, and Rheinmetall-Borsig believed it had the answer in the recoilless gun.

The recoilless gun had first seen the light of day as an aircraft weapon during the First World War. Known then as the 'Davis Gun' after its inventor, a Commander Davis of the US Navy, it had been adopted in small numbers by the Royal Naval Air Service for shooting at ships and submarines, though since it did not get into service until the final weeks of the war its efficiency was never really tested. The problem facing the RNAS was to be able to fire a heavyweight shell from a stick-and-string aeroplane without the recoil shaking the aircraft to pieces, The Davis Gun was, in its essentials, two guns joined back-to-back; a shell went into the gun pointing forward and a 'counter-shot' of grease and buckshot into the gun pointing backwards. Between the two projectiles went a cartridge. When the cartridge was fired, the shell went out of the front to hit the target, while the counter-shot went out of the back to disperse harmlessly in the air.

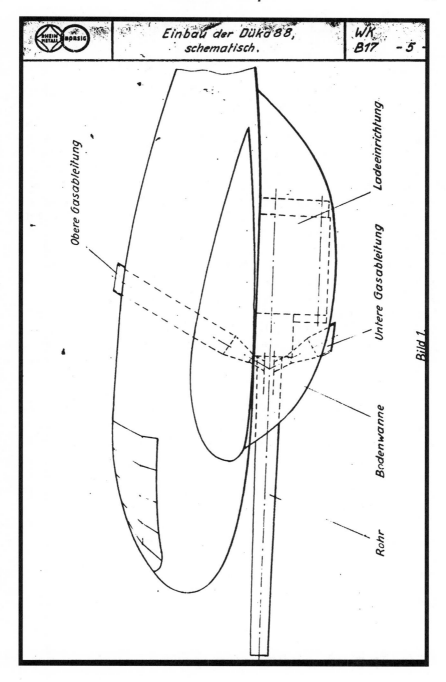

An original Rheinmetall drawing showing the fitting of an 8.8cm
Düsenkanone *recoilless gun, with the gas vents leading up and down.*

Since shell and counter-shot weighed the same and left with the same velocity but in opposite directions, each gun recoiled the same amount, the two cancelled each other out, and the result was a recoilless gun. Obviously, the gunner had to be careful how he pointed it, or the counter-shot could blow his own tail off, but as long as he bore this slight drawback in mind, he had a formidable weapon.

Using the Davis Gun as the starting point, the Rheinmetall company began developing its ideas in about 1937, starting with a 30mm gun. Once they had proved that they could make it recoilless on the ground, it was fitted to an aircraft, whereupon the troubles really started. The system adopted was not to use a counter-shot, but to allow some of the gas from the cartridge to be exhausted from a jet at the back of the gun at high speed. Provided the mass of gas multiplied by the its speed was the same as the mass of the gun's shell multiplied by its speed, then the two effects balanced each other and the gun stayed still. But the high-speed jet did some unfortunate things to the underside of the aircraft beneath which it was fitted, even after the floor was reinforced by 3mm-thick steel plates. Work began on modifying the design to use a jet pipe which directed the blast away from the fuselage, but simply turning the pipe upset the arrangement because the angle of the back-blast also slewed the aircraft tail to one side and upset the aim. The next solution tried was to split the jet between two pipes, leading one downward and the other up, through the aircraft body, to exhaust above and below. This balanced matters and the gun was now considered successful.

Now came the question of reloading it; obviously, a single-shot weapon in such a small calibre was more or less useless. After more trials a rotary magazine feed was developed which allowed ten rounds to be carried. In order to get the release of gas needed for the jets, the cartridges had their forward sections made of plastic. When fired, the plastic disintegrated and allowed some of the gas to pass into the jets while the rest was pushing the shell forward through the barrel.

The gun was subsequently developed to the point of installing it into a Junkers 88, but the priority of the demand had almost vanished by the time it was ready and it never went into service. There is some doubt as to whether, in fact, it was as good as the designers claimed. One of the design team claimed in 1943 that trials in aircraft had shown no damage, but the pilot of one of the test machines, interviewed in 1945, said that every ten-round burst sprang rivets out of the fuselage.

Gerät 104 and *Sondergerät 113A*

Once the basic recoilless principle had been proved, work also began on a monster gun in response to a request from the *Luftministerium* for an anti-ship weapon capable of firing a 1,400lb armour-piercing shell to penetrate battleship deck armour. The object was to use this to bombard the British fleet as it lay at anchor in Scapa Flow. The result of this was *Gerät 104* ('Equipment 104'), a 35cm calibre gun slung beneath an aircraft and retracted hydraulically during flight. With a weapon of this size, a jet efflux would doubtless have wrecked the carrying aircraft completely, so the Rheinmetall engineers went back to Davis' idea and produced a counter-shot weapon. Instead of using a second barrel and special counter-shot, the same result was achieved by making the cartridge case with a special heavy steel casing which weighed 1,400lb, the same as the armour-piercing shell. As the cartridge fired the shell forwards, so it fired the cartridge case back-wards, achieving the necessary balance and recoillessness. Obviously, reloading a 1,400lb shell plus a cartridge of equal weight while in flight was out of the question, so the *Gerät 104* was strictly a one-shot weapon.

But before flight trials could take place, war broke out, and since it was thought that other things were more important, further development of the *Gerät 104* was stopped. A similar weapon, code-named *Münchausen*, was a 54cm calibre gun on the same lines, to be slung beneath the Ju 87 *Stuka* dive-bomber, but this proved to be too much of a good thing. The strain, even of a recoilless gun, was far too much for the smaller aircraft, and the blast which came out of the breech end as the heavy cartridge case was ejected was sufficient to disturb the aircraft in flight. As a result, the whole project was abandoned.

However, other slightly less ambitious recoilless gun ideas were more successful. One of the best was *Sondergerät 113A* ('Special Equipment 113A', or SG 113A), more popularly called the *Jägerfaust*. This was also based on the Davis gun principle of using a counter-shot. A single tube was mounted behind the pilot of a fighter aircraft, and in this was loaded a 5cm anti-tank armour-piercing shell together with a cartridge and a counter shot. The tube was open at top and bottom and the round was retained in place by a shear pin. The technique was very simple: the pilot simply flew close beneath the bomber and then fired the cartridge electrically. The explosion launched the armour-piercing shell upwards and fired the counter-shot downward to balance the recoil. The effect of such a shell striking an aircraft can be imagined, since it was originally designed to wreck a heavily-armoured tank.

After proving that the idea worked, it was improved by being mounted beneath the wings of the aircraft, in order to attack from directly ahead of the bomber. The Me 163 carried six barrels, three beneath each wing, while the Me 262 was scheduled to carry thirty. The tubes were set at a slight angle so that the shells diverged to give a spread of about 20 yards at 100 yards range. At the end of the war there were twelve Me 163s equipped with *Jägerfaust* at Brandeis airfield near Leipzig, and according to some reports at least one bomber was brought down by this weapon.

The SG 113A was the beginning of a series of weapons all known by SG numbers. SG 116, 117, 118 and 119 were all similar counter-shot devices but they used the 30mm cannon shell as their standard projectile. While the 5cm AP shell of the SG 113A was a fearsome weapon, a lighter projectile could do as much damage as was necessary while allowing more armament to be carried on the aircraft. SG 116 was the first model, a single-barrel device of which numbers could be installed in various places on the aircraft as opportunity offered. SG 117, 118 and 119 were all improvements using 'barrel blocks', packs of barrels which could be fitted as complete assemblies and fired in salvos to give a better chance of hitting the target. SG 117 and 118 both used 7-barrel blocks, the only difference between the two systems being in the method of mounting, while SG 119 used a 49-barrel assembly. In order that the discharges should not interfere with each other, a timing device was included in the firing circuit which gave a very slight interval between the firing of each barrel, giving an effective rate of fire of 1,200 rounds a minute to the assembly.

Having got all this into the aircraft the only problem remaining was to make sure the pilot pushed the button at the right moment, and that was not as easy as it looked. With the Me 163 passing under the bomber at 500mph and the bomber passing over the attacker at 300mph, the margin of error was incredibly small, and if the pilot was a tenth of a second wrong in his assessment, he would miss. To solve this problem a photo-electric aiming device called *Zossen* was developed by a Doktor Orthuber of the AEG company at Neustadt. This contained a light source, and a photocell arranged so that the light reflected from the target above would enter the photocell and automatically fire the weapon at the right moment. This was first tested at Werneichen airfield near Berlin in mid-1944, using an aircraft fitted with an ordinary 20mm cannon and flown beneath a cloth target suspended between two balloons. It worked quite well and production began, but very few were ever finished and it is believed that only two were ever installed in aircraft for service.

Other variations on the same idea were *Bombersage*, a 60-barrel 30mm upward-firing gun mounted behind the pilot of a Fw 190, and *Harfe*, a similar battery of 20mm barrels.

Bordwaffen

Another field of research which all the combatants entered was the question of mounting ever-larger orthodox guns into aircraft. The best-known of these were the British and American 75mm guns, but they were small beer compared to some of the armament proposed by the *Luftwaffe*. However, it must be pointed out that the prize in this field goes to the British who managed to mount a 32-pounder (94mm) anti-tank gun in a Mosquito aircraft and fire it successfully, though this was not actually achieved until after the war had ended.

In Germany the trend came about gradually as part of the logical progression in aircraft armament from rifle-calibre machine guns to 20mm cannon, then to 30mm and larger calibres. The root of the problem was the combination of increased speed of the aircraft in combat, which led to shorter engagement times, and stronger construction of aircraft which meant that something more powerful than a rifle-type bullet was needed to do any worthwhile damage. When the two were put together the whole problem resolved itself into doing as much damage as possible in the shortest possible time. There were two ways of solving it; either by exceptionally fast-firing guns of the normal small calibre or by slower-firing weapons from which one shot would do all the damage needed. Each point of view has its adherents. The Americans, for example, chose the first method and after the war produced the General Electric Vulcan Cannon firing the normal 20mm cannon shell but at the phenomenal rate of 6,000 rounds per minute. The Germans were not averse to this solution either, and did quite a lot of research into aircraft cannon design. Just one example was the Mauser MK 213C 20mm cannon which reached a rate of fire of 1,400 rounds per minute. But far more work went into heavier weapons, the so-called *Bordwaffen* of calibres from 37mm to 55mm.

The first requirement was, of course, to make sure that one shot from such weapons would be sufficient to wreck an aircraft, and much research went into designing *Minengeschoss* ('Mine shells') which had a much thinner wall of high-quality steel in order to carry the maximum amount of high explosive inside. At the same time, new types of high explosive were tried which gave much more violent detonation and consequently caused much more damage than was possible with the conventional TNT fillings. With these matters settled, work could then go ahead on producing the guns to fire them and the more difficult task of fitting them into aircraft. The first model was the 5cm *Bordkanone*, which was constructed by taking the now-obsolete 5cm tank gun Model 39, fitting it to a suitable recoil-absorbing mounting, and putting it into an aircraft. This was satisfactory, the recoil being well within the Ju 88's ability to resist, and the next stage in the development was to produce a method of loading while in flight. Hand-loading by a crew member was scarcely feasible, and eventually a 22-round rotary magazine and automatic loader was produced. This allowed a rate of fire of 45 rounds a minute, and by the end of the war no less than 300 of these guns had been produced and fitted. They were almost all sent to the Eastern Front where, with armour-piercing ammunition in their magazines, they were a formidable tank-busting instrument.

The Mauser company now took a hand and developed its 5cm Maschinen Kanone 214, which was the same gun with a magazine of Mauser's own devising, capable of producing a rate of 140 rounds a minute. But development was only completed in the early days of 1945, and before series production of this model could get under way the war was over.

One of the major anti-aircraft developments attempted by the Germans was a 5.5cm automatic gun, the story of which will be told later. While this weapon was being developed, it occurred to several people that it might make a very powerful aircraft cannon, and steps were taken to modify it to suit. Rheinmetall-Borsig designed two models, the MK 112 and MK 115; the 112 used recoil to operate the magazine and reload, while the 115 tapped off gas from the barrel to drive the magazine mechanism. Both achieved a rate of fire of over 300 rounds per minute. Krupp of Essen also produced a design which combined the features of both the Rheinmetall models by using both gas and recoil to drive the mechanism, also giving 300 rounds a minute, but the recoil strain on the aircraft was too much. Like the anti-aircraft gun, the 5.5cm *Bordkanone* never got close to production, since development began too late and the war ended before it was completed.

Finally came the 7.5cm aircraft cannon. This was no more than the standard 7.5cm anti-tank gun Model 40 with a new recoil system and a highly efficient muzzle brake, mounted into a Henschel 129 attack bomber. A 12-shot automatic magazine and loading mechanism was provided. Development began in the summer of 1944 and went so smoothly that by the end of that year 30 guns were contracted for. Early in 1945 the first equipments were issued and were flown into action against Soviet tanks, and it has been reported that the first 14 missions flown knocked out nine heavy tanks. But, like many another idea, it came on the scene too late to have much effect on the hordes of tanks which were by then rolling across eastern Germany.

Air-to-ground rockets

The prospect of attacking tanks from the air with rockets appears to have been thrust into prominence in Germany by the RAF Typhoon fighters which scoured through France in 1944 firing rockets at anything which moved. Two German developments appear to have been tried. The first was *Panzerblitz*, a simple rocket with an armour-piercing head to be fired from fighter aircraft. The warhead was the same 8.8cm hollow-charge head as used on the *Panzerschreck* infantry rocket launcher, but fitted with a more powerful rocket motor. *Panzerblitz I* had a velocity of 300 metres per second and was soon replaced with *Panzerblitz II*, which used a more powerful motor from the R4M rocket and reached 370 metres a second. Both these were developed by Waffenwerke Brünn in Czechoslovakia. The *Panzerblitz* was accepted for service with the intention of mounting it in the Hs 132 jet fighter, but since the Hs 132 never got into the air, the *Panzerblitz* never had a chance to show its paces. Two more models, the *III* and *IV*, were being worked on by the Deutsche Waffen und Munitions company as the war ended. These had the same warhead with more powerful rocket motors which gave velocities up to 600 metres a second.

Another anti-tank weapon in the design stage when the war ended was *Förstersonde*, which was quite normal as far as the rocket went, but somewhat unusual in its method of firing. Like the recoilless anti-bomber armament, *Förstersonde* was mounted vertically behind the pilot, and in order to avoid the problem of aiming it manually, a complicated fire control system was evolved which detected the magnetic field of the tank as the plane passed over and fired the rocket down at the correct moment, without the pilot having to do anything more than keep a course straight over the top of the tank. Very little is known of this project except that trials were made in early 1945 on the fire control system which proved that it was feasible if not immediately perfect, but the weapon never got into service.

Fritz-X

The other system of attacking ground targets which attracted the *Luftwaffe* was the possibility of controlling a bomb after it had been released. The first of these, and probably the most successful, was the FX 1400, which was also known variously as SD 1400 and (most commonly) *Fritz-X*.

The FX 1400 was a glide bomb which was radio controlled from a parent aircraft. It was designed for use against armoured ship targets. Basically the missile was a standard 1400kg *Esau* amatol-filled aerial bomb fitted with a standard bomb fuze and modified to permit the attachment of four wings and a tail unit. This tail unit contained the radio equipment and stabilising gyroscopes and had attached to it at its after end a set of four fins in a 12-sided framework. These fins were equipped with radio controlled, solenoid-operated spoilers which were made to protrude, at radio command, into the slipstream and thus effect a change of range or azimuth. The bomb-aimer followed the course of the bomb by watching a flare in the extreme rear of the weapon. Provision was made for the substitution of an electric lamp for night drops since the brightness of the flare tended to dazzle the bomb-aimer and an electric light was less dazzling but sufficiently bright to be seen.

The development of FX 1400 was begun by Dr Max Kramer of DVL – Deutsche Versuchsanstalt fur Luftfahrt – at Adlershof, Berlin, in 1939. The bomb itself was built by Rheinmetall-Borsig, originally at Düsseldorf, later at Berlin-Marienfelde. Since it was to be remotely controlled by radio, Strassfurth Rundfunk AG was called on to build the receiver and Telefunken to build the transmitter The original tests were carried out by DVL in the Jüterbog area (about 60km south of Berlin) using a Heinkel 111 as the parent aircraft. In the spring of 1941 the experimental station at Peenemünde was drawn into the development (mainly because of the availability of its wind-tunnel) and conducted a second series of tests on its own proving ground. Inasmuch as the technical problems were apparently solved by the autumn of 1941, and since weather conditions in Germany were unfavourable for further tests, DVL and Peenemünde decided to conduct further demonstration tests in Italy in 1942. Siponto, near Foggia, was chosen as the proving ground. The tests took place and ran so true to predicted performance that the whole development was regarded as being completed.

The FX 1400 was an ugly weapon. The forward wings were set rather far up towards the nose, had no sweep-back to the leading edge, were square tipped with a pronounced taper to the trailing edge and were arranged in an asymmetrical cruciform with the broad axis lying in the horizontal plane. The 12-sided tail framework was wider than it was high. It was constructed of flat metal plates at the leading edge and bent steel rods at the trailing edges. One of these rods was insulated and acted as the antenna. The control system, with its simple operation, gave a performance of high nominal accuracy. Error of the order of 2 feet from 20,000 feet was theoretically possible, but the accuracy was, in practice, reduced by controller errors. The whole weapon weighed 3,454 lb, and the warhead was a 1,400 kg armour-piecing bomb fitted with a BZ 38-B Rheinmetall fuze and loaded with poured 40/60 or 50/50 amatol/TNT. Two rows of pressed TNT pellets wrapped in brown paper ran along the axis of the bomb and there was a base surround of pure cast TNT about one inch thick. The total weight of explosive was 300 kg.

From the very beginning of this design spoiler control, hitherto unknown, was used. Years before, Dr Kramer had studied this method of control, appreciated its advantages, and had explored the possibilities of its use. He decided that the disadvantages of spoiler control (greater aerodynamic resistance and greater delay in aerodynamic effect) were unimportant. On the other hand the advantages (simple mechanical construction and immediate response to the control impulse) were of great significance in view of the short flight time of this type of weapon. In FX 1400 a complete aerodynamic tri-axial control mechanism was installed in which the same mechanism could be used for all three axes. In this manner a complete and self-contained steering apparatus could be installed in the bomb.

Steering was achieved by means of spoilers located in the elevators and rudders. These were actuated by solenoids at a rate of 10 times a second in such a way that the mean of the rudder movements corresponded to the desired steering value. The rate of vibration of the spoilers was made to coincide with the mechanical period of vibration of the system. Extensive tests were necessary to establish firmly that this system was feasible for a speed of 280m/sec. It was fortunate that during the first tests of the FX 1400 the first high-speed wind tunnel was brought into use.

The first FX 1400 went into service about the middle of 1943. About 2,000 were built, of which about 200 were dropped operationally. After its efficiency had been proved, in the spring of 1942, Kramer, with his associates, set about replacing the remote radio control with a more jam-proof system using wire control. At that time the drawback of the wire system was that the critical speed at which the wire could be paid out was 150 meters per second. The reason for this low uncoiling rate was due to the whipping of the wire, and steps were taken to remedy this by paying out the wire from the wing tips of the bomb. With this the critical speed could be increased to a value of 300 metres per second. Meanwhile efforts were being made to improve the aerodynamic properties so that the bomb could be dropped from a higher altitude and attain supersonic velocity, thus increasing its penetrative powers.

The first attempt on these lines was the FX 1400 X-2, the principal change being to the steering gear, which was redesigned. It was dropped from 9,000 metres and attained a speed of 300m/sec. Only one test model was built because Kramer had more radical design changes in mind, and when these were incorporated the result became the X-3. This was spin-stabilised by attaching trim tabs to the trailing edges of the main fins and allowing the whole weapon to rotate about its longer axis at a speed of 1 to 1.5 revolutions per second. Originally, when X-1 was gyro-stabilised, the construction necessitated an assembly tolerance of 0.1 per cent in order to obtain the desired trajectory with sufficient accuracy. By adopting spin-stabilisation a construction tolerance of plus or minus 1 per cent was sufficient, since the slowly rotating projectile had an in-built tendency to compensate for construction inaccuracies. This lesser demand for accuracy paved the way for mass production.

In this new version both the main and tail fins were swept back sharply at an angle of 45 degrees. A spoiler was also introduced into the tail fin for the first time in order to give steering control. A gyroscope-driven distributor system also had to be evolved in order to translate up/down and left/right steering commands into the proper pulses to be fed into the spoilers, since the missile was now rotating and any spoiler could be functioning as an azimuth or range adjuster according to its position at any given instant.

The result of all these changes was a missile which could be dropped from 12,000–14,000 metres and attain a supersonic speed of 400m/sec. The experience gained in the development of the X-3 was to be used later in two designs using 2,500kg bombs as their starting point, the FX 2500 X-5 using an armour-piercing bomb, and the X-6 with a high explosive blast bomb. An order to build 100 X-5s and 100 X-6s was cancelled because the change in war conditions made it necessary to shift from an offensive to a defensive war and there appeared to be no useful military task that such weapons could perform.

The principal use of the X-1 was against major enemy warships. However there was a possibility that if mass-production methods could be used to turn out a rotating missile such as the X-3 it might be produced cheaply enough and in sufficient quantities to warrant its use against smaller craft. Obviously FX 1400 was a weapon easiest used in broad daylight and in good visibility. In these conditions the parent aircraft was somewhat limited in its manoeuvrability during the bombing run and thus presented an excellent target to AA fire. The Germans therefore attempted to use FX 1400 as a night weapon by providing it with a tracking flare and having the target illuminated by flares dropped by pathfinder planes equipped with radar.

Probably the most successful mission on which FX 1400 was used was the one in which three Do 217s scored two direct hits on the 35,000-ton Italian battleship *Roma*, one in the forward ammunition magazine and one in the engine room, and a glancing hit on the port side. The ship sank in 30 minutes. Other unsubstantiated German reports state that two cruisers were severely damaged and several smaller craft sunk by the use of the bomb.

Henschel 293

Another successful controlled bomb was the Henschel 293 rocket-boosted bomb. This looked more like some sort of missile than a bomb, and indeed it was what would today be called a 'stand-off missile' insofar as the bomb-aimer let it go well clear of the target. The warhead carried 550kg of high explosive and was helped along by a Walter rocket motor which burned for ten seconds during flight. Once launched, and after the rocket was burned out, the remaining glide could be radio-controlled to the target, the bomb-aimer merely having to keep the bomb between him and the target until it

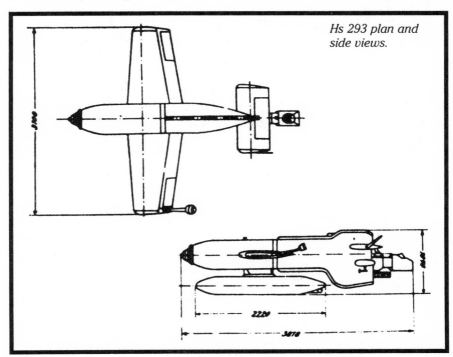

Hs 293 plan and side views.

hit. Though it must be said that aiming it in the face of hostile gunfire and aircraft was a little more difficult than the scientists had imagined.

Development of the Henschel 293 under Professor Herbert Wagner began in July 1940, and the first plan was simply to take a standard 500kg service bomb and put some wings with control surfaces on it, then add radio control to actuate these control surfaces and thus end up with a controllable glide bomb. Several of these Hs 293 V-1s were made and dropped successfully.

Some modifications to the controls brought the V-2 model, and the addition of the *Strassburg-Kehl* radio link next produced the V-3. By this time sufficient experience had been gained to show that the fundamental problem with a glide bomb was that by the time the bomb got to the target the parent aircraft was well ahead of it, and the bomb aimer therefore had a most difficult job trying to obtain a hit.

The answer to this was to put a rocket on the bomb so as to drive it at speed, well clear of the aircraft, before it could start its dive. The dive phase of the attack would then be taking place as the bomber caught up with the bomb, after which the pilot would curve off to one side, avoiding the need to fly directly over the target, while the bomb-aimer could still have a commanding view of the situation. And so the Hs 293 A-0 appeared in December 1940, with a pod beneath the body carrying a small bi-fuel rocket made by Walter of Kiel. The tail was fixed, steering being done by banking the weapon, and the tail contained a powerful flare so that the bomb-aimer could pick it out at long range. Some more minor changes were made and the design then went into production as the Hs 293 A-1.

In common with many German projects and weapons, one has to say that the Hs 293 was over-engineered. The following extract from a postwar report is illuminating:

> 'The whole weapon is characterised by robust construction apparently greater than is required by aerodynamic considerations. The wing had a tubular front spar which tapered from 3⅜ inches to 2½ inches, and a cast trailing edge which is the rear spar. The taper on the trailing edge is of about 10 degrees and a there is a sweep-back of about 2 degrees on the leading edge. The wing tip is almost square. The trailing edge to a depth of 9.5 inches is formed by a single magnesium casting of a mean wall thickness of about 0.3 inch, with cut-outs for the ailerons and with lugs for five ribs and a strengthened triangular root attachment. Particular care is taken in machining the trailing edge and some 200 dial indicators are used during manufacture to maintain the very close tolerances required by the aerodynamics of the missile. The wing ribs, all the same size, are attached to spars by eight screws. The wing section is symmetrical and the thickness tapers from 5 inches at the root to 3.4 inches at the tip. The airfoil is a standard profile with 12 percent

thickness 10 percent back of the leading edge. Although not designed for it, this wing performed very well at high Mach numbers. The skin, which is about 16 SWG [standard wire gauge], is in two pieces, inboard and outboard, meeting at the centre rib of the wing, and each piece is carried forward from the rear casting.'

A tubular front spar; a single magnesium casting; machining of such precision that 200 dial indicators are needed to ensure its accuracy; all this on a throw-away weapon?

Nevertheless, the A-1 went into production, training took place with aircrews over the Baltic, and in the summer of 1943 an operational squadron of Dornier 217 E-5 aircraft equipped with the necessary control equipment was activated in France. Their first success came on 27 August 1943 when a plane patrolling the Bay of Biscay found the British sloop HMS *Egret*, launched the bomb, scored a direct hit and sank her. There were several more successes in 1943, another four British destroyers among them, but the Allies were swift to sum up this new threat and swifter to counter it. It was soon realised that the bombs used one of 18 channels in the 48–50 MHz band; all that was necessary was to use a panoramic receiver to identify the signal and determine the frequency, after which a powerful transmission on that frequency would jam the steering signal circuit into a full left or full right command and the bomb would immediately veer off to one side and dive into the sea, the bomb-aimer no longer having any control over it. As a result, of some 40 attacks made against Allied warships during Operation Shingle, the landing at Anzio in January 1944, only a few were successful.

The *Luftwaffe* personnel had previously said that provided jamming did not result in more than a 70 per cent failure rate, they would be content to continue with radio control, but the virtually 100 per cent failure rate at Anzio led them to withdraw the Hs 293 from service. The designers, however, had foreseen the possibility of jamming and had already begun work on producing a replacement.

Indeed, the A-1 pattern had already undergone a change while the weapon was in service. The technique of using 'spoilers' rather than conventional ailerons and rudder for directional control had been developed and applied, producing the Hs 293 A-2. The spoiler was a comb-like metal strip buried in the trailing edge of the wing, fin or tail surface and controlled by a simple electro-magnetic solenoid. When current was applied the solenoid thrust the spoiler up or down from its concealed position, into the airstream. This deflected the air flow and caused the missile to turn, climb or dive according to which spoiler or combination of spoilers was being activated. Turn spoilers were generally in operation; they were either in or out and remained in either position as long as the control was energised so that they had either nil or full effect. Elevation spoilers worked on a timing system; they were energised in sequence for one-tenth of a second. In the 'rest' position this brief pulse had little effect, but moving the control stick in the parent aircraft would cause the necessary spoiler to receive a greater share of the $\frac{1}{10}$th second pulses, until in the 'full up' position, for example, the 'up' spoiler received the full 10 pulses per second and was thus fully extended and kept out in the airstream. This system was used because range was the more critical of the two senses; direction was fairly easy to visualise from the controller's position in the aircraft, but range was a rather more delicate matter and therefore a more delicate control was necessary.

The other advantage of the spoiler system was cheapness and simplicity; instead of a heavy motor and linkages to push up a hinged surface against the pressure of the airstream, a light and simple solenoid, directly connected to the spoiler, could push it up with far less effort; a spoiler stood only 5.5mm above the airfoil surface and was generally no more than 15cm in length. Its effect was out of all proportion to its insignificant size.

From the A-2 work moved on to removing the *Strassburg-Kehl* radio control. (So called because the transmitter was code-named *Strassburg*, and the associated receiver was named *Kehl*, the combination coming from the two linked towns in Alsace. This highly insecure method of identifying control pairs was duplicated in other missiles, as we shall see.) It was replaced by the *Dortmund-Duisburg* (another twin town combination) wire guided system, the modified missile being named Hs 293B, Some 200 completed A-1 airframes on the production line were modified, after which the design was changed so that the basic airframe could be fitted with radio or wire control as desired. This became the A-2, which was just entering production when the war ended. Numbers of 239Bs were used in Italy and the Mediterranean, and one *Luftwaffe* squadron was sent east in April 1945, armed with the 293B, in order to demolish as many bridges over the River Oder as they could before the Red Army got to them.

Hs 293 variants

Because the Hs 293 worked, and was well understood, it became the favoured test-bed for all sorts of improvements and ideas, which caused a formidable and confusing list of variant models, which I shall list here without going into too much detailed explanation.

The Hs 293C series was a variation in which the missile was used for attacking enemy ships below the waterline. Like the Hs 294 (*see below*) it was designed so that the wings, tail and propulsion unit sheared off on striking the water. The bomb body had a spherical nose with a spoiler ring around it which played a vital part in governing the underwater trajectory. It was fitted with a direct action impact fuze and had a self-destruction element controlled by a turbine wheel which would detonate the warhead after 45 metres of underwater travel. All in all, one is at a loss to understand why this was being developed at the same time as the Hs 294, which did the same job. The only difference that can be seen is that the Hs 293 used a

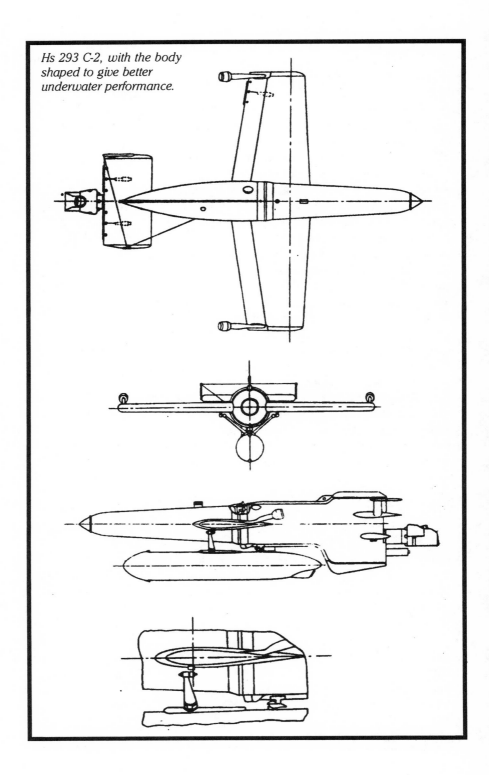

Hs 293 C-2, with the body shaped to give better underwater performance.

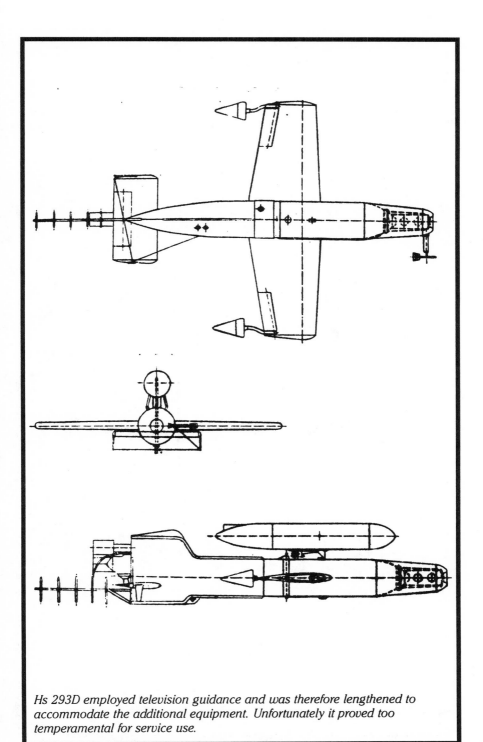

Hs 293D employed television guidance and was therefore lengthened to accommodate the additional equipment. Unfortunately it proved too temperamental for service use.

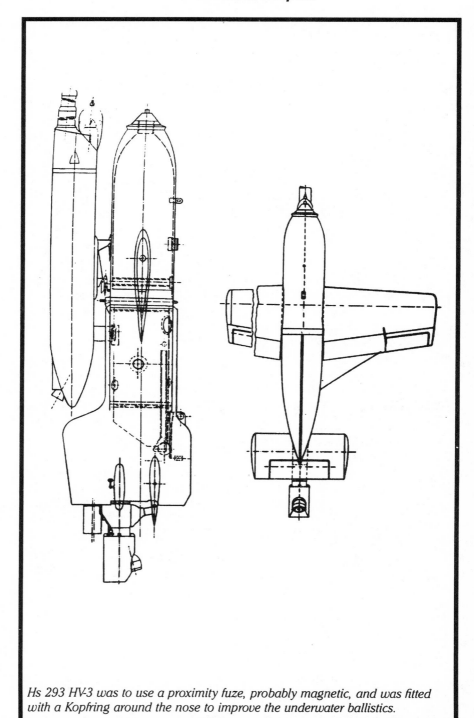

Hs 293 HV-3 was to use a proximity fuze, probably magnetic, and was fitted with a Kopfring around the nose to improve the underwater ballistics.

standard light-case blast bomb while the 294 used a heavy-case armour-piercing bomb and a fuze which incorporated a delay so that the bomb's piercing head could enter the target ship before detonating. The Hs 293 C-1 was the first of this series; it was followed by the CV-2, C-2 and C-3 which differed in various details of the body contour in an endeavour to find the perfect underwater shape; the C-2 used radio control, the C-3 could be fitted for radio or wire. C-4 had steel replacing alloy in much of the rear body and tail construction. C-1-0 and C-3-0 became the definitive production models and 630 were ordered, but few were made before the war ended.

Hs 293D was a television-guided version of the 293 A-1. Other than the new type of radio equipment, the extension of the nose and centre section of the fuselage to carry part of the equipment, and the addition of the TV antenna on the rear of the fuselage, this model is exactly the same as the A-1. Accompanying the above changes the overall length was increased and the weight went up by 85lb.

Development of the television system was begun in 1940 by Dr Weiss, Oberpostrat of the Reichspost Forschungsanstalt, and it was first tested in 1942 with little success. It was too complicated and only worked when it was operated by the laboratory staff who had designed it and who obviously knew the correct incantations and rituals.

The Hs 293 HV series were simply experimental (*Versuchs*) models built in order to follow some promising developmental path. HV-1 tried a different arrangement of spoilers; HV-2 tried a new method of detonating the warhead. HV-3 was designed to use a proximity fuze of unknown type; and HV-4 was designed to use the *Kakadu* proximity fuze. HV-5 was an HV-2 fitted with television guidance and with a means of detonating the warhead by command, and HV-6 had a barometric fuze which detonated the warhead when the missile dropped below a certain altitude so that any rogue test missile would not reach the ground in a condition where it might yield information to an enemy agent. (This may sound paranoid but exactly this happened during the development of both the *FZG 76*/V-1 and A4/V-2.) HV-7 was an improved HV-5 fitted with an infra-red proximity fuze.

The Hs 293 V series is another experimental branch; although no documentary evidence has been found, it seems likely that the HV series was instigated by Henschel, the original designers of the Hs 293, while the V series was developed by the *Luftwaffe* experimental station, since they all have changes which would have been suggested by their operational use. The V-4 was an improved model of the Hs 293 A-0 which incorporated new altitude control and some electrical circuit changes. The V-5 had a clipped wing and was intended to be launched from a jet aircraft, and the V-6 had stronger wings and control surfaces so as to withstand being launched at higher speeds from a jet aircraft and had an automatic correctional system built into the controls to compensate for variations in speed of launch. None of this series reached production.

Other Henschel designs

A derivative of the Hs 293 was the Hs 294, which was designed to be launched from aircraft for sub-surface attacks against shipping. Direct bombing was thought to be too difficult and dangerous, given that the bomber had to get within gunfire range of the target, so the idea arose of using the guidance capability of the Hs 293 to dive the missile into the water close to the target and then have it continue underwater so as to strike the target in its most vulnerable area. The difficulty here is that what is a good shape for flying through the air is not necessarily a good shape for travelling through water. The result of this thinking was the Hs 294 V-1 which had a head of special shape to allow it to enter the sea and then carry on, following a predictable underwater trajectory, to hit the ship like a torpedo. To achieve this the extraneous equipment such as the wings, tail and propulsion unit had to be got rid of as soon as the missile struck the sea, and this was achieved by attaching all these parts with explosive bolts. These were then wired up to feeler fuzes on the nose and wing tips, so that as soon as the fuzes detected the sea the bolts were fired and everything was blown clear, allowing nothing but the 650kg warhead to plunge under the surface, level out and travel on for about 45 metres with accuracy. After 50 metres or so the speed had dropped significantly so that its path was no longer predictable.

Work on the Hs 294 V-1 began in 1940. In general construction the missile was similar to the Hs 293 A-1 though the warhead was of a different shape. The missile was powered by twin liquid rocket units identical to those used in the Hs 293 programmes. These were fastened to the wing and fuselage and had no rigid connection with the warhead, thus allowing them to be blown clear when the time came. The missile was intended to be used at ranges from 4km–14km and to enter the water at an angle of about 22 degrees. Launching weight was 2,176kg

Only a few Hs 294 V-1s were built, largely, it would seem, to prove that the idea worked. Once that was satisfactorily resolved, improvements were called for. The next version was the Hs 294 A-0. This was similar to the V-1 and was used largely for hydro-dynamic testing. The most important change was that the jettisoning of component parts was now achieved by grooving the strength-carrying members between the component parts and the warhead. As soon as the various parts entered the water the drag was sufficient to snap off the wings and other units at the weakened points without the liability, found with the explosive bolt solution, of blowing the warhead off-course. Another improvement was the addition of a self-destroying fuze fitted into the warhead which would detonate the explosive charge after 45 metres of sub-aqua travel. If it hadn't hit the target by that time, well, the self-destruction might do a bit of damage and save the day. Tests were carried out, the weapon worked well, and the *Luftwaffe* issued a contract for 1,130 production missiles to be built at a rate of 50 per month.

The only question to be settled was to define the production model, and here the usual yearning for improvement undermined the whole project. The first change appears to have been to the control system; instead of controlling the flight by the standard ailerons and rudder, a new system using spoilers was adopted, on the grounds of saving energy and weight. This became Hs 294 V-2 and it is reported that 56 airframes to this specification were built, presumably the first part of the contract for the *Luftwaffe*.

Next, the designers, fearful of the jamming threat, decided that it would be wiser not to pursue a radio-guided solution but go, instead, for a wire-guided one. This meant a fresh design and the Hs 294B appeared, with wire spools on the wing tips controlling the spoilers. The production schedule was again changed, the airframes re-worked to the new specification, and production began once more.

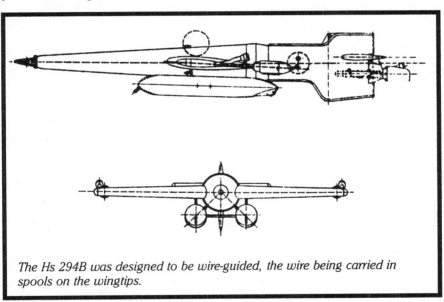

The Hs 294B was designed to be wire-guided, the wire being carried in spools on the wingtips.

By this time (summer 1944) the idea of using television to give the bomb-aimer the best chance, had taken hold, and nothing would now do but that a TV system should be built into Hs 294. A small (for those days) camera was mounted in the front of the right-hand motor unit; it is not entirely clear whether this signal was to be relayed back to the bomb-aimer by radio or by wire. The probability is by radio, since it is known that, production having been halted once more, 25 Hs 293 A-0 airframes were earmarked for modification to the new Hs 294D standard. And that was where the Hs 294 came to an end when the axe fell in February 1945, with a collection of miscellaneous models on the drawing board and 25 examples in the process of modification.

The next developments in this series are the Hs 295 and Hs 296, design of which began early in 1942 at the Henschel factory under Professor Wagner. The object in view appears to have been a high-velocity bomb with an armour-piercing capability to attack warships. The basis was a 1,000kg armour-piercing bomb, to which the airframe and control surfaces of the Hs 293 were added. Two Walter rocket motors were suspended underneath instead of the usual one, giving 6,000kg thrust and pushing the speed up to Mach 0.625, or about 475mph. Some 50 of these, under the name Hs 295 V-2,

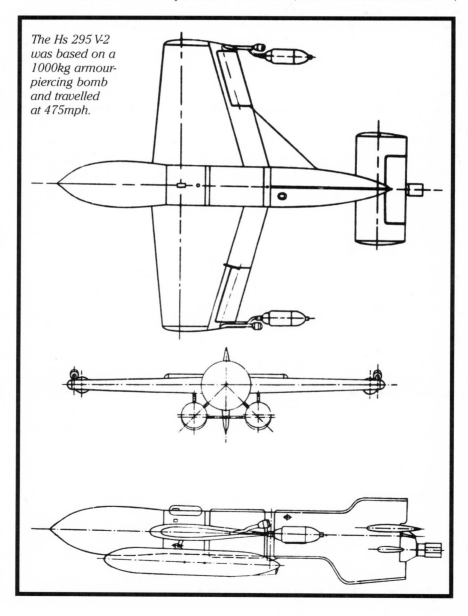

The Hs 295 V-2 was based on a 1000kg armour-piercing bomb and travelled at 475mph.

are said to have been manufactured, but there is no record of any tests having been carried out. The Hs 295D was a V-2 with television control, but whether this got any further than the drawing office is in some doubt.

Hs 296 was similar in concept to the 295 but used a 1,400kg bomb as its starting point and apparently used some of the Hs 294 components in the tail section. It used the two-rocket propulsion system but with a change in the fuel composition which improved the thrust to 6,500kg/sec and attained a maximum speed of 240 metres per second or about 540mph. One or two test models were built and flown, but the design had got very little further before the war ended.

Anti-ship weapons

Henschel might be thought to have had enough on its plate with the production of Dr Kramer's various missiles, as well as making tanks and aircraft and numerous other sorts of munition. However, the company managed to find time to develop an entirely independent set of anti-ship missiles which seem to have been inspired by the Hs 294, but which became a different line of development. The point appears to have been that the Hs 294 was an air-to-surface glide bomb which had been adapted to become an anti-ship bomb. As a result of this adaptation its shape was not the best for underwater performance. Much better, thought some unrecorded Henschel designer, to start again, design for the underwater performance and then adapt as much as possible from the existing series to provide the parts that are needed.

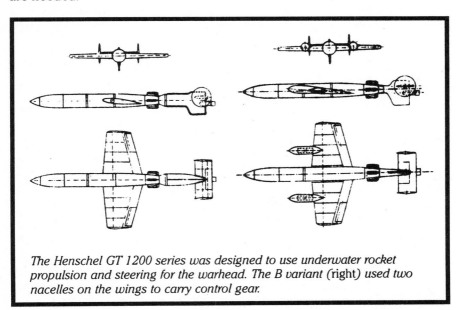

The Henschel GT 1200 series was designed to use underwater rocket propulsion and steering for the warhead. The B variant (right) used two nacelles on the wings to carry control gear.

The first model, GT 1200A, differed from Hs 294 in that it provided under-water propulsion and steering for the warhead. A second rocket motor was ignited as the missile struck the water and this gave it greater speed and greater underwater range than had been possible with the Hs 294. It was so constructed that the wings and tail sheared off on entry into the water in much the same way as the Hs 293C and 294 A-0. GT 1200B decreased the overall length by shortening the moment arm of the control surfaces, made possible by mounting the control gear in two nacelles in the leading edge of the wing. This version used the same warhead as the GT 1200A. The final model, GT 1200C, was longer than either of the two previous models but still used the same warhead. It had a chin-shaped nacelle under the forward end, which is believed to have been designed to accommodate either the control gear or some sort of forward-looking target-seeking device. Firm information on the GT series is scant; it is not at all certain that any of these missiles ever got as far as the prototype stage; they certainly never got into production.

Perhaps the last air-to-sea missile to go on to the drawing board was *Zitterrochen* or 'Torpedo fish', developed by Doktor Vöpl of Henschel who may probably, if the drawings are anything to go by, have had something to do with the GT series. But the reports are conflicting; some sources say that *Zitterrochen* was a missile; others, notably documents found at the Henschel works after the war, claim that it was simply a model developed for wind-tunnel tests at velocities up to Mach 1.6. It had a well-streamlined body with small triangular wings, an underslung tail fin, twin rocket motors in pods beneath the wings, and used spoilers for guidance. It is known that wind-tunnel experiments were successful, and it is also claimed that the project was ready for production in October 1944 but was then stopped. This latter claim seems unlikely; far less advanced missiles were nowhere near production at that date, and there is no record of a full-scale missile ever having been built.

Blöhm und Voss, being primarily a firm with naval interests, became involved in the development of a gliding torpedo in the middle 1930s. Dropping torpedoes from aircraft was by that time a commonplace, but it was a rough and ready technique which simply took a standard naval torpedo and dropped it in the water from as low as the pilot dared to go. The Blöhm & Voss *Luft-Torpedo* (LT F5b) began with a standard 750 kg fleet torpedo and added tail surfaces and apparatus for setting the steering and depth controls from the aircraft. This worked well and improved the accu-racy of the aviators, and it was followed by the LT 10 *Friedensengel* ('Angel of Peace') which used the same torpedo but added wings and tail-planes so that it could make a long glide before entering the water at the proper speed and angle. About 450 of these appear to have been manufactured during the war years, though accounts of their employment are certainly very scarce. Production was halted in 1944 and changed to the LT 11 or

Schneewittchen ('Snow-white'), a rather more advanced model, but few of these were ever made.

Blöhm and Voss had also made an earlier attempt at an air-launched bomb, called the Bv 143 or the 'Flying Torpedo', but this somehow got changed during its development and emerged as a guided missile. Using a liquid rocket motor, it was provided with radio-controlled steering, gyro-stabilisation and automatic altitude control by a radio device produced by Zeiss. The Bv 143 was tried out at Peenemünde in March 1941 and again in September 1942, but from the remaining accounts it seems that the altitude control was unreliable and as a result the weapon was uncontrollable.

Hagelkorn

One of the Allied devices which the Germans were keen to counter was the long range radio navigation system which allowed Allied bombers to roam over Germany with uncanny accuracy. The *Luftwaffe* soon discovered where the 'Loran' transmitters were in the south of England, but several attempts to attack them ran into severe trouble, as the RAF was equally well aware of their value and was quick to swamp the area with fighters when any German aircraft appeared. A Doktor Vogt of the Blöhm und Voss ship-building firm produced a solution which seemed to hold promise: a gliding bomb with a radio controlling system actuated by the transmissions of the stations.

The Bv 246 or *Hagelkorn* had actually been conceived as a long-range 'stand-off' bomb to be radio-guided to its target from a parent aircraft, provided a jam-proof guidance system could be developed. By the end of 1942 it seemed that Allied electronic prowess rendered this a forlorn hope, and at that point came the idea of a system which relied on the enemy to provide the guidance. Tune the command radio to the frequency of the Loran station and allow that signal to control the steering. All the pilot of the bomber needed to do was get within 200 kilometres of the target and let the bomb go; its aerodynamic shape was exceptionally good, allowing a glide of this distance, and the homing system would keep it pointed at the Loran station until it finally landed dead on target. This idea was so attractive that 400 were ordered immediately, without waiting to see whether the bomb worked. Flight tests which took place at the Unterlüss Proving Ground late in 1944 were not particularly successful, since the gyroscopic stabilisation gave trouble and only two out of ten flew properly. At the same time the A4 rocket (more usually known as the V-2) and the *FZG 76* (or V-1) were both operating with considerable success, and it was thought that with a little care in setting these up they could probably be induced to land on the offending Loran stations. As a result, the Bv 246 or *Hagelkorn* project was dropped.

Mistel

Without doubt, though, the glide bomb to end all glide bombs was *Mistel* ('Mistletoe'). It is said that this idea was put forward by the chief test pilot of the Junkers company in 1941 as a method of putting war-weary Ju 88 bombers to some practical use. In the 1930s Britain's Imperial Airways had proposed an air mail service on the Atlantic and other routes by using a seaplane mounted on top of a flying-boat. The flying boat took off, carrying the seaplane, transported it some distance along its route, and then the seaplane released itself and flew off to continue the trip while the flying boat returned to base. The object was to use the greater power of the flying boat to get the heavily laden (with fuel and mail) seaplane into the air, as well as carry it some distance without using any of its fuel.

The proposal that now came forward in Germany was a reversal of this. The Ju 88 bomber was stripped of its interior fittings and had the cockpit space filled with a gigantic shaped charge weighing about 3,500kg. A fighter aircraft was attached above the bomber and the controls connected. All engines were started and the fighter pilot flew the combination off. On approaching his target he put the whole combination into a dive calculated to deliver the bomber to the target, then disconnected himself. He then flew an accompanying course, correcting the bomber's flight by radio until he had steered it into impact with the target, after which he flew home satisfied with a job well done.

As might be imagined, such a revolutionary concept in 1941 was promptly thrown out, but in 1942 it re-appeared but as a means of lifting a glider into the air and then releasing it. This appeared to work successfully, then somebody in the *Reichsluftministerium* remembered the fighter/bomber combination and brought the idea forward again. In 1943 it was put into development and a combination Ju 88A/Messerschmitt Bf 109 flew a series of tests, leading to an order for 15 sets to be built under the code-name *Beethoven*. The shaped-charge warhead was built and tested, first against a redundant French battleship and then against reinforced concrete, against which it could defeat 18 metres thickness.

Once the design was perfected and made operational, it became *Mistel 1*, and the machines were operated in 1944 from a base in France against Allied shipping in the Bay of Biscay. It is reported that several hits were made, though no ship was sunk as a result. Now a crash programme was begun to assemble 100 units, to be called *Mistel 2*, which were to be used in Operation Iron Hammer against the advancing Allied forces nearing Germany. The order was then increased to 250, and several other combinations of fighter and bomber, according to what machines could be rounded up and converted, were put in hand, but, as with so many other last-minute schemes, the war ended before the force could be built and assembled.

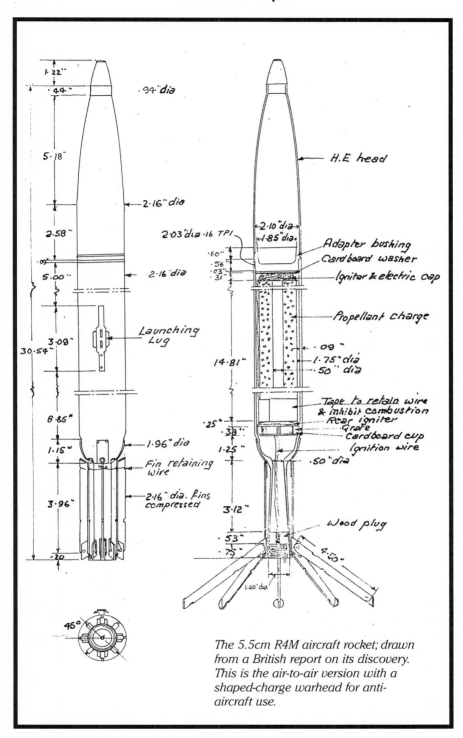

The 5.5cm R4M aircraft rocket; drawn from a British report on its discovery. This is the air-to-air version with a shaped-charge warhead for anti-aircraft use.

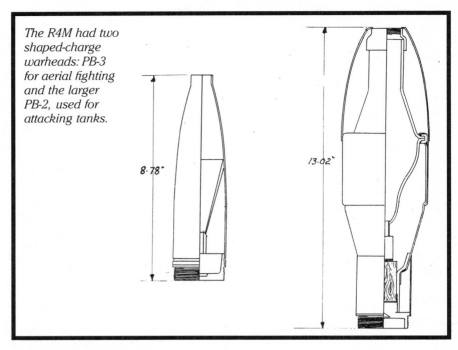

The R4M had two shaped-charge warheads: PB-3 for aerial fighting and the larger PB-2, used for attacking tanks.

8·78˝

13·02˝

Air-to-air weapons

When it came to attacking other aircraft, there seemed to be less interest in the rocket field than there was in the gun field. The only air-to-air rocket which reached any production was the R4M, a straightforward solid-fuel design with a high-explosive warhead fired from the He 162 jet fighter. The rocket, weighing 32.2kg with its high explosive warhead, was a simple steel tube with spring-out fins.

When the anti-aircraft programme of 1944 produced the *Föhn* rocket, discussed in a later chapter, several aircraft designers saw in this a worth-while air-to-air weapon. Of 73mm calibre and weighing about 3kg, it was spin-stabilised and carried a 285g explosive charge of RDX/TNT with both an impact fuze and a self-destroying fuze. Propulsion was by a simple stick of solid propellant powder and, having been designed as an anti-aircraft weapon, it had ample range and velocity for air-to-air use. Being spin-stabilised it required no more than a simple tube to launch it, and a number of designs for clusters of tubes were developed, but it appears that few of these, if any, got into service, since production began too late to be of any use.

Far more ambitious was the Henschel 298, a rail-launched missile to be carried on Dornier 217 or Focke-Wulf 190 machines. Weighing 120kg, 2.05m long and with a wing-span of 1.22m, it carried a potent 48kg blast warhead fitted with a proximity fuze. As might be guessed from the nomenclature, this was another design from Dr Kramer, though it bore little resemblance to the other members of the '290' series of missiles.

The fuselage was made in three sections, nose, body and tail. In the nose were the radio receivers, gyroscope, proximity fuze and a wind-driven electric generator. The body section held the explosive charge and propulsion unit, in a most unusual manner. The propulsion unit was a solid-fuel rocket with a burning time of 25–30 seconds, mounted on the axis of the missile, and secured by two bulkheads. The 106lb explosive filling of the weapon was poured, in its molten state, into the axial space around the rocket body until the space was full. The explosive solidified on cooling. Therefore provision had to be made for insulating the explosive from the heat of the rocket body during the 10-second burning time. This was achieved by placing a thick insulating jacket around the rocket body before pouring in the explosive. The tail section was used for supporting the tail surfaces and was in two halves welded together.

The proximity fuze was to be *Fuchs* ('Fox'), the radio fuze used with the Hs 117. This was designed to operate within 10 metres of the target and was armed by a clockwork mechanism six seconds after launch. Should the missile miss the target entirely, a self-destruction timer was also fitted; this came into action 50 seconds after launch and blew the missile to pieces so that it could not come back to earth in a live condition. And as a final piece of insurance there was also an impact fuze which would function in the event of a direct hit combining with a malfunction of the proximity fuze. An alternative suggestion was the use of the *Kranich* ('Crane') acoustic proximity fuze instead of *Fuchs*; the real question was which of the two would reach operational status first.

The Hs 298 was suspended from the parent aircraft by two lugs. Before the missile was independent it was guided by a launching rail which provided a run of about 6 feet. Guidance was by radio command, and the observer steered it onto his line of sight and kept it there until it reached the target. Test firings were made on 22 December 1944 from a Ju 88G parent aircraft, but the results were not encouraging; three missiles were fired, one detonated prematurely in flight, one dived into the ground and the third stuck on the launching rail. Development was supposed to be completed by December 1944 and production begun in January 1945, but these dates came and went with no sign of the missile, and production was stopped on 6 February 1945 as it seemed unlikely to reach a satisfactory stage of development in time to have any effect on the war.

Another potential air-to-air missile was the X-4, developed by Ruhrstahl AG. This was intended to circumvent the jamming problem and do away with the involved development of radio devices. It was an air-to-air guided missile intended to be launched from fast fighters such as the Fw 190 and the Me 262. It was unique in that during flight it rotated about its longer axis at 60 revolutions per minute. By this rotation, it was claimed, there was a symmetrical cancellation of any manufacturing errors and a consequent simplification of manufacture. A non-rotating missile of this design would have required gyroscopic stabilisation both in azimuth and elevation, but the X-4 was stabilised in the line of flight by a single gyroscope, another useful economy. The fuselage was cigar shaped and consisted of three sections: the warhead, body and tail. The warhead was made of steel, loaded with 22kg of explosive, and was to be fitted with the *Kranich* acoustic proximity fuze at its front end. The body section was of cast aluminium and held the compressed air and fuel cylinders of the propulsion system. The missile was propelled by a bi-fuel liquid rocket and stabilised in flight by four fins symmetrically placed around the fuselage roughly amidships.

The tail section was made from four thin aluminium sheets spot-welded together. It contained the gyroscope, battery, fuel lines and propulsion unit. The propulsion unit was held by three adjustable steel tubes. Remote control was performed by electrical signals transmitted down a pair of fine wires from the parent aircraft. The wire was paid out by the missile from spools mounted on the tips of two opposite fins. Control of direction was done by comb-like spoilers operated by double-acting electro-magnets and fitted to the four symmetrically-placed tail fins which were mounted at 45 degrees with respect to the main fins.

The X-4 was selected, released and controlled by the pilot of the parent aircraft. Separate switches were used for pre-selection of one of the four missiles carried and for starting the stabilising gyroscope prior to launch. The pilot aimed at the target using a reflector sight and pressed the release button which engaged the gyroscope, fired the propulsion rocket, armed the fuzing, ignited the wing-tip flares and released the missile, all in the same instant. He subsequently guided the missile by using a joystick mounted below the instrument panel. The missile was to be fired from behind the target, up to 30 degrees right or left and slightly above or below; aiming commenced at 2,000 metres. No accuracy figures are available, though claims were made of several successful test runs.

The *Kranich* proximity fuze was actuated by the acoustic radiation from the propeller of the target aircraft. It consisted of a vibratory reed with a diaphragm tone filter sensitive to frequencies between 140 and 500 cycles. The vibrations of the diaphragm excited the resonances of the reed. When the vibrations of the reed exceeded a certain limit it touched an electric contact and fired the igniter. By making use of this resonance phenomenon it was possible to use a relatively insensitive acoustic-mechanical system instead of a complex electronic circuit. It was claimed that the fuze would function within 15 metres of the target when activated by the propeller noise. A $\frac{1}{50}$th second delay allowed the missile to close up a further five metres before detonating.

Kranich and *Fuchs*, a radio-operated fuze, are generally thought to have been the two German proximity fuze developments which stood a reasonable chance of working in actual service conditions. It has to be said that compared to the Allied development of the radio proximity fuze to be fired from guns, development of a fuze to be launched in the far less stressed environment of a guided missile was a much simpler task, and had the Germans begun their work at the same time as the British (1940) they would undoubtedly have had a working fuze in use by 1944. But *Kranich* and *Fuchs* were only the tip of the proximity fuze iceberg; there were something like 35 proximity fuze projects unearthed by investigators after the war, almost all for aircraft or anti-aircraft missiles.

The most popular form was the infra-red sensor intended to react to exhaust or engine heat; *Paplitz* was one of the many examples of this class. Made by the Elektro Akoustik Institut of Namslau it was tested in March 1945 by flying aircraft over a static specimen at gradually decreasing height; this showed a sensitivity of between 12 and 20 metres. It also became apparent in the course of the tests that the fuze would have to be used at night, since solar radiation by day was sufficient to mask the heat from the targets.

Photo-electric reaction was also popular. *Pistole* was an 'active' photo-electric fuze, the missile carrying a light source which would be reflected back from the target and into the P-E cell, thus triggering the fuze. But while the *Luftwaffe* was contemplating *Pistole*, another of the same breed, *Wassermaus* came along and looked like being a better product, so the *Pistole* and *Wassermaus* design teams were brought together and continued on *Wassermaus*, a most unusual piece of co-operation. No tests had been done on this fuze when the war ended, and it was considered unlikely to have been made workable much before the end of 1946. It is worth remembering that this active P-E principle had been patented by a Swede in 1937, and that the British had used a passive P-E fuze in their anti-aircraft rockets in 1941, a device which relied upon the shadow of the aircraft falling on it to trigger the detonation.

Acoustic fuzes were another popular choice, though some were unusual; BAZ 55A, for example, was developed by Rheinmetall-Borsig for use in drop bombs. The first bomb of the stick would be fuzed with a normal impact fuze; the remainder would be fuzed with BAZ 55A. On dropping the stick, the detonation of the first bomb as it landed was 'heard' by the fuze of the next bomb, which detonated about 20–25m above the ground to produce maximum destructive blast. And, in turn the next bomb heard that explosion, and so on until the last bomb of the stick went off. On the face if it, one tends to visualise a series of higher and higher detonations, but bear in mind that drop bombs do not fall vertically; they have a forward component, too. This fuze actually went into service use in the summer of 1944.

Fuchs, made by AEG of Berlin, was the leading radio fuze, relying, as the official text put it, 'on the effect on the oscillation amplitude of the transmitter of the change in the radiation resistance in the antenna as the missile neared the target.' This gave a radius of sensitivity of around 50 feet, which

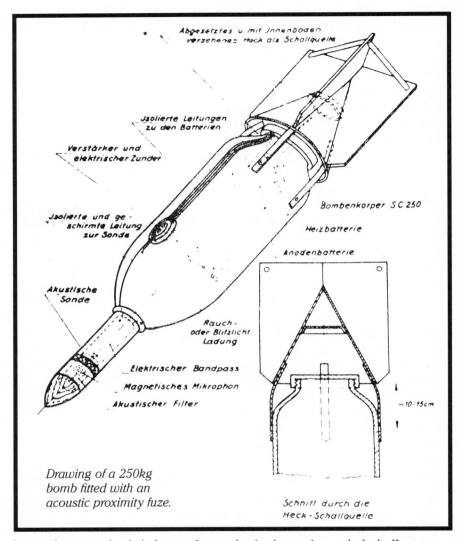

Abgesetztes u mit Innenboden
versehenes Heck als Schallquelle

Jsolierte Leitungen
zu den Batterien

Verstärker und
elektrischer Zünder

Jsolierte und ge-
schirmte Leitung
zur Sonde

Akustische
Sonde

Bombenkorper SC 250

Heizbatterie

Anodenbatterie

Rauch -
oder Blitzlicht
Ladung

Elektrischer Bandpass

Magnetisches Mikrophon

Akustischer Filter

~10-15cm

*Drawing of a 250kg
bomb fitted with an
acoustic proximity fuze.*

Schnitt durch die
Heck - Schallquelle

by modern standards is far too far to obtain the optimum lethal effect on an aircraft target. Nevertheless, it worked and was scheduled to go into production in January 1945 for fitting to Hs 117 and Hs 298 missiles. It is doubtful that any were ever made.

Kakadu ('Cockatoo') was another radio fuze, by Donaulandische Gesellschaft mbH of Vienna, and perhaps the only one which got into any sort of production, some 3,000 of a 23,000-fuze contract having been made in Vienna in late 1944/early 1945. They were intended for use in Hs 293 missiles, and apparently worked quite well, although Allied engineers who subjected them to post-war examination were of the opinion that they were too complicated and difficult to manufacture and should have been revised by a production engineer before going to production. Specifically matched to the Hs 293, *Kakadu* relied on the Doppler effect set up by the signal reflected from the target. (When either target or missile is moving, then the signal returning to the receiver enters at a slightly different frequency than that which was originally sent. This change in frequency, called the 'Doppler Effect' after its discoverer, can be measured and used to operate a circuit.) *Marabou*, *Kugelblitz*, *Marder*, *Pinscher* and *Trichter* were other designs of radio proximity fuzes of which *Trichter* is worth a remark, since it was designed for an anti-aircraft drop bomb. The idea was for the fighter-bomber to get above the Allied formation and then drop a heavy blast bomb fitted with this fuze into the middle of it. It had got as far as field testing by 1945, but indications were that the sensitivity was not good enough. The design began by using the Doppler shift effect, but abandoned this in favour of using the change in resistance loading of the antenna since this looked like being immune to jamming.

Electro-magnetism was a popular choice; *Isegrimm*, developed by the Orlich Institut of Danzig used two induction coils and relied on the inductive effects of the target to produce the necessary proximity reaction. The designers got into serious problems with the design and manufacture of thermionic valves for this fuze and were saved at the last minute by a general ban on electro-magnetic fuze work because it had been discovered that the suppression of interference from the earth's magnetic field presented a virtually insuperable problem.

The Orlich Institut was also responsible for *Marder*, a radio fuze which transmitted a signal to the target, detected the reflection and used this to trigger an oscillator which then sent another signal back to a ground station, which in turn sent up a signal to trigger the fuze and detonate the warhead. This appears never to have got past the bread-board laboratory model stage. And with all the better ideas floating about at that time one is inclined to wonder why it even got that far.

Kurt, Germany's Dambuster?

During the night of 16/17 May 1943, 617 Squadron RAF raided the Möhne and Eder dams in the Ruhr, their aim being to breach them and thus interfere with the supply of electricity to the many armaments factories in the region. To achieve this, a special 'rolling' bomb had been developed by Dr Barnes Wallis, a Vickers designer. This was spun up before being dropped from a low altitude above the water, and then skipped along the surface of the water until it struck the dam, whereupon it sank to a pre-determined depth and detonated.

The damage was not as severe as the RAF had hoped, and was fairly quickly repaired. But the Germans were intrigued by the Wallis bomb, and late in

1943 the *Luftwaffe* Experimental Centre at Travemünde set about improving on its design. Like the RAF bomb, *Kurt* was intended to skip along the surface of the water up to its target and then sink until detonated by an hydrostatic fuze. The bomb itself was spherical and weighed about 385kg. Dropped from an altitude of 18m from an aircraft flying at 640km/hr it would roll on the surface for about 400m before sinking.

To obtain more range, and thus provide safer conditions for the dropping aircraft, which, it appeared, would usually be above the bomb when it detonated, a rocket rail unit was fitted. This increased the range but also showed a tendency to push the bomb off course if it happened to be yawing at the instant of ignition. To cure this a gyroscope stabilising unit was designed, which would have been run up before the bomb was dropped but while the aircraft was aimed at the target, and which would subsequently detect any tendency to veer off-course and apply the necessary corrections to the tail unit to steer it back again. But, in November 1944, before this could be built and tested, the project was closed down. The one thing that remains to be discovered about *Kurt* is what target the *Luftwaffe* planned to use it against?

Air Defence Weapons

The war in the air also involved the question of ground defences against aircraft. In the case of the anti-aircraft gun the first and most obvious step was simply to make it bigger, but every time the gun designers got down to their drawing boards to solve the latest problem, the *Luftministerium* arrived with a fresh set of demands for higher velocity, greater ceiling, faster rates of fire, heavier shells and increased lethality, and the designers had to tear everything up and start again.

Bigger and better guns

At the outbreak of war the heaviest anti-aircraft gun in German service was a 12.8cm (5.03-inch) weapon which fired a 25.8kg (57lb) shell to a height of 48,000 feet at a rate of 25 rounds per minute. In 1939 that was a superlative performance which nothing else in the world could match. This gun had been requested in 1936, and at the same time another gun of 15cm calibre had also been asked for.

In the early part of 1938 the pilot model of the 15cm gun was tested, and the trials soon revealed that so far as performance went it was little, if at all, better than the 12.8cm gun. Moreover it could not be transported in one piece but had to be dismantled for movement, carried on a number of special trailers, and then re-assembled before it could be fired, a procedure which was something of a drawback for what was intended to be a mobile anti-aircraft weapon. A lot of work went into trying to improve things, but eventually, in mid-1940, the project was abandoned and the *Luftministerium* issued a fresh specification for the designers to meet. This time it asked for a gun which could travel in a single load and fire a 92 lb shell to 60,000 feet altitude. While the designers were still struggling to make sense out of this, the Luftwaffe changed its mind and decided that mobile guns over 12.8cm calibre were not practical and told the designers kindly to forget it. Then it changed its mind again and said well, it might not be practical as a mobile gun, but try it as a static design. Another year went by and finally, in late 1943, the decision was taken not to waste any further effort on heavy guns but to rely on missiles.

So much for the 15cm gun; but in 1941 the Luftwaffe had asked for even bigger guns for static mounting around cities and vulnerable points. They had asked for a 21cm gun firing a 270lb shell to 60,000 feet and for a 24cm gun firing a 435lb shell also to 60,000 feet. (The layman may wonder at what sort of damage a 435lb shell could do to, say, a formation of Flying Fortresses; a practical gunner is more likely to wonder at what sort of a burden the gunners were going to have, attempting to load a 435lb shell into a gun elevated to 70 degrees or so.) It so happened that the German Navy had also expressed a desire for two really powerful anti-aircraft weapons, and, an unusual event in itself, the two projects were merged. But the mechanical requirements for a *Luftwaffe* gun bolted down in concrete and a *Kriegsmarine* gun attached to a warship and connected to its power supply and magazines, were somewhat different, and trying to marry the two together was proving very difficult when the 1943 ban on heavy AA artillery came along, no doubt to the delight of the hard-pressed designers.

One important project which was close to completion when the war ended was the production of an 'intermediate' anti-aircraft gun. The light guns of 20mm and 37mm calibre were effective against low-flying raiders; the medium (8.8cm) and heavy (10.5cm and 12.8cm) guns were effective against high fliers. But between about 4,000 and 10,000 feet altitude was a difficult zone for the defences; aircraft in this region were too high for the light guns, and their crossing speed was too great for the heavier guns to track them with any hope of accuracy. This was not due to any mechanical defect, simply to the physical difficulties in swinging a heavy gun fast enough to keep up with a target. As a result of this, work began before 1939 on a 5cm AA gun, an automatic weapon which was more or less an enlarged 20mm cannon. It was produced in moderate numbers and extensively tried, but proved disappointing; among other defects it had a distressing habit of rolling over when towed too fast, and when it fired it vibrated so severely that the gunner could no longer use his sights properly. So production stopped and the designers promised to think about a new design.

By 1942 the Germans had gained enough experience of air raids to show that in some cases even one bomber getting through the defences was enough to do all the damage necessary; the Möhne and Eder Dams raid testified to that. Therefore it was considered that if an anti-aircraft weapon system could be developed which absolutely guaranteed knocking down 100 per cent of the attackers, then no matter what it cost in terms of development effort or money, for some very vulnerable and critical targets it would be worth it. From this came a very advanced plan for a complete anti-aircraft system, comprising six automatic guns, radar, predictor, height-finder and tracker, all coupled together to give absolute certainty of finding and hitting any attacker in the medium height zone. The gun was to be an improved version of the 5cm model, but by this time there had been some improvements in the design of shells, and it was particularly demanded that the shell should carry sufficient explosive to guarantee downing a four-engined bomber with one hit. There was no problem in making a shell to carry this charge of explosive, but there was a good deal of trouble when it came to making it fly straight to the target; because of various ballistic defects, every shell design tried turned out to be inaccurate.

After over a year of failure the designers gave up and decided that the only solution was to change calibre, and after some discussion a 5.5cm gun was proposed. There was little problem in designing an accurate and lethal shell in this calibre, and in the early months of 1944 the 5.5cm *Gerät 58* project finally got under way. But too much time had been wasted, and although some guns were assembled and fired before the war ended, the power-operated mountings, radar, predictor and all the other gadgetry were nowhere near completion. There is some evidence to show that a good deal of the development equipment was spirited off to Russia after the end of the war, where work was continued and a good deal of the German design eventually reached service as a Soviet 57mm gun in the 1950s.

It is worth noting that this failure to develop an intermediate gun was not confined to Germany; Britain (with a 57mm) and the USA (with a 75mm) both attempted something similar and neither was successfully completed before the war ended. Indeed, the British design never did reach completion; its specified performance was outmatched by the arrival of jet aircraft and the project was abandoned in 1946.

All wind and noise

As the war progressed and the Allied air raids increased, the question of anti-aircraft defence became a vital one, and because of this a lot of ideas were given consideration which, in more normal times, would have been quashed as soon as they appeared. There was, for example, Doktor Zippermeyer's 'Whirlwind Cannon'. This sounds like something out of a comic strip, but it was actually built and tested, and according to some reports one was actually deployed in an operational position, protecting a vital bridge.

Zippermeyer's idea was, like many weapon ideas, sound in many respects but more suited to a laboratory model than a full-sized device. In the course of aerodynamic studies he had discovered that strong whirlwinds of air could rack and strain the airframe of an aircraft to such a degree as to break it, or at least render the machine uncontrollable. He therefore proposed to produce such whirlwinds by generating explosions in a combustion chamber and directing the blast into the air through specially-shaped nozzles. Experiments showed that four-inch planks could be shattered at 200-yard range, and a full-sized 'Whirlwind Cannon' was built. Unfortunately it proved impossible to produce the desired effects at altitudes high enough to have any effect on enemy aircraft, and the project was abandoned.

The same laboratory also invented a 'Sound Cannon', since it was known that at certain intensities sound waves could also have a destructive effect, not only on aircraft but on the occupants as well. This machine burned methane and air to produce an explosion, which was then beamed by sound-mirrors into the sky. A series of explosions followed rapidly on each other and the noise emitted soon built up into a high-pitched tone which, trials showed, was lethal to animals at close range and distinctly uncomfortable for human beings at 300 yards. But, as with the 'Whirlwind Cannon', the problem was to get the effect up into the sky where the raiders were, and since this proved completely insoluble this project also came to an end.

Electric power

Just as unorthodox, though slightly less ridiculous, was the project for an electric gun. As every schoolboy knows, if a coil of wire is wrapped around a soft iron core and an electric current is passed through it, the core will jump out of the coil. This is the solenoid, a well-known electrical control mechanism. In the 19th century it occurred to various experimenters that if the coil was made big enough and the current strong enough, then the core could be made to leave at high speed and might thus become a projectile. But try as they might, nobody ever managed to develop enough electric current to get a worthwhile speed out of the core.

During the First World War a French experimenter, Fauchon-Villeplee, came up with a new idea using a winged arrow connected across two conducting bars; this worked quite well but before he could do much with it, the war ended and nobody was interested any longer. His idea was later developed into what is today known as the 'linear motor' and occasionally used as a propulsion device. During 1944 a German company looked once again at this proposition and came to the conclusion that, since there had been considerable advances in electrical science since 1918, the idea might now be workable.

In October 1944 a preliminary specification was agreed with the *Luftwaffe* for a 40mm electric anti-aircraft gun, with a velocity of 1,980m/sec (6,500 ft per second) and a rate of fire of 6,000 rounds per minute. Each shell was to carry one pound of explosive, and six 'barrels' were to be connected to a single power supply.

The work went ahead, although nothing but small laboratory experiments were achieved before the war ended. It is doubtful if anything would ever have come of it, as the gun demanded 1,590,000 amperes of power at 1,345 volts in order to get the velocity and range predicted. Even today it would demand formidable engineering to produce a machine which could withstand that sort of power, as well as requiring a complete power station for each gun.

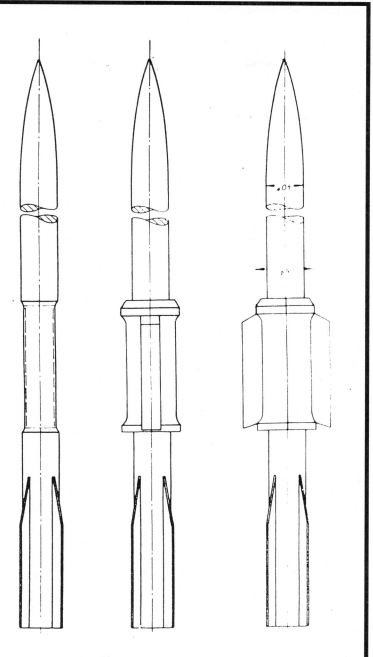

Line drawings of a proposal for a 40mm electric gun projectile. The centre section 'wings' rode in the electro-magnetic bus bars and the whole centre section was discarded at the 'muzzle' of the gun. In theory, anyway.

Anti-aircraft rockets

As the need to produce anti-aircraft defences became imperative in the middle 1930s, Britain began experimenting in 1937 with unguided rockets, and eventually produced a wide variety of such weapons for air defence. Germany was better off for anti-aircraft guns and took very little interest in rockets until about 1943, when it became apparent that extra defences were needed and needed fast. This reluctance to look at rockets earlier in this field is all the more strange when one remembers that the Germans were the first to see the military possibilities of rockets in general and had some of the finest research facilities in the world at their service. It seems that simple 'firework' rockets were beneath their dignity, and all the work that went on was aimed at more sophisticated pieces of equipment. However, the advantages of the simple rocket were too great to be denied, and after some initial argument, designs for air defence were put in hand.

The first to make an appearance was the 7.3cm *Föhn*, a 35-barrel launcher mounted either on a trailer or set in a concrete bed for static sites. The rocket was a short and stubby article which, at first glance, resembled an ordinary gun shell. The nose carried 250 grams of high explosive and a percussion fuze, while the rest of the body contained a solid fuel motor burning for $\frac{9}{10}$th of a second to boost the speed to 850mph. As it fired in salvos, the Föhn was a useful weapon but its chief liability was an impact fuze which demanded a near impossible direct hit on the target. Numbers of these launchers were deployed in Germany and, towards the end of the war, several were used as makeshift field artillery weapons, but so far as can be determined they were never successful in downing aircraft.

More ambitious was *Taifun* ('Typhoon'), a 46lb rocket driven by a liquid-fuel motor, which travelled at over 3,000 feet per second to reach an altitude of nine miles or more. Work on this began at the latter end of 1944, and the design was accepted for production in October. Production began in January 1945, but only 600 rockets had been made before the war ended. One of the more remarkable things about it was that in spite of being liquid-fuelled, with all the apparent complexity which that arrangement brought with it, the cost was estimated at being 25 marks – about £2.25 in 1940s' prices. A parallel design was *Wirbelsturm* ('Tornado'), basically the same rocket but one which used a solid-fuel motor. The performance was almost the same, but because of the shortage of propellant materials affecting Germany by the beginning of 1945 there was some reluctance to approve Tornado for production. While the arguments were still going on the war came to an end.

All these weapons, of course, were crew served and quite large, but with the introduction into service of one-man anti-tank weapons, such as the *Panzerschreck* (copied from the American Bazooka) and other designs, it seems to have occurred to somebody to try and produce an equivalent one-man anti-aircraft weapon. The result of this was the *Fliegerfaust*, a little-known development which, had it come earlier in the war, might have made life very unhealthy indeed for low-flying aviators. It consisted of nine 20-mm tubes in a simple frame, with a shoulder rest and a pistol grip. Into the end went a clip carrying nine small rockets, and squeezing the trigger generated an electric current to ignite them. Five rockets were immediately fired from alternate tubes and the other four a tenth of a second later. This delay allowed the rockets to launch without disturbing each other by their blast and also gave a dispersion to the salvo which improved the chance of hitting. The rockets were adaptations of the standard 20mm aircraft cannon

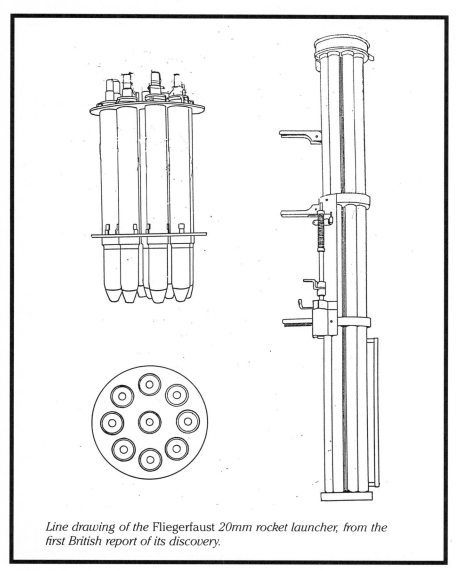

Line drawing of the Fliegerfaust *20mm rocket launcher, from the first British report of its discovery.*

shell in which a steel tube holding a stick of smokeless propellant was crimped to the base of the shell. In the base of the tube were four angled vents and an electric ignition squib. When the squib fired and lit the propellant, the blast came through the angled vents and in addition to providing the forward thrust caused the rocket to spin in flight, stabilising the whole affair in the same fashion as a bullet fired from a rifled gun.

Fitted with a simple optical sight, *Fliegerfaust* was a highly effective and dangerous weapon out to a range of about 2000 metres. But like many ideas, time was against it: it was approved early in January 1945 and arrangements were made to manufacture 10,000 for immediate issue. Very few were, in fact, made, and as far as is known they never got into the hands of the soldiers who so desperately needed them. Indeed, it seems that only one or two specimens ever survived to be found by the Allies.

Another low-altitude device was the *Kurzzeitsperre* ('Short Time Barrage'), more properly known as RSK 1000, intended for the defence of airfields. Developed by Rheinmetall-Borsig, this consisted of a number of 21cm rocket motors buried in short mortar-like launching tubes around the perimeter of an airfield. Attached to the rocket was a parachute container and a steel ribbon 1,000 metres long. When aircraft approached, a battery of these mortars was fired and the rockets soared up to the height of the cable, where they burst and released the parachute. This slowed the descent of the cable and thus, by firing several at once, put a wire barrier across the approach to the airfield. The cables were flat steel ribbons, and on contact with an aircraft wing would twist and cut their way through very rapidly. So far as is known, few aircraft were brought down by this system, but there is plenty of evidence to show that the sight of these rockets streaming up ahead was enough to cause many pilots to have second thoughts about shooting up a German airfield – and, after all, that was the object of putting them there. The success of air defences is not measured by the number of aircraft brought down but by the number of aircraft deterred or prevented from attacking their assigned target.

Anti-aircraft missiles

In contrast to the relatively small effort put into unguided rockets by the Germans, the amount of research which went into guided missiles was tremendous. Much of the initial interest was developed from the research on rocket propulsion and advanced aerodynamics which was done at the Peenemünde Research Station, and once the results of this work began to be appreciated, the possibilities of controlling rockets attracted a number of experimenters. Probably the first in the field was Henschel with the Hs 117, which later became known as Hs 297 and then as *Schmetterling* ('Butterfly'). Development began under Professor Wagner in 1941, but since it was classified as a 'defensive' weapon, at that stage of the war he could raise no interest. But in 1943 the *Luftministerium* changed its opinion and gave an order for experimental production to begin, with the hope of the project reaching the stage of issue to troops by early 1945.

The Hs 117 was a mid-wing monoplane with swept-back wings, rectangular stabiliser surfaces and two vertical tail fins, one above and one below the fuselage. It was of all metal construction and about 4m (13 feet) long with a 2m (6.5-foot) wing span. A liquid-fuel rocket motor furnished the main propulsive force, but for additional thrust during take-off two rockets were provided. One was attached above and the other below the fuselage and both were jettisoned after four to five seconds of burning. A tail flare was provided as an aid for tracking. At launch it weighed 445kg (980lb), but after the take-off units had fired and dropped off, the all-up weight came down to 258kg (570lb). It had a constant governed speed of 865km/hr (535mph) and a maximum range of 40km (44,000 yards); its accuracy was estimated to be an eight-yard circle at ten miles range, which sounds a little optimistic for 1945.

The missile was launched from a platform which could be inclined and rotated to direct the weapon towards the target. About 40 yards away was the aiming stand where two operators were stationed. One operator oriented the stand and aiming devices, while the other guided the missile

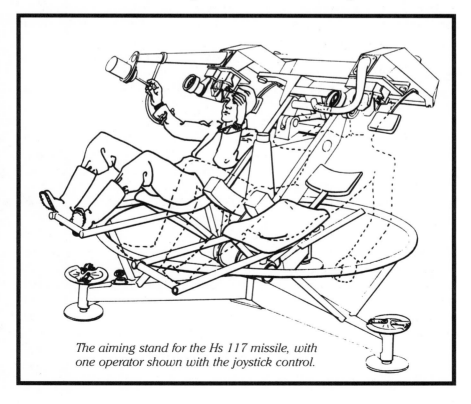

The aiming stand for the Hs 117 missile, with one operator shown with the joystick control.

by means of a joystick control. The missile was remotely controlled by radio throughout its flight and was governed to fly at a constant speed of 537mph (865km/hr), irrespective of its altitude, to give accuracy in control. Electric power for operating the radio receiver and controls was supplied by a generator which was driven by an airscrew located at the nose of the missile.

Propulsion was by a liquid-fuel rocket motor using *Tonka* a hydrocarbon mixture of aniline, monoethylaniline, dimethylaniline, petrol, naphtha, triethylamine and isohexylamine, and the oxidiser was *Salbei*, a mixture of nitric acid with a small percentage of sulphuric acid to suppress corrosion. The fluids were held in separate cylinders under pressure, one in front and the other aft of the centre of gravity so that the CofG did not shift as the fluids were consumed. A piston in each cylinder, acted upon by compressed air maintained the pressure of the fuel. The compressed air was held under 200 atmospheres of pressure in an air bottle located in the forward part of the body of the missile.

The rocket motor was located at the rear of the tail section. It comprised a combustion chamber surrounded by a cooling jacket through which the *Salbei* was circulated before entry into the combustion chamber. Besides cooling the combustion chamber walls, this arrangement pre-heated the *Salbei* for more efficient combustion. A counter-flow system was used; the *Salbei* entered the combustion jacket from the exhaust end and flowed in a direction opposite to the stream of exhaust gases. The fuel and oxidiser were forced separately through holes at the front of the combustion chamber and struck a special refractory block to atomise the spray. The mixture ignited spontaneously on contact.

The warhead contained 25kg (55lb) of explosive and produced a blast rather than fragments. No other facts about it are known.

Two fuzes were used, one of which was a radio proximity fuze made by AEG called *Fuchs*. It was said to be effective up to 10 metres from the target and, in contrast to various infra-red fuzes which had been put forward, it was not adversely affected in its operation by exhaust gas from the target. The other fuze was a delayed action device for self-destruction of the missile should it go astray or otherwise fail to get close enough to the target. Both fuzes were armed when the launch rockets were jettisoned.

Guidance was performed by radio command from an operator who had the missile and target in view all the time, using the *Strassburg-Kehl* system. As an anti-jamming measure, 18 different channels were available to the operator; there was also an additional channel which could be used to detonate the warhead on command from the ground if desired. To avoid further the possibility of jamming, wire control was proposed to supplement the radio system. The plan was to retain and use all the control circuits except for the radio receiver, with a resultant flexibility in the substitution of one type of control for the other. Against low-altitude targets the missile had an effective range of 10 miles. Its ceiling was 35,000 feet.

Because of Allied bombing of the factory and also of the works of the various subcontractors, the planned production schedule went wrong and the weapon never got into service. Moreover, the problems associated with controlling rockets at high speed were entirely new and they took a lot of solving. Out of 59 test missiles launched, only 25 flew successfully and responded to guidance.

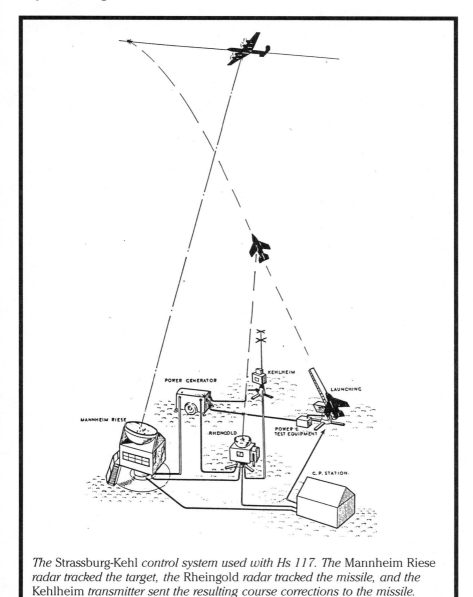

The Strassburg-Kehl *control system used with Hs 117. The* Mannheim Riese *radar tracked the target, the* Rheingold *radar tracked the missile, and the* Kehlheim *transmitter sent the resulting course corrections to the missile.*

A report on the training requirements brings out some additional interesting points. Men picked for training came from all ranks in the army and no special skills were demanded. However, good eyesight and eye/hand coordination were essential and 60 per cent of trainees were eliminated by a preliminary physical examination. It seems that men with technical skills did not always make the best students. Pilots, usually unavailable because they were needed elsewhere, appear to have had the best results, which is perhaps not surprising, since they would have had some experience of manoeuvring a machine in flight. Each trainee was given one or two hours, morning and afternoon, on a 'training device' over a period of two months. During that time expert operators gave demonstrations with actual missiles to acquaint the trainees with guiding techniques. At the end of the training period the student was required to make three practice launchings. Some 20 per cent of trainees are said to have made hits on their first attempt. After these practice launchings the best trainees were selected to take the advanced course which ultimately would make them qualified operators. This 'training device' was not explained in the document, but it might very well qualify as the grandfather of all the expensive simulators which have accompanied missiles since then.

Some time in 1944 it occurred to somebody in the Henschel design offices that if you could fire the Hs 117 upwards, you could also fire it in other directions, and from that came the idea for the Hs 117H. This was an air-launched version of the Hs 117 and was designed to be launched from large bombers, specifically the Dornier 217. All dimensions were the same as those of the Hs 117, with the exception of the upper tail fin which was reduced in height to permit suspension beneath the fuselage of the parent aircraft. Unlike on the original Hs 117 no launching rockets were required, since the aircraft gave the missile an initial speed and the launch would usually be horizontal or slightly downward,

The missile was planned to have an effective horizontal range of 12,000 metres and a vertical range of 5,000 metres above the point of launch. Development tests were still in progress at the Henschel works up to the end of the war, and records showed that six of 21 test launchings had failed.

Next came *Wasserfall* ('Waterfall'), a 7.9m (26ft) long liquid-fuelled rocket which bore a considerable resemblance to the A4 bombardment rocket – not surprisingly since, it was developed at Peenemünde. It was proposed in 1942 as a weapon for the defence of large cities, and the plans envisaged 200 batteries in three zones, 50 miles apart, which would virtually seal off Germany from the North Sea. A later revision of this idea proposed 300 batteries, which it was claimed would completely defend all Germany if suitably spaced out. To back up this deployment, a production of 5,000 rockets per month would have to be achieved.

Wasserfall was a supersonic rocket similar to the A4 in principle of operation, but weighing about one-third as much. It could be carried on a standard railway freight car and lifted into the vertical launch position without requiring special handling equipment. The use of nitric acid and aniline for propulsion instead of liquid oxygen simplified the transport, storage and handling of fuel to a very important degree. The mechanical construction was simplified compared to the A4 by the use of a compressed gas fuel feeding system in place of turbine pumps and by replacing many of the valves with diaphragms which fractured on the application of pressure to the fuel container.

Wasserfall was designed in response to a specification which called for a weapon to ensure the destruction of a bomber flying at 20,000 metres (65,000 ft) altitude, at 900 km/hr (560 mph) and at a range of up to 50 km (31 miles) from the launcher. The assumption was made that any type of aircraft could be destroyed with a warhead of 100 kg (220 lb) of explosive, and perhaps several aircraft if they were in close formation. In order to fulfil the required performance it would be necessary to have a very accurate control system. The first method to be suggested involved the use of two radar sets, one tracking the target and one tracking the missile. The signals from each radar were to be displayed to a controller who would operate the radio control transmitter in such a manner as to guide *Wasserfall* to intercept the target aircraft, and the controller would then detonate the warhead by radio. A second proposed method involved similar radar and radio control but employed an infra-red homing device and proximity fuze to control the missile in the final approach and to detonate the warhead at the nearest point of approach.

Wasserfall was a torpedo-shaped missile almost 26 feet long mounting four stub wings about 11 feet back from the nose. There were four guiding fins at the rear incorporating both jet rudders and air rudders. The whole assembly was broken down into eight sections to expedite mass production. The fuel containers were made a part of the framework since their construction had to be strong enough to withstand internal pressure.

The propulsion system of *Wasserfall* was similar in arrangement and principle of operation to that of the A4, although the construction was greatly simplified. Fuel feed to the combustion chamber was accomplished by applying nitrogen pressure to the fuel containers through a pressure-reducing valve. The nitrogen, in a spherical tank, was under pressure of about 4,000 lb/in^2 which was reduced to 450 lb/in^2 by the valve before entering the fuel containers. Frangible membranes which took the place of check valves in the pressure line, were broken and the pressure of 450 lb/in^2 was applied to the fuel tanks.

The fuels were fed to a mixture regulator in front of the combustion chamber. This compensated for the varying internal resistances of the fuel lines and maintained a uniform fuel mixture ratio. The fuel was *Visol* (vinyl isobutyl ether) and was injected directly into the front portion of the combustion chamber. The oxygen carrier was 90 per cent nitric acid plus 10 per cent sulphuric acid, and was circulated through a cooling jacket around the venturi and combustion chamber and then sprayed into the chamber from a circular manifold on its rear section. Provision was made in the mixture regulator for the *Visol* to lag behind the acids long enough to allow the acid to enter the combustion chamber first, thereby avoiding the possibility of an explosion caused by an accumulation of *Visol*.

The fuels ignited spontaneously upon mixing. The combustion chamber pressure of 280lb/in^2 produced an exhaust velocity of 1,900m/sec (6,230ft/sec) and a total thrust of 800kg. The fuel tanks carried 360kg (793lb) of *Visol* and 1,500kg (3,300lb) of acid mixture and the compressed gas weighed about 143 pounds. This fuel load was sufficient to produce a total impulse of 360,000kg-sec over a period of 45 seconds.

The warhead was constructed originally to contain 100kg (220lb) of explosive, but the explosive weight was later increased to 305kg (670lb). A proximity fuze was specified for the *Wasserfall*, but up to the date of termination of the project none had been developed sufficiently to warrant production. It is believed that for the first operational use of the weapon detonation was intended to be accomplished through a special channel of the radio control transmitter.

The development of a high-performance and expensive rocket device to destroy aircraft meant that something better than mere aiming was required, and the missile would actually have to be controlled throughout its flight and guided either to impact or at least into very close proximity with its target and then detonated. The target location and aiming system employed in test flights was a ground system known as *Elsass* and was similar to the *Burgund* system which was developed for use with subsonic missiles. The *Elsass* system consisted of a radar set for locating the target (either a *Mannheim Riese* or an *Ansbach* set) and a control unit designated *Rheingold*, developed by Telefunken. This consisted of a joystick, a telescope and an oscilloscope linked to the radar set used for locating the missile (a *Würzburg* set), employing a 3m parabolic dish antenna mounted on the roof of the *Rheingold*. A remote power control system was used to control the telescope from the target-tracking radar.

In operation, the *Mannheim* or *Ansbach* radar would detect the target and, by remote control, would point the telescope at it, after which the operator acquired the target in his field of view. Since the telescope was obeying the tracking radar, the operator saw the target as a stationary object, which he then had to keep covered by the missile as it flew. If the engagement was entirely by radar – for example at night – then the operator performed the same sort of thing on the screen of his oscilloscope display, keeping the spot representing the target covered by the spot representing his missile. In either case, the necessary movement of the missile to cover the target was done by his joystick control.

A second proposal was to use a radar which tracked the missile and triggered a transponder, the signal from which was picked up by a direction-finding set, thus establishing the azimuth and elevation of the missile. This was to be fed into a comparator in which it would be compared against similar information from the target-tracking radar. The differences being established, the necessary corrections would then be calculated electronically and relayed to the control transmitter and thus to the missile, bringing the missile into the beam of the target-tracking radar. Once in the beam the corrections would be zeroed and it would simply ride the beam to the target. A homing device to take over the steering when the missile was within a few miles of the target was also under development, because it was felt by the designers that the radar system alone was inadequate for a missile flying at supersonic speeds as did *Wasserfall*.

In addition an improved system of guidance was under development by Telefunken in which the radar would issue commands directly to the missile without the intervention of an operator. This was expected to bring the missile close enough to the target so than an infra-red homing device could then take over. However, this system was still in the laboratory stage and had not been tested in flight.

Whatever the system of guidance, *Wasserfall* was controlled in azimuth and elevation by four jet rudders and four air rudders mounted at the tail of the missile, as in the A4. They were arranged so that an alternate pair acted as elevators while the remaining pair acted as rudders. The jet rudders were in the stream of rocket gases so that they functioned when the rocket burned. The air rudders were mounted outboard in the slipstream, and functioned at all times during flight. Every jet and air rudder combination was operated by an Askania hydraulic servo-motor acting through a linkage system. These control servos executed the commands received from the radio receiver .

Wasserfall was launched in the vertical position in a manner similar to the A4/V-2. The complicated fuelling procedure of the A4, however, was unnecessary for *Wasserfall* since the missile was designed to be fuelled in a rear area and then stored ready for use at the launch site completely filled except for the high pressure gas tank. The missile was set vertically on a transport trolley, rolled out to the launching position, and fired from the trolley.

The actual launching procedure consisted simply of closing an electrical circuit which fired the detonators on the blast valve, allowing the fuels to flow into the combustion chamber and ignite. The missile took off with an acceleration of 72ft/sec/sec and was controlled in the desired direction of flight by the radio controller as soon as it was airborne. Peak velocity was about 2,530ft/sec and the terminal velocity could vary between 1,150ft/sec and 2,530ft/sec depending upon range.

Work on *Wasserfall* began late in 1942 at Karlshagen near Peenemünde, an establishment known as the 'AA Research Station of the *Luftwaffe*,

Karlshagen'. Between 500 and 600 men worked on the project. A provisional model of the combustion chamber was tested at Peenemünde in March 1943 and in July a pre-production model was tested. By September 1943 sufficient parts for three complete rockets had been produced at Karlshagen. The first launching test was carried out on 28 February 1944 on Greifswalder Oie. On this occasion the missile reached a ceiling of slightly below 23,000 feet but failed to reach supersonic speed.

By July 1944 seven more missiles had been tested and additional firings were made by the latter part of the year, but the destruction of the *Wasserfall* workshops at Karlshagen by an air raid late in 1944 slowed down the development for some weeks. By 5 January 1945 another 17 launches had been made to complete the total of 25 missiles fired, 24 with radio control; 10 of those fired failed to operate. A status report dated 22 January 1945 mentions that some difficulties were encountered with the propulsion unit in the first tests but that these had been overcome. Development was stopped on 6 February 1945 but there are indications that work continued in a desultory manner for some time after that date.

The total estimated time for production for *Wasserfall* was 500 man-hours compared with an estimated 4,000 man-hours for the A4. The entire *Wasserfall* production programme could be carried out with 14,000 workers using 60,000 square metres of floor space (24.2 square miles!). The development of *Wasserfall* was never entirely completed, although much of the engineering and design work had been done by the end of 1943.

Enzian

Next came *Enzian* ('Gentian'), a design which came very close to success. *Enzian* was an extremely powerful rocket which could almost be considered a pilotless aircraft. It carried a warhead of 500 kg of high explosive and was particularly intended for use against formations of heavy bombers. It was designed by Dr Wurster of Holzbach-Kissing AG as a subsonic ground-to-air missile, with a future option of developing it into a supersonic weapon. There were also suggestions of converting the design into ground-to-ground and anti-tank configurations, but these got no further than suggestions

The missile consisted of three main parts: the warhead, of steel or moulded wood; the monocoque fuselage in which were two fuel tanks and two steering control motors; and the tail section holding the power unit, control panel and stern cap, to which vertical fins were attached. This stern cap could be removed in one piece for access to the power unit and control panel. Two swept-back wings of conventional aircraft type were fitted to the fuselage. There were only two control surfaces, mounted in the wings and operated by electric motors through a simple rod transmission system

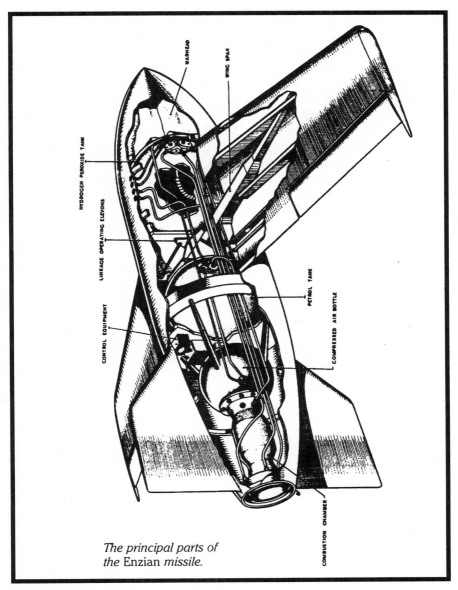

The principal parts of the Enzian *missile.*

The warhead carried 500 kg of explosive and was to be fitted with a proximity fuze. Several competing designs were under consideration, among them *Fuchs* (radio), *Kugelblitz* (radio), *Paplitz* (infra-red) and *Kranich* (acoustic), but no decision had been taken, since none of them ever completed development.

Four auxiliary take-off rockets were mounted in two pairs outside the fuselage, held in place by explosive bolts. The nozzle of each of these rockets was displaced by 30 degrees so that the axes of the exhausts passed through the centre of gravity of the missile. These rockets burned for 5 seconds after launch, after which the explosive bolts were electrically fired and the expended rocket casings fell away, aided by small wing sections which ensured that the casing diverged from the missile and did not interfere with its stability. At the usual launch angle of 75 degrees this separation occurred at about 2,400 feet altitude. The main sustainer motor was to be a Walter bi-fuel rocket burning a nitric acid/benzene mixture which was fed to the motor by turbine pumps

The fuselage was made of moulded plywood which consisted of several layers of beech veneer pressed into the required shape of the various components and glued together. The wood components were produced by the Behr works at Wendlingen. An alternative form of construction designated *Schnittholz* had been suggested by Herr Beyer of Holzbau Kissing AG; this had the advantage that the wings and main fuselage units of *Enzian* could be constructed at various small wood-working factories. The *Schnittholz*

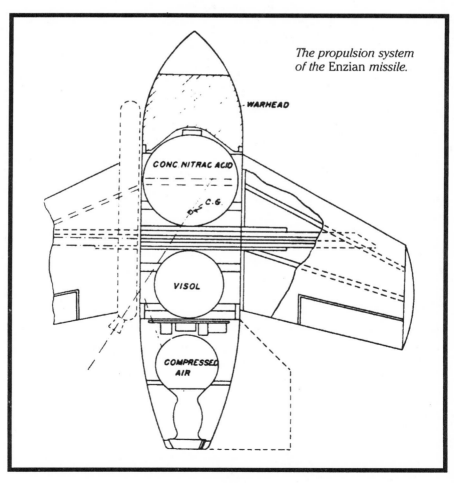

The propulsion system of the Enzian *missile.*

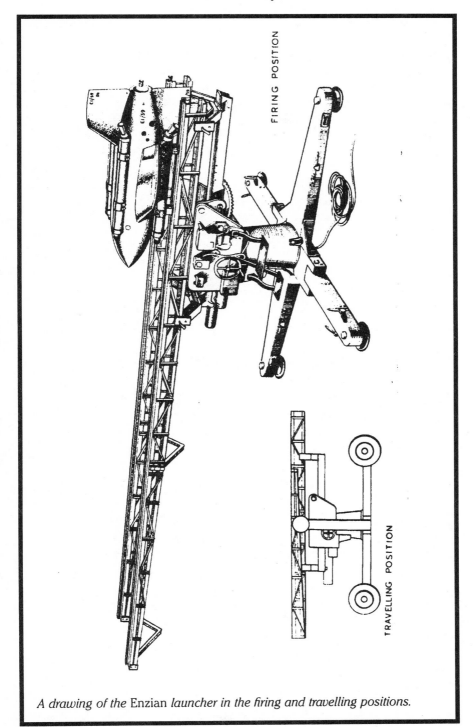

FIRING POSITION

TRAVELLING POSITION

A drawing of the Enzian *launcher in the firing and travelling positions.*

construction consisted of building up the shapes from planks glued together in the manner of a wooden barrel, and it had the further advantage that the wood was spruce which had no supply problems. By the time the production of *Enzian* ceased, little or no practical progress had been made with this form of construction. Only a few components had been tested, and the properties of the *Schnittholz* method were still not proven.

Although Dr Wurster was the originator, the project soon got beyond his company's capabilities and was transferred to Messerschmitt AG in late 1943. The first experimental models of the *Enzian* were built at Augsburg during the latter part of 1943 and early 1944. Allied bombing caused the work to be transferred to the Kissing plant at Sonthofen, which proved inadequate when pressure to produce in quantity increased. So the *Enzian* project was moved again, to a branch of the Messerschmitt factory near Oberammergau. Here a new plywood version was hastily developed between November 1944 and January 1945. The project came to an official halt on 18 January 1945, when a general order stopped work on several

FR and *Enzian* models

FR 1   (June 1943): The drawing board original design with two wings and two fins at 90 degrees to each other.

FR 2   (August 1943): A drawing-board project only; as for the *FR 1* but the lower vertical fin was removed. It was to be fitted with rudder control and ailerons.

FR 3   (September 1943): An improved *FR 1* with wing and tail tips streamlined and a cylindrical body. All control was performed by wing ailerons.

FR 3a   (September 1943): As *FR* 3 but with the body streamlined.

FR 3b   (October 1943): As *FR 3a* but with the wing-span increased from 11ft to 12ft 2in.

FR 4   (October 1943): As for *FR 3* but with the tail removed and replaced by two more wings at 90 degrees to the main wings.

FR 5   (November 1943): As for *FR 3* but with a cylindrical body and using a Walter RI 203 assisted take-off unit as a motor, since the intended Walter pump motor was not ready.

FR 6   (October 1943): The *FR 3b* modified to take the Walter pump motor 109-739.

Enzian 1   (February 1944): As for *FR 5* but with some small changes in the location of components and with enlarged tail fins. A number of these were built and flight tested.

Enzian 2   (Mar 1944) As for *FR 6* but with the body entirely constructed of wood, rectangular fuel tanks instead of spherical ones, projects in order to concentrate available effort on one or two selected programmes. In spite of this, work continued while interested individuals, including Professor Messerschmitt, tried to get the order rescinded and production authorised, but the attempt failed and in mid-March 1945 the project was finally stopped.

Development began in June 1943 under the designation *FR 1* (*Flak Rakete 1*), and a number of *FR* designs followed before the project acquired the name *Enzian* in January 1944. The various development models are tabulated below.

Enzian 4 was expected to fly at something over 500mph, or Mach 0.66, and it was hoped that *Enzian 5* would reach Mach 1.6 or even Mach 2.0. The Walter turbine pump rocket motor was expected to produce a ceiling of 52,000 feet, but all the flight trials were done using the solid-fuel Walter assisted take-off rockets which gave a maximum ceiling of only 23,000 feet.

Altogether, 60 *Enzians* were built, and 38 *Enzian 1* models were launched in a series of test flights, about 16 of which used radio control.

---

and with pods at the tips of the tail fins for installing flares, transponders or wire spools, according to which guidance system was selected. This model was never built.

Enzian 3A (Jun 1944): As for *Enzian 2* but with spherical fuel tanks and no tail fin pods.

Enzian 3B (Jan 1945): As for *Enzian 3A* but designed to accept a new motor, the Konrad VFK 613-AOI bi-fuel type which differed from the Walter motor in using compressed gas in bottles to force the fuels to the rocket motor instead of turbine pumps, and was hence a lot easier to build. Neither model of the *Enzian 3* was ever built.

Enzian 4 (February 1945): This was intended to be the definitive production model and was based on the *3B* but with a larger body and wing span. It was intended to use the Konrad motor, since by then there appeared to be no chance of the Walter motor ever appearing in time to be used.

Enzian 5 (February 1945): A development of *Enzian 4* with overtones of *FR 4* and designed for supersonic flight. It had four very swept-back wings at 90 degrees to each other and a more streamlined body. An improved Konrad motor was to be fitted and the warhead reduced in size to 250kg. Drawings and calculations were done but the design got no further.

Enzian 6 (February 1945): A proposal for a simplified wire-guided version for use as an anti-tank missile. No detailed studies or drawings were ever made of this version.

Had the weapon been given a chance there is every possibility that it could have become operational, but the *Flak Ministerium* was biased against it on the grounds that it was diverting the Messerschmitt factory from its prime task of making aircraft. As a result the project was always struggling against official hostility and low priorities for obtaining the necessary materials and components. Moreover post-war investigation showed that many of the flight trials had been carelessly carried out and much of the data that had been determined from them was suspect.

Rheintochter

The last anti-aircraft missiles to be developed were the *Rheintochter* series. This project began in 1942 when the Luftwaffe asked Rheinmetall-Borsig to develop an anti-aircraft rocket which would go to an altitude of 12,000 metres.

Rheintochter I was a ground-launched, subsonic, radio controlled, ground-to-air rocket developed by Rheinmetall-Borsig of Berlin-Marienfeldt. It was launched from a rail attached to a converted 8.8cm Flak 36 gun mounting, the rail being aimed towards the target in a manner similar to the barrel of a conventional gun. The missile had a torpedo-shaped body with six stabilising wings attached to the rear portion of the frame, and four control fins mounted on the pointed forward section. A solid-fuel assisted take-off rocket was connected to the main body by an explosive bolt connection which was fractured by detonation when the assisting rocket was expended and the main propellant powder ignited. The radio control system used in tests of *Rheintochter I* was of a conventional audio-modulated type and gyroscopic roll stabilisation was used. Optical tracking with the aid of flares attached to two stabilising wings was employed in the test launchings but it was planned to equip operational batteries with radar tracking units as well as optical units.

The rocket body can be subdivided into five sections: fuze, control compartment, electrical unit, explosive warhead, and propellant container. The fuze housing was fitted to the control compartment by a sleeve arrangement secured by six screws and was intended to house the *Kranich* acoustic proximity fuze. The control compartment was made of Elektron alloy, chosen because of its light weight and comparatively high tensile strength. It was attached to the electrical unit by 12 stud bolts and contained the various mechanical components concerned with the control of flight. The electrical unit was housed in a steel tubular container attached to the explosive warhead and contained the radio receivers and other equipment.

The explosive warhead was made of steel plate and had a maximum capacity of 150kg (330lb) of explosive. The warhead was secured to the forward plate of the propulsion chamber with a flanged joint and stud bolts. The propulsion chamber, with an overall length of about 2.4m, carried the

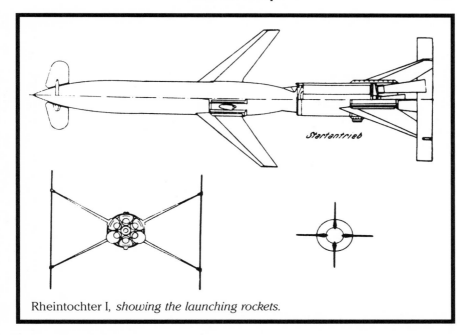

Rheintochter I, *showing the launching rockets.*

main solid-fuel rocket. At each flanged connection along the rocket a thin sheet steel strip was welded to produce a smooth exterior surface. Both the stabilising wings and the control surfaces were made of a highly compressed laminated wood called Lignofol.

Both the starting rocket and the main propulsion rocket motors used Diglycol in sticks about one metre in length. The starting rocket with a total weight of 650 kg (1,432 lb) contained 240 kg (530 lb) powder in a casing. The main unit contained 210 kg (465 lb) powder which burned in 10 seconds, with an impulse of 40,000 lb-sec. Fuel consumption was 48.4 lb/sec and the specific impulse 82.5 lb-sec/lb.

Rheintochter I reached a velocity slightly below that of sound inside a distance of 1,000 feet. The starting unit had a thrust of 143,000 lb, and at the end of the 0.6 sec burning time the missile was travelling at a speed of about 1000 ft/sec. At this time the starting rocket was disengaged from the weapon and the main rocket was ignited. The velocity continued at slightly less than 1,000 ft/sec for the 10-second duration of the main unit. A target at maximum range would be reached shortly after the termination of thrust, while the velocity was still 985 ft/sec.

Compared with several other missiles under development, *Rheintochter I* had the poorest performance of any, and for this reason mass production was never seriously considered. There are indications that as far back as June 1944 the Germans did not consider *Rheintochter I* for mass production but rather as an experimental model for accumulating data for the development of *Rheintochter III*.

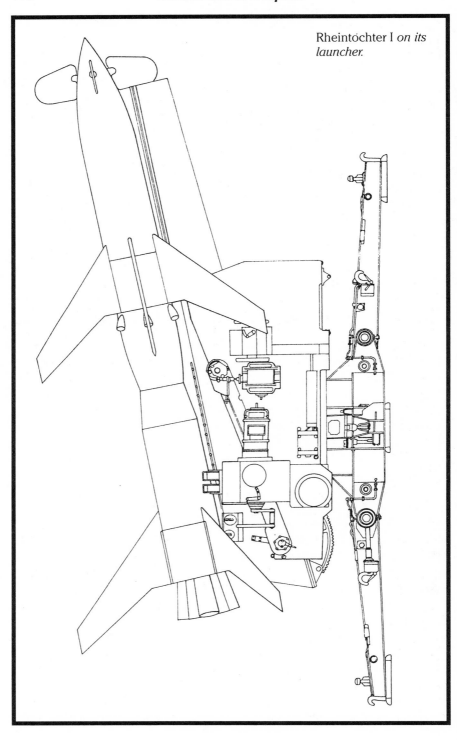

Rheintöchter I *on its launcher.*

A handbook on *Rheintochter I* was published by Rheinmetall-Borsig in April 1943, and we may therefore assume that the engineering had been completed by that time. The first tests were made in August 1943 at Leba, on the Baltic coast. Up to the beginning of July 1944, 34 experimental missiles had been launched, but it is not known if any of these were radio-controlled. A further 48 were fired between July 1944 and January 1945. Of this total of 82, 22 were radio controlled and all but 4 operated satisfactorily. Correspondence from Rheinmetall-Borsig files indicated that 20 *Rheintochter I* rockets were to be fired at Karlshagen on 20 February 1945; it is not known whether this test firing was carried out, but it is unlikely, as all development had been stopped on 6 February 1945.

After extensive development work had been done on *Rheintochter I* the Luftwaffe rejected the missile on the grounds that its range was now too short. Work then started on a new model called *Rheintochter III*. This incorporated many of the features of the *R I* except the propulsion unit which was entirely new. Two assisted take-off rockets were mounted on opposite sides of the weapon and the length of the rocket body was increased by one metre to give greater fuel space. Provision was made to use either solid or liquid fuel in a system patterned on that of the *Wasserfall* missile.

The guidance system of *Rheintochter III* was identical to that of *R I* except that roll stabilisation was not provided. The missile was free to rotate and incorporated a gyroscopically controlled commutator to feed the control signals to the proper control surfaces in the correct sequence.

An entirely new launching ramp was developed, which was permanently emplaced in a circular pit about 25ft in diameter and 10ft deep. The rails were a few feet above ground level when the ramp was in the horizontal position. The rails from which the rocket was actually fired were part of a firing car to which the rocket was attached by T-shaped guides at the preparation bunker. The car and rocket were then taken to the launcher where the car was attached to the ramp by two bolts. The launcher could be elevated to 90 degrees and had 360 degrees' traverse.

The liquid propulsion unit was developed as a result of experiments with power plants for the V-2 at Peenemünde. The hydrocarbon fuel called *Visol*, with *Salbei* (nitrous oxide) as the oxygen carrier, provided a self-igniting mixture. Fuel tanks were arranged so as to keep the centre of gravity constant during flight.

A time switch operating one second after launch blew the explosive bolts of the assisted take-off rockets and started the main rocket, fracturing a diaphragm in the main air pressure system. As pressure built up so diaphragms in the fuel lines burst at different pressures, the acid going first so as to allow it to circulate around the cooling chamber and be injected before the fuel was injected.

The fuel load was 88kg (194lb) of *Visol* and 335kg (740lb) of *Salbei*. Thrust varied from 3,750lb to 5,080lb over a burning time of about 45 seconds.

The rate of fuel consumption was 10kg/sec (22lb/sec) and the specific impulse was 85kg-sec/kg (188lb-sec/lb). The alternative solid fuel motor was five sticks of diglycol powder 18cm (7 inches) in diameter and 2.2m (7ft 3in) long weighing 90kg (200lb) each, a total charge of 450 kg (1,000lb) with a burning time of 50 seconds. The grains were unperforated but had a six-leafed clover-shape section to give the desired burning characteristics. No report on performance has survived, but apparently five of the six experimental missiles fired in late 1944 were of this type.

The explosive weight in *Rheintochter III* was 150kg (330lb). In the liquid-propelled model the explosive charge was carried between the acid tank and the fuel tank. In the powder-driven model the charge was contained in a separate section between the electrical unit and the propulsion unit. One proposal was to use solid cast explosive and depend only upon blast, while another proposal was to use a charge of 60-gram incendiary pellets, but neither warhead was ever tested. The warhead was to be detonated by means of a *Kranich* acoustic proximity fuze, as in *Rheintochter I*, but there was also a separate radio channel which would allow the warhead to be detonated by radio command from the ground if desired.

In July 1944, by which time 34 *R I* missiles had been fired, *Rheintochter III* was still in the process of construction. By 5 January 1945 six *R IIIs* had been fired, five with solid and one with liquid fuel, None was radio-controlled, but the commutator system had been tested and it was thought that control would offer no problem. Rheinmetall-Borsig records indicated that 15 *Rheintochter III* were to be fired at Karlshagen on 20 February 1945 but it is doubtful if this demonstration ever took place.

More ambitious still was the manned *Rheintochter* project. This envisaged a pilot, prone in the nose of the weapon, guiding it towards its target on instructions from the ground. Once set on a target interception course, the pilot would take to his parachute and leave the missile to go on and hit the target. This project never got off the drawing board, and in some post-war accounts has become mixed up with the A series of missiles, resulting in reports of a 'manned V-2 with which to bombard New York, steered there by a pilot who parachuted out before impact'. There was no such proposal.

Feuerlilie

A missile which occasionally crops up in lists and reports is *Feuerlilie*, of which there were two models. It was not, in fact, a missile, and the reason that it features in the lists is a fine example of the chicanery necessary to get things done in Nazi Germany.

The *Feuerlilie 25* was, in fact, a sounding rocket; a rocket designed to go up into the atmosphere carrying scientific instruments and transmitters which would send back information on whatever the scientists were attempting to measure. In this case it was the performance of a missile at trans-sonic speeds, figures which were needed by the Ardelt company of Breslau in connection with aerodynamic work which it was doing, quite properly, for the *Luftwaffe*. But the bureaucracy was unable to comprehend such a device and consistently refused the various instruments and materials necessary to make one. Finally Ardelt designed the rocket as an anti-aircraft missile, with suitable spaces for the warhead and fuze. Since it was now a weapon, the demand went via another department, and was approved. So Ardelt built the 'missile', filled the spaces with the measuring equipment, and completed six. Three were fired in April 1943, with two failures. The remaining three were fired in July 1943; all three worked and produced the desired information.

Feuerlilie 25 was a simple cylindrical body, 34.5 inches long, with a pointed nose. There were two in-line vertical fin surfaces, one above and one below the fuselage. Unlike conventional aircraft, no rudders were attached to these surfaces. Two horizontal stabilising surfaces were fixed to the fins, one well above and one well below, the fuselage. Only the upper surface was fitted with an adjustable elevator. Both the wing and the tail sections were made of cast aluminium alloy.

Since the function of the *F 25* was simply to obtain trajectory dynamic data, no attempt was made to guide it. The elevator was pre-set before launching, and gyroscope control of the ailerons was sufficient to prevent roll in flight. Propulsion was by two Rheinmetall-Borsig assisted take-off rocket units, designated the RI 502, which used a solid diethylene glycol dinitrate propellant. A throttling valve was regulated to give the rocket an even thrust of 500kg for 6 seconds.

Feuerlilie 55 was similar to the earlier *F 25*, but it was larger with much of its design based on lessons learned from its forerunner. Like the *F 25* it was built for the purpose of collecting aerodynamic data in the trans-sonic region and was launched from the ground.

The missile had tapered swept-back wings mounted well back in the rear section of the cylindrical fuselage. On the extremities of the wings were a pair of vertical airfoils. The airfoil area was large enough to permit the elimination of tail fin surfaces, and it also furnished a streamlined housing for the electromagnets which operated the ailerons on the trailing edge of the wings. The fuselage used the lattice method of construction. Space was provided in the forepart for an explosive charge, a parachute, instruments and control apparatus. In the actual flight tests the explosive space was filled with 100kg of ballast.

Propulsion was by means of four assisted take-off units, similar to these used with *Enzian*, located in the tail section of the fuselage. The projected total impulse was 13,000kg-sec at 6,000kg thrust, with which the *F 55* could reach to 6,000 metres. Altitude could be increased by extra assisted take-off units mounted outside the fuselage. This, it was calculated, would increase the ceiling to 9,000 metres.

No firm data on control is available. It is generally assumed that it used a gyroscope in the same manner as in *F 25* to control ailerons via electromagnets. Tests apparently showed that the missile flew within one metre of its predicted trajectory with a scatter of one or two metres.

Development of the *F 55* began in the summer of 1943. The first test, made at Leba, on the Pomeranian Baltic coast, in May 1944 was successful, giving a Mach number range between 0.85 and 1.2 (639mph and 900mph). At the second test at Peenemünde in November 1944 the missile fell out of control. A third missile sent to Peenemünde in the same month was never tested.

Artillery

Artillery is not a field in which you might have expected, in 1939, to find anything secret; it appeared to be a fairly pedestrian field of activity, with developments limited simply to making minor improvements in metallurgy or fire control or detail design. Surely there was nothing that one nation could come up with which would have escaped the attention of every other artillery-producing nation? Or was there?

The taper-bore guns

In 1903 a German called Karl Puff patented a design for a gun in which the bore, instead of being the same diameter from end to end, was tapered; it started out at the breech end at, let us say, 10mm diameter and then gradually got smaller until at the muzzle it would be 7mm diameter. He completed the idea by designing a bullet with an expanded sleeve around its waist; this was of 10mm diameter, so that it loaded correctly into the bore, but when fired it passed down the bore and the gradual taper squeezed the sleeve down until it left the muzzle with the sleeve firmly reduced into a prepared groove in the bullet so that the bullet had the usual smooth exterior shape.

His object in designing this device can be explained by some simple arithmetic. Suppose the base area of a bullet when loaded to be 10 square centimetres. And suppose the gas pressure generated by the propellant charge to be 10,000kg. The pressure on the bullet will therefore be 1,000kg per square centimetre, which will produce some specific velocity. But as the bullet goes down the bore, the base diameter shrinks and thus the base area shrinks with it. The design of the charge can be adjusted to provide a constant gas pressure, so that by the time the bullet reaches the muzzle the pressure remains the same at 10,000kg but the base area has, let us say, halved. So the pressure on the bullet is now 2,000kg per square centimetre, and this will have increased the velocity by a considerable amount. Tapering the bore therefore develops a far higher muzzle velocity than could be achieved by a conventionally rifled parallel bore.

Puff's intention was to obtain high velocity so as to get a flatter trajectory and a shorter time of flight, and thus improve the accuracy of the weapon. And everybody thought it was rather a clever wheeze, but how do you drill a tapering hole and then rifle it? And how do you make these complicated little contracting bullets? Ah, said Herr Puff, that's your problem. But if you do succeed, than I'll take my percentage in licence fees.

Puff's patent duly expired without ever being worked, and some time in the 1920s another German, a gunmaker this time, decided that technology had moved along a little since 1903 and perhaps Puff's idea might be workable. The gunmaker was Hermann Gerlich, and in conjunction with a partner called Halbe he eventually produced a taper-bore sporting rifle which he marketed as the *Halger*. With the aid of the RWS ammunition company he also developed a practical bullet, and, as Puff had predicted, the *Halger* rifle had high velocity and a flat trajectory which, even though it was expensive, made it popular with hunters, so Halbe and Gerlich were able to make a living. But Gerlich, like many a gun inventor before him, had his eyes firmly fixed on a military contract, and in 1928–33 he walked the corridors of war departments in Germany, Britain and the USA in an attempt to interest them in a powerful sniping rifle. They were all interested, but the cost of such a weapon was daunting, and there were no takers. The Americans experimented at Springfield Arsenal and developed a number of bullets, one of which produced a muzzle velocity of 7,100 feet per second (compared with around 2,800 fps for a standard military rifle), but the programme was abandoned early in 1939.

Gerlich went back to Germany in 1933 and got in touch with the Rheinmetall-Borsig company. Hitler had become Chancellor, the Versailles Treaty was repudiated, re-armament was beginning, and ideas were wanted. They were particularly wanted in the field of anti-tank gun design, because the problem there was to produce a weapon light and handy enough to be easily moved about and emplaced by a couple of infantrymen but powerful enough to penetrate the armour of tanks. Fortunately, at that period, the armour on tanks was not of any great thickness, since it was only intended to keep out ordinary small arms bullets and shell splinters.

Reduced to its basics, the penetration of armour is simply a question of momentum; throw something hard enough and the mass and velocity will carry it through. Even a plain lead ball will go through armour steel if you can get it moving fast enough. So the *Halger* rifle, with its high velocity, was a promising idea. In order to survive the impact with the target, the bullet was given a core of tungsten carbide; this was enclosed in a soft steel casing which had two flanges or 'skirts' which could be squeezed down in the bore so as to present a smooth outline at the muzzle.

Rheinmetall, after various experiments, decided on a barrel tapering from 28mm to 20mm; for security reasons it was known as the *schwere Panzerbuchse 41* ('heavy anti-tank rifle') but in every respect it was a small conventional artillery piece on a two-wheeled, split-trail carriage, with a small gun-shield and a hydro-pneumatic recoil system. The whole equipment weighed only 505lb (229kg) and it fired a 131-gram bullet at 4,595 feet per second (1,400 metres/second) to go through 2.6 inches (66mm) of steel armour at 500 yards range.

It would be idle to suppose that security was so tight that nobody outside Rheinmetall knew what was going on, and there was soon a whisper around the armaments engineers in Europe that somebody was playing with a taper-bore weapon. As a result one or two other people began looking at the idea; one was a Czech who, in 1938, got out of Czechoslovakia just ahead of the occupying Germans and fled to Britain. There he began trying to interest the military in his taper-bore theories. He met with a stony response. In the July 1940 the Ordnance Board, tired of his supplications, poured cold water on the idea.

> 'The principle has been investigated in the past. It is quite clear that, as regards attack of armour, a weapon of this type cannot be regarded as possessing any advantages over a normal weapon of equal weight and of the same calibre. As regards the application of the principle to the 2-pounder gun, the Board recommend No Further Action.'

A few days later a liaison officer lately returned from France submitted a report on the *Halger* taper-bore rifle, an example of which he had acquired in France. He got much the same treatment:

> 'The system was investigated by the Small Arms Committee some years ago (See SAC Mins 1935 or so, under 'Halger Rifle'), Herr Gerlich himself being employed by the War Department. He was not the inventor of the coned bore and skirted projectile, the credit for this being due to Karl Puff whose patent was taken out in about 1903. [Actually Brit Pat 18601 of 27/8/1904]. The system was developed by Gerlich in collaboration with Halger. It is still being pursued by Kern, in Switzerland, and by Pacetti at Otterup in Denmark. The Kern proposal is being dealt with in current Proceedings. Neither ammunition nor weapons are yet within measurable distance of becoming fit for use in war. No Further Action to be taken.'

About eight months later the British Army captured a *Panzerbuchse 41* in the Libyan Desert and flew it back to Britain to be examined. It was found to have a muzzle velocity of 1,388m/sec (4,555ft/sec) and to penetrate 70mm of homogenous armour at 100 yards range.

By that time Rheinmetall had moved on and had designed the 4.2cm *Panzerjager-kanone 41* ('tank-hunting cannon') which was more or less an enlarged version of the first weapon. This started out at 42mm calibre and ejected the projectile at 29.4mm calibre. The shot weighed 11.8 ounces (336g), had a velocity of 4,150ft/sec (1,265m/sec) and could go through 3.43 inches (87mm) of armour at 500 yards range, or 2.36 inches (60mm) at 1,000 yards. This weapon came into service early in 1941.

Krupp, that other famous German gunmaker, had also looked at the taper-bore idea. In 1939, looking well ahead to the inevitable increase in the size and strength of tanks, the army had asked Krupp and Rheinmetall for a 7.5cm anti-tank gun. Rheinmetall produced a conventional gun. Krupp was attracted to the taper bore but was faced with a major engineering problem in producing a tapering gun barrel of that calibre and size and therefore invented a variation which became known as the 'Squeeze-bore'.

The 7.5cm *Pak 41* gun was a conventionally rifled gun with a barrel 116 inches (2.95m) long. To the end of this barrel was attached a smooth-bore extension 37 inches (950mm) long which had a varying internal taper. As the flanged shot left the muzzle of the rifled section and passed into the extension, it first went through a section tapered at 1-in-20 for about 10.6 inches (270mm), then into a more sharply tapered section at 1-in-12 for another 6.7 inches (170mm) and then into a parallel-sided section for the rest of its travel, emerging squeezed down to 5.5cm calibre. The advantage of this method of manufacture was that only a short length of the barrel had to be tapered and this did not have to be rifled. The wear on this taper as the shot passed through at high speed was such that the extension piece was worn out after about 500 shots, but it was simply held on the barrel by a screwed collar and could be replaced in a very short time in the field and with the minimum of tools.

The gun fired a tungsten-cored shot weighing 5.7lb (2.6kg) at a muzzle velocity of 3,690ft/sec (1,125m/sec) and could defeat 7 inches (177mm) of armour at 1,000 metres range, striking at a 30 degree angle, or 4.9 inches (124mm) at 2,000 metres. This was a really formidable performance for 1941 and but for one thing this might have been the standard German army anti-tank gun for the remainder of the war. The one thing which defeated it, and also defeated the other two taper-bore guns, was the demand for tungsten to provide the cores for the projectiles. Tungsten was not native to Germany and had to be imported; the supply was restricted, and there was a constant demand for it for the manufacture of machine tools and other vital production equipment. A tungsten machine tool could be sharpened or rebuilt when worn; a tungsten projectile fired at an enemy was so much tungsten lost for ever. And since production was the more vital of the two conflicting demands, tungsten for ammunition was cut off in the late summer of 1942. And once their special ammunition was gone, the taper-bore guns went to the scrap pile. So effectively, indeed, that few specimens of the 7.5cm *Pak 41* survived the war.

But if the shortage of tungsten ruled out the taper-bore as an anti-tank weapon, it certainly did not rule it out in other applications, and now the anti-aircraft specialists began to look at the system. In the anti-aircraft business the principal problem was the interval between firing the gun and having the shell arrive in the vicinity of the target; a great deal could happen during that time, and any way of shortening the shell's time of flight by increasing its velocity was carefully scrutinised. Therefore the taper bore, with its substantial increase in velocity, was a highly attractive idea; the difficulty lay in the design of the projectile. In an anti-tank gun the 'payload' was a lump of inert metal, but in an anti-aircraft gun the payload had to be high explosive. And the dangers which lay in squeezing a high explosive shell were self-evident. With armour-piercing shot the core acted, as it were, as an anvil, while the tapering barrel acted as a hammer, but with an explosive filling the squeezing action had to be carefully controlled so as not to place excessive pressure on the shell body.

Two solutions appeared to work satisfactorily. In the first type, the shell was of smaller diameter than the bore and was fitted with two supporting bands of sintered iron, one at the shoulder and one at the base. These were attached in the manner of driving bands, and performed the same function in spinning the shell, but they were malleable so that as the bore reduced they were swaged down and folded back, so that at the muzzle the shell left with two smoothed-down bands which set up minimal air drag.

The second method was rather more complex. Three soft studs were fitted at the shoulder of the shell and the base was deeply indented with a semi-circular groove around the body. Into this grove went a malleable skirt with a circular base which fitted into the groove and acted as a sort of flexible ball-joint, turning backwards as the skirt was squeezed down by the reducing bore. At the same time the soft studs at the shoulder were pressed down and deformed until they were mere bumps on the outside of the shell. Again, the result was that as the shell left the muzzle the studs and skirt had been reduced to streamlined excrescenses which set up minimal drag. It was claimed that either of these designs could give a reduction in the time of flight by about 30 per cent, though there appear to be no trials results to back this up. Like so many other developments, the taper-bore anti-aircraft gun was overtaken by events and the war ended before the design could be perfected.

Gustav and *Dora*

One of the myths of the 1930s which sustained the French and their allies was the inviolability of the powerful Maginot Line defences. It had its effect upon the Germans, too; their thoughts were directed towards methods of overcoming them. There are, of course, only two solutions to that sort of problem; either you go around it (as the Germans eventually did) or you go through it, and for that option you need some powerful weapons.

In 1935 the *Heereswaffenamt* sent a query to the Krupps; what size of weapon would be needed to defeat the fortifications of the Maginot Line in the same manner that Krupp's 42cm howitzers had defeated the fortifications of Liège in 1914? The Krupp staff did some calculation and responded with ballistic data for three possible weapons, guns of 70cm (27.5in), 80cm (31.5in) and 100cm (39.3in) calibre. And there the matter briefly rested.

In March 1936 Adolf Hitler visited the Krupp works, and in the course of his inspection he asked the same question about defeating the Maginot Line. The same figures were given to him, and when he asked about the possible manufacture of such weapons he was told that, whilst difficult, it would not be impossible. Hitler left the matter hanging in the air, but Gustav Krupp von Bohlen und Halbach knew that, if Hitler had a weakness, it was for grandiose engineering projects, and he ordered plans to be drawn up for an 80cm gun. Early in 1937 these were sent to the *HWA* to see what it thought of the idea, and very rapidly came back with a firm order to build three guns. Work began in the summer of 1937, the first gun to be delivered by the spring of 1940.

It would be well to understand the magnitude of the problem; the ballistic solution for 80cm postulated a concrete-piercing shell weighing 7 tons (7,100kg) and propelled by a cartridge containing 4,631lb (2,100kg) of propellant powder to attain a range of 23.6 miles (38km). Alternatively, it could fire a 4.73-ton (4,800kg) high explosive shell from a 4,939lb (2,240kg) cartridge to a range of 29.2 miles (47km). We are looking at a shell weighing the same as a fully-laden 40-passenger bus, fired by a charge of propellant powder weighing as much as a large Mercedes car. It follows that the gun itself has to be big; more than big, enormous. And somehow it had to be capable of movement to and from the battlefield.

The equipment was therefore designed so that it could be transported piece-meal on special railway trucks, each part being carefully dimensioned so as to lie within the standard railway loading-gauge limits. The gun portion split into several sections: the breech ring, breech-block, the barrel in two halves, jacket, cradle, trunnions and trunnion bearings, all of which were carried on specially-fitted flatcars. The carriage was split both vertically and longitudinally; the bottom-most layer, the wheeled sub-structure, was simply trundled along in its own train, but the remaining layers which formed the main carriage and upper carriage were moved on more special flatcars. In addition to this caravanserai there were trains of ammunition wagons, crew coaches, machine-shops and a dismantled travelling gantry crane, two anti-aircraft battery trains and a protection and security company. Each gun was accompanied by no less than 1,720 men under the command of a general officer.

On arrival at the firing position a special four-track spur was laid on a curve, so that the gun could be given direction by moving it around the curve. The two outer tracks were laid for the gantry crane. The right and left halves of the bogie sections were pushed into place on the gun tracks, bolted together and anchored. The carriage components were then shunted up to the crane, lifted from their flatcars, transported to the bogies and lowered into place. Once the upper carriage had been fitted, the trunnion bearings were put in position and the cradle and its trunnions fitted. The jacket was then lifted on to the cradle and the rear half of the gun

Left: *Few V-1s failed to detonate; this one was shot down south of London and landed relatively undamaged.*

Left: *A V-1 on the launch ramp. The combustion chamber has been fitted, and the crew are making the various connections preparatory to firing. The men in white coats suggest a test at Peenemünde rather than a combat launch.*

Below: *The piloted Fi 103* Reichenberg *was originally devised as a test machine, but was later proposed as an air defence fighter.*

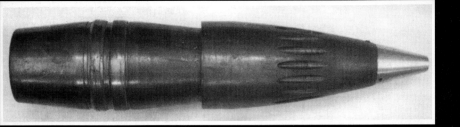

Top: *An experimental athodyd shell in 10.5cm calibre. The details of the construction differ considerably, but the principle remains the same. This shell has a small capacity for explosive towards the base end. Air entered through the holes in the forebody, mixed with fuel and ignited, and was exhausted from the mid-point skirt.*

Above: *The stub-wing solution in 12.8cm/10.5cm calibre; the stubs did not discard, but gave added lift to the shell in flight and an increase in range.*

Left: *A 15cm gun shell with jack-knife fins extended. The 'driving band' behind the fins rides on roller bearings and is primarily designed to seal the propellant gases and not to spin the shell.*

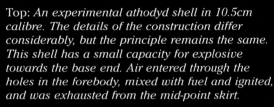

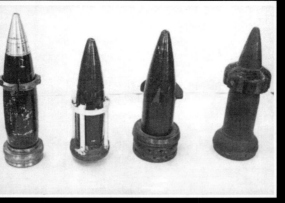

Left: *A collection of 10.5cm/8.8cm sabot shells for the 10.5cm anti-aircraft gun, showing a variety of approaches: from the left, a three-part shoulder ring and a blow-off base; a 'cage' sabot; stub wings and a blow-off base; a forward sabot of synthetic material and a segmented base.*

Left: *A 37mm PAK 36 anti-tank gun loaded with the 3.7cm Steilgranate shaped-charge bomb.*

Below: *The ultimate anti-tank gun; the 12.8cm PAK 44 had a truly formidable performance but it weighed ten tons and demonstrated the impracticality of using such huge weapons in the field.*

Left: Maker's mock-up of the proposed 10.5cm PAW anti-tank gun.

Left: The cartridge and projectile of the 8cm PAW 600.

Below left: Another view of the PAW 600, showing the holes in the cartridge closing plate through which the high pressure gas passed into the gun.

Below: The 8cm PAW 600 weighed only 1,323lb (600kg) but could defeat 150mm of armour.

Above: *The rocket-assisted shell for the 28cm K5(E) railway gun, cut open and showing the time fuze, the rocket propellant in the forward section, and the blast pipe passing through the high explosive section to the efflux at the rear.*

Left: *The 31cm Peenemünde Arrow Shell, without its fuze.*

Below: *The first 60cm Karl howitzer, with eight roadwheels.*

Bottom: *The 54cm version of Karl, showing how the ammunition was supplied from the munitions carrier.*

Top: *An A4 rocket is moved into place on its* Meillerwagen *transporter.*

Above, centre: *The rear section of the A4 rocket, showing the combustion chamber and fuel supply lines; photograph taken in the underground Mittelwerke assembly factory.*

Above: *The V-2 fuzes: left, the nose fuze; centre, the base fuze; and, right, the exploder capsule which detonated the main filling of the warhead when initiated by one of the fuzes.*

Above: *The V-3, or High Pressure Pump. This is one of the two 15cm test guns found at Hillersleben. The two splayed girders at the far end were part of a bracing system to resist the recoil shock.*

Left: *One of the more successful projectile designs for the High Pressure Pump. The forward sabot is shown partially dislodged, and the pusher piston behind the fins is shown in the firing position. It would discard shortly after leaving the bore, together with the front sabot.*

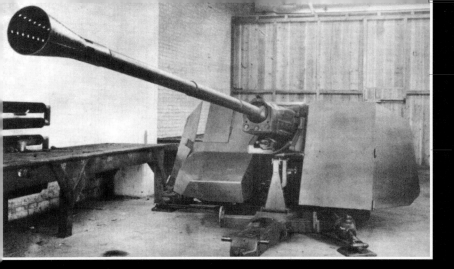

Top: *The 5.5cm Gerät 58 anti-aircraft gun has a good claim to being part of the first integrated weapon system.*

Above: *One of several proposed projectiles for the 40mm Electric Gun, with a conventional 40mm gun shell for comparison.*

Left & above left: *Two views of Doktor Zippermayer's Whirlwind Cannon, as found on the Artillery Proving Ground at Hillersleben in 1945.*

Left: *The 75mm* Fohn *anti-aircraft rocket launcher. The rocket resembled an artillery shell, exhausting throug canted vents in the base to produce spin as well as thrust. It saw more use as a last-ditch field artillery weapon than it ever did as an air defence weapon.*

Below: *An American soldier demonstrating the* Fliegerfaust; *note the canister with a spare clip of rockets hanging at his waist.*

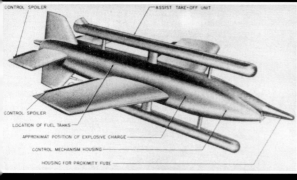

CONTROL SPOILER
ASSIST TAKE-OFF UNIT
CONTROL SPOILER
LOCATION OF FUEL TANKS
APPROXIMAT POSITION OF EXPLOSIVE CHARGE
CONTROL MECHANISM HOUSING
HOUSING FOR PROXIMITY FUZE

Top: *A side view of* Enzian *on its launching platform; the launcher was based upon a redundant anti-aircraft gun mounting.*

Above: *The Hs 117* Schmetterling *missile, showing the principal parts.*

Right: *A detailed drawing of the* Dusenkanone *showing the rotary magazine for the gun, and the gas jets, roughly as they would have appeared when mounted in a Junkers Ju 88 aircraft.*

Left: *A 5cm* Bordkanone *mounted on a Henschel Hs 129 aircraft. Note the large and elaborate muzzle brake, required in order to reduce the recoil as much as possible.*

Left: *A Junkers Ju 87 Stuka mounting two 37mm* Bordkanonen.

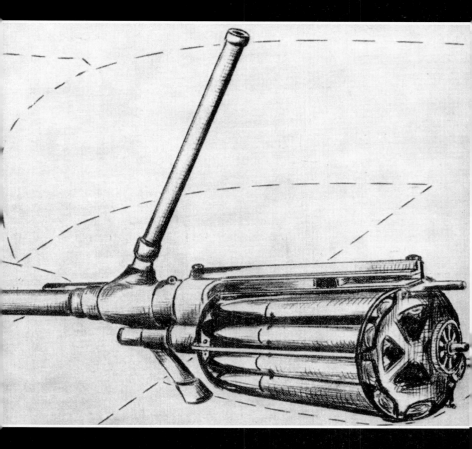

Above: Gustav *complete and in position.*

Left: *Removing the empty cartridge case after firing* Gustav.

Above: *A damaged* Natter *found in St Leonard by American troops.*

Right: *American troops examining one of the four* Natter *machines found at St Leonard.*

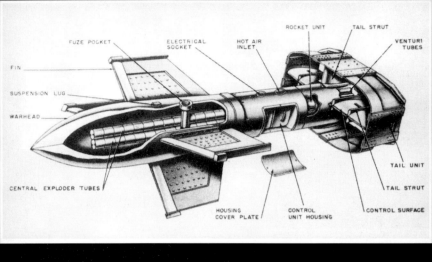

FIN —
SUSPENSION LUG —
WARHEAD —
CENTRAL EXPLODER TUBES —
FUZE POCKET · ELECTRICAL SOCKET · HOT AIR INLET · ROCKET UNIT · TAIL STRUT · VENTURI TUBES · TAIL UNIT · TAIL STRUT · CONTROL SURFACE · HOUSING COVER PLATE · CONTROL UNIT HOUSING

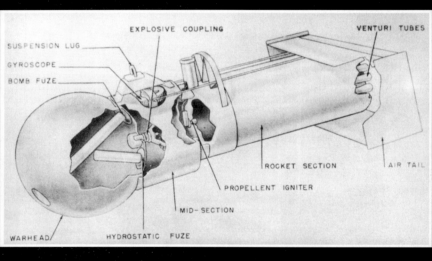

SUSPENSION LUG —
GYROSCOPE —
BOMB FUZE —
WARHEAD —
EXPLOSIVE COUPLING · VENTURI TUBES · ROCKET SECTION · AIR TAIL · PROPELLENT IGNITER · MID-SECTION · HYDROSTATIC FUZE

*Top: The squeeze-bore projectile for the 7.5cm
PAK 41. The holes in the front skirt are to
release air trapped between the skirts as they
are squeezed down during the passage through
the reducing gun bore.*

*Above, centre: The taper-bore projectile for the
2.8cm Panzerbuchse 41 (to the same scale as
7.5cm shell at top).*

*Above: An experimental squeeze-bore high
explosive shell for an anti-aircraft gun.*

*Right: A 10.5cm/8.8cm squeeze-bore shell
using soft metal studs and a soft metal skirt.*

Top left: The principal components of FX-1400.

*Centre left: Kurt, the rocket-assisted skip bomb
designed to better the more famous Barnes
Wallis design.*

*Bottom left: The X-4 wire-guided air-to-air
missile; the wire spools have been detached
from the wingtips and one has been opened*

Above: Natter *on its vertical launching rails.*

barrel inserted into the jacket. The front half of the barrel was then fitted and locked in place by a massive joint nut (and one can imagine the performance, attempting to line up two halves of a gun barrel weighing well over 100 tons, one half of which is dangling from a crane.) The breech ring was then assembled to the barrel, the breech block inserted, and after some three weeks of work the gun was at last ready to fire. The equipment was some 141 feet (42.97m) measured over its couplings; the gun itself was 106.5 feet (32.48m) long and the entire weapon weighed 1,329 Imperial tons (1,350 tonnes).

In 1940 all that lay in the future. The barrel proved a great deal more difficult to manufacture than had been imagined and the Maginot Line was out-manoeuvred without the assistance of the 80cm gun. It is said, though no authority is quoted, that after the French campaign was over Hitler had some harsh words to say to the Krupp management, hinting that it was required to overpower the fortress of Gibraltar should General Franco prove amenable. But Franco was not amenable, and the Gibraltar project faded away. Nevertheless the gun barrel was completed towards the end of 1940 and successfully proof-fired early in 1941. The rest of the year was spent building the carriage (there had been no point in doing much work on this until the gun was known to be viable) and early in 1942 the first gun was moved to Rügenwalde firing range on the Baltic coast, assembled and fired in the presence of Hitler himself. Once he pronounced himself satisfied, the gun, now named *Gustav Gerät* by the Krupp management in honour of the proprietor, was presented by Gustav Krupp to Hitler as the company's contribution to the war effort. And by that time a second gun, named *Dora* after the wife of Erich Muller the chief designer, was ready for delivery and components for the third gun were under construction.

After its tests at Rügenwalde, *Gustav* was moved down into southern Russia to join the siege of Sebastopol, It took up a position as Bakhchisary, some 16km north-east of the city, and fired 48 shots at various targets. The most spectacular of these was the concrete-piercing shell which penetrated into an underground magazine at Severnaya Bay and detonated the contents. After Sebastopol fell *Gustav* was dismantled and shipped back to the factory at Essen to have the barrel re-lined; proof, ballistic tests and the few rounds fired in the siege added up to over 300 shots and the barrel was worn out.

Dora, the second gun, was now sent into action outside Stalingrad. The records of this action are scanty and conflicting but the gun must have been withdrawn after a short stay, since the Soviet counter-attack surrounded the German Sixth Army in a matter of days and there would have been no time to dismantle and move it had it waited until the attack began. *Gustav* is said to have been sent to join the siege of Leningrad late in 1942, and it has also been stated that one of the two guns was used against the Warsaw uprising in 1944, but it seems probable that the weapons used in these two actions were the *Karl* 60cm self-propelled howitzer (discussed later in this chapter). Both guns were moved to the Rügenwalde ranges for a training session in 1943, but thereafter they were never seen again until May 1945 when the US Third Army found parts of *Gustav* in Bavaria. Parts of *Dora* were later found near Leipzig, and parts of the third gun, which was never completed, were found at the Krupp factory and at Krupp's Meppen proving ground. But from all these parts there was not sufficient to construct a complete gun, and eventually everything was scrapped.

After the successful debut of *Gustav* at Sebastopol a number of grandiose projects were suggested. One was the manufacture a 52cm (20.47-inch) gun to fit on the same mounting and fire a 3,131lb (1,420kg) shell to a range of 68 miles (110km), or a 52/38cm sabot shell to 93 miles (150km) or a 52/38cm rocket-assisted shell to 118 miles (190km) range. This was proposed as a cross-Channel bombardment gun which would have put a considerable stretch of southern England in danger. But the obvious threat of air retaliation, and the impossibility of hiding such a monster weapon, put this project into the discard pile. The next idea was to manufacture a smooth-bore barrel and fire a dart-like 'Peenemünde Arrow Shell' to about 100 miles range, but this idea never got past the drawing board stage.

As a technical achievement *Gustav* and *Dora* were remarkable; as practical weapons of war they were a total waste of time, money and manpower which could have been put to better use elsewhere. Each gun cost something in the region of seven million Reichsmarks (approximately £610,000 in 1939) without considering the cost of the ancillaries such as the trains and the special transporter cars, the cranes or even the two air defence batteries. For the price of *Gustav* you could have had 28 Tiger tanks.

And although these guns were never known to the Allies as anything else but rumours and suggestions, one wonders whether they were quite as secret as they were thought to be. Among my possessions is a notebook written by an officer on an artillery intelligence course in February 1940; on one page he has some figures about potential German guns, amongst which is an 80cm gun firing a 4-ton shell for 29 miles. This was before the gun had even been made; so perhaps it wasn't so secret after all.

Adam, Eve, Odin, Thor, Loki and *Ziu*

Germany, as you might expect of a country in the heart of a continent and surrounded by potential enemies, owned a respectable collection of railway artillery of various calibres. And yet in 1937 the *OberKommando des Heeres* authorised development of a self-propelled 60cm howitzer firing a 2,200kg concrete-piercing shell. Surely, one would think, there were several railway guns capable of doing whatever this weapon could do? But a look at the 1939 map of the Polish–Russian border offers a clue; there were a mere nine railway lines which touched the border in all its 500 miles length. Moreover, of course, the Russian railway gauge was 5ft 6 inches, whilst the German and Polish gauge was 4ft 8½ inches. Perhaps the invasion of Russia in 1941 was not such a spur-of-the-moment decision as it is sometimes claimed to be.

Design of the weapon was done by Rheinmetall-Borsig, and the prototype was tested in the spring of 1940. The chassis was a massive box carried on a tracked suspension with eight road-wheels on each side. The howitzer was a quite conventional stubby-barrelled weapon using a dual recoil system – the barrel recoiled in its own cradle, and the mounting recoiled along the chassis, both being controlled by hydro-pneumatic cylinders. Tests revealed a few problems with stability and the chassis was re-designed to use 11 road-wheels on each side, suspended on torsion bars which ran across the hull. These were attached to a gearing system so that once the vehicle had arrived at its firing position the torsion bar anchorages were revolved, the wheels raised, and the hull was lowered until it rested on the ground and the suspension was relieved of the firing shock. Propulsion was by a massive 44.5-litre Daimler-Benz V-12 diesel engine generating 580bhp, and the whole equipment weighed 120 tonnes.

For all that, the performance was not in the record-breaking class. The 2,200kg anti-concrete shell carried a charge of 240kg of explosive and was propelled by a four-part cartridge weighing only 32kg. The lowest charge pushed the shell to only 3,260 metres and the highest charge to 4,320 metres. It was obvious that this machine was meant to clatter its way close to a fort and then fire half-a-dozen of these great shells to reduce it to rubble. The shell was capable of piercing up to 2.5 metres of reinforced concrete before bursting, and it could also defeat up to 35cm of armour steel. A lighter 1,575kg anti-concrete shell was provided, which gave a maximum range of 6,650 metres, but with rather less penetrative power, and there was also a high explosive shell of similar weight which had a maximum range of 6,580 metres. Both these used a different, five-part, cartridge.

The six service equipments, which were known officially as *Gerät 041*, less officially as *Karl* (for General Karl Becker of the *OKH* who had initiated the design) were delivered to the army in 1940/41 and issued to 628 schwere Artillerie Abteilung (Motoriziert), who promptly christened them *Adam, Eve, Thor, Odin, Loki* and *Ziu*. Then they trundled off to Russia in July to batter down the forts at Brest-Litovsk, Lvov and various other strong-points. Together with *Gustav*, they attended the siege of Sebastopol in 1942, then Leningrad, and appeared outside Warsaw during the 1944 rising. But the army was less than happy with the performance; it felt, rightly in my opinion, that a weapon as cumbersome as this ought to offer more range in order to compensate.

In May 1942 the army suggested that a smaller calibre and lighter projectile might be a sensible exchange, and asked for a design of 54cm barrel which could be interchanged on the same mountings. This was duly done and six 54cm barrels provided, but instead of completely changing over, it seems that the barrels were fitted as and when the range was desired. If the heavy shell was of greater importance in a particular tactical situation, then the 60cm barrel was used; where range was the primary consideration, the 54cm barrel was fitted. At the end of the war two of these weapons were captured by the US Army; one had a 60cm barrel while the other had a 54cm barrel. The 54cm version fired a 1,600kg anti-concrete shell to 10,500 metres range using a 57kg propelling charge. It also fired a 1,270kg high explosive shell to 12,500 metres. The rate of fire with either was about 6 to 8 rounds per hour.

On the face of it *Gerät 041* was another case of giantism, but given the paucity of railway communications on the Eastern Front and the strength of some of the border fortresses, they were a practical solution to a tactical difficulty. At any rate, they seem to have been in steady, if not continuous, employment throughout the war.

K5 *Glatt*; the 150km cannon

One of the better German artillery designs was the 28cm K5(E) railway gun, some 28 of which were built between 1936 and 1945 and which became more or less the standard German railway piece, used in every theatre of war. One attained fame as 'Anzio Annie', firing into the Allied beach-head at Anzio; it was actually called *Leopold* by the German gunners who operated it, and it now stands on a short length of track in the display area of Aberdeen Proving Ground in Maryland in the USA. (Another is on display in a museum at Cap Gris Nez in France.)

The K5(E) had one unconventional feature, which had been first explored in the Paris Gun of the First World War, and that was the use of ribbed shells in conjunction with very deep rifling grooves. The gun was rifled with 12 grooves of 7mm depth, and the shells all had 12 curved ribs on their exterior which matched the curvature of the rifling. Loading was therefore a critical business, to ensure that the ribs entered the rifling grooves, and the gas sealing was taken care of by a wide copper sealing band behind the ribs.

Good as the K5(E) was – and it fired a 563lb (255kg) shell to a range of 38.6 miles (62km) – there were those who felt it could stand some improvement, and it soon became the vehicle for a number of innovative designs. The first of these was a shell with rocket assistance.

A rocket-assisted shell had been devised for the standard 15cm howitzer; it was not particularly successful but it enabled a number of problems to be identified and solved, so that the shell for the K5(E) was a much better article. The interior of the shell was divided into two compartments by a steel plate just below the shoulder. This carried two impact fuzes and had a central hole from which a blast pipe ran down to the base of the shell. The nozzle was sealed by another steel plate. The rear section, around the blast pipe, was filled with high explosive, an insulating jacket being placed around the pipe. The nose section was filled with solid rocket propellant and the nose carried a time fuze permanently set to 19 seconds. The shell was loaded in the normal way and fired by the normal cartridge; the time fuze ignited the rocket after 19 seconds of flight, just as the shell was approaching the peak of its trajectory. The rocket's blast went down the pipe and blew off the sealing plate, and the thrust accelerated the shell and extended the trajectory. On impact, the two fuzes inside the shell sensed the sudden deceleration and detonated the explosive payload. The shell weighed 248kg, slightly less than the standard shell, and achieved a maximum range of 53.7 miles (86.5km).

The only defect of this projectile was occasional inaccuracy. At the instant of the rocket's ignition, the shell might be perfectly aligned with the trajectory, or it might be yawing slightly off it, and if so the thrust of the rocket would drive the shell further off the trajectory in the direction of the yaw. As a result half the shells were likely to fall in a rectangle some 3.5km long and 200 metres wide around the target, while the worst cases could land over 13km away.

As we have already seen, the research station at Peenemünde owned a supersonic wind tunnel, and when not concerned with rockets it did other ballistic research for the *HWA*. There, Engineer Gessner had developed a long finned shell to be fired from a smooth-bore version of the K5 gun, calling it the *Peenemünde Pfeilgeschoss* ('Peenemünde Arrow Shell', or *PPG*). The dart-like shell was 4.7 inches (120mm) in diameter, with four fins at the rear and a three-piece sabot around the waist, both these items being of 31cm calibre to fit in the bore; the gun was thereafter known as the K5 *Glatt* (*glatt* means smooth). The 28cm rifled barrel was reamed out to 31cm smooth-bore and a special propelling charge launched the shell at 5,000ft/sec (1,525m/sec) velocity. As it left the bore the three-piece sabot fell clear and the dart went to a maximum range of 93.8 miles (151km). The body of the shell was loaded with 55lb (25kg) of high explosive and had an impact fuze screwed into the nose.

Development of this shell began in 1940 but was slow; the successful design described above was, in fact, the third attempt and it demanded some high-grade steel for the long body to withstand the acceleration inside the gun. It was not until late in 1944 that issues began, and records of their use appear not to exist. It has been reported that a few rounds were fired against the Americans in the final weeks of the war but there is no confirmation of this. It is perhaps worth noting that a similar but smaller projectile was under development for the 10.5cm anti-aircraft gun in an attempt to reduce the time of flight and increase the practical ceiling; a velocity of 3,125ft/sec (952m/sec) was achieved but there are no figures

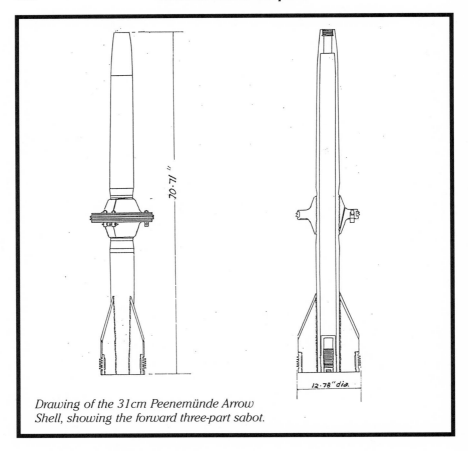

Drawing of the 31cm Peenemünde Arrow
Shell, showing the forward three-part sabot.

available on its altitude performance.

Although not directly connected with the K5(E) gun, one further development can be conveniently considered here, and that is the athodyd shell of Dr Tromsdorff. The drawback of the rocket shell, as Tromsdorff saw it, was the need to carry both components of the propulsive power, the fuel and the oxygen-carrier; since the shell was flying through the air, with unlimited oxygen on tap as it were, he opted to develop a jet-propelled projectile which, like the engine of the V-1 missile, would only require to carry its fuel.

There were a number of designs developed by Tromsdorff at the Hillersleben Proving Ground from 1935 onwards. In general, his projectile consisted of an inner unit containing fuel (carbon disulphide) and shaped so as to form, in conjunction with the outer wall of orthodox shell shape, an air-flow channel and combustion chamber. Distance pieces provided the correct spacing, and there was provision for attaching an orthodox driving band. The liquid container had to contain baffles in order to prevent the liquid 'taking control' of the projectile by moving during flight. A capsule of carbon dioxide was fitted into the liquid container and punctured when

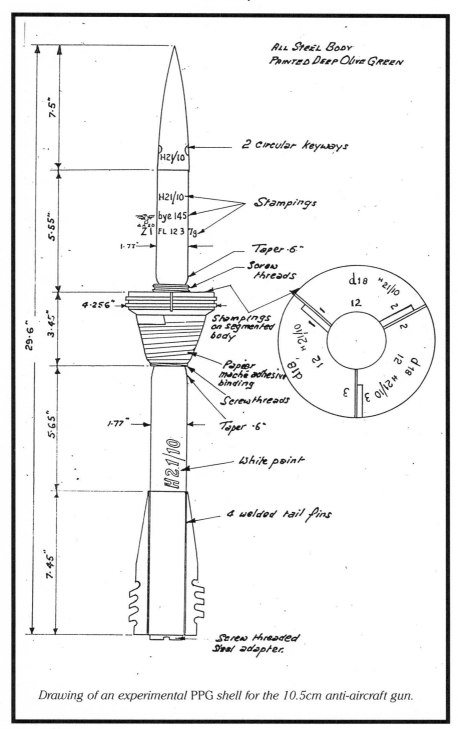

Drawing of an experimental PPG shell for the 10.5cm anti-aircraft gun.

the shell was fired, and the released gas forced the liquid through orifices in the combustion chamber wall, assisted by centrifugal force from the shell's spin. Ignition was due to compression of the air and fuel at supersonic velocities, and the resulting blast passed out of the rear of the combustion chamber and added thrust to the shell.

By 1945 a number of projectiles had been made and fired successfully, though they were only experimental and carried no explosive filling. Nevertheless, a 15cm shell had been fired at a muzzle velocity of 1,000m/sec and it had been calculated that it would be possible to reach 180km with it. Ranges of 200km for a 21cm gun and 400km from a 28cm gun such as the K5(E) were theoretically possible. The principal problem appears to have been fitting in the explosive payload and making it worth firing; the postulated 28cm shell would have carried only 13kg of high explosive instead of the 30kg or so normally found in conventional shells of this calibre. Various reports in the period since 1945 have suggested that further research into the athodyd shell has been carried out in Soviet Russia and in the USA, but that this question of finding room for a worthwhile payload has not yet been satisfactorily solved.

K12; the cross-Channel gun

In 1918 the German Navy built the *Kaiser Wilhelm Geschütz*, popularly called the 'Paris Gun' because it was used solely to bombard the city of Paris from gun positions in the Forest de Gobain some 70 miles away. (One of the minor incidental mysteries of the First World War is what happened to the Paris Gun? It was withdrawn in the face of the Allied advance in the autumn of 1918 and was never seen again. The Allied Disarmament Commission searched high and low and questioned everybody they met, to no avail.)

The Navy was somewhat smug about this super-gun, and the Army somewhat put out. And in the 1920s Army planners decided that Something Must be Done to relegate the Paris Gun to second place in the history books. Design studies took place, and when, in the early 1930s, the political climate became favourable, work began in earnest. The major question was that of achieving the very high velocity needed to get the shell into the stratosphere, where the air resistance was negligible and where the shell could thus achieve most of its range. The same technique had been employed in the Paris Gun though at a terrible cost in erosive wear; the rifling wore away at a rate of about ten inches for every shot fired, and after fifty shots the barrel had to be replaced. To combat this wear problem the shells for the Paris Gun were made in a numbered series, each slightly greater in diameter than its predecessor, so as to compensate for the wear; and it is said that one gun was destroyed by inadvertently loading a shell out of numerical order and trying to fire a shell which was too big for the state of the barrel.

Problems of this sort needed to be avoided, and it was decided that the new gun would be rifled with a few deep grooves and the shell would be given curved ribs or splines which would locate in these grooves so as to produce the desired spin on the shell, with the rotational acceleration spread over the entire shell body instead of being concentrated into the narrow area of a conventional driving band. Again, this same technique had been used in 1918, though with shallower grooves. Sealing of the propellant gas behind the shell would be done by a copper band, in the place usually occupied by the driving band, backed up by graphite and asbestos packing. To test this idea a number of smaller barrels were made up with various rifling profiles, and tested in 1935, as a result of which an eight-groove barrel was selected.

The mounting was fairly simple; it was to be a railway gun, and thus a box-like carriage supported on double bogies was designed. The main box structure rested upon two sub-frames, and each of these had two bogies beneath it, the front sub-frame two eight-wheelers and the rear two ten-wheelers. The gun was carried in a cradle with a hydro-pneumatic recoil system; but since the recoil force was expected to be fairly substantial, the entire box structure with gun was able to recoil over the two sub-frames, again controlled by hydro-pneumatic braking cylinders.

The gun was 33 metres (105.25 feet) long, and posed a few problems of its own. Firstly, elevating such an enormous length of tube was going to cause it to bend under its own weight, so an extensive bracing system had to be attached to keep the barrel straight. Secondly, elevating such a mass of metal needed some precision in setting the position of the trunnions so as to get a reasonable distribution of weight, and so the trunnions were set as far forward as possible and the breech area made as heavy as possible. This, in turn, meant that when the gun was elevated there was not sufficient room between the breech and the track below for it to recoil; therefore, before firing, the box structure and gun had to be lifted one metre above the sub-frames by hydraulic jacks. And since it was not possible to load the gun when it was in the 'up' position, it had to be lowered and raised again between shots.

The first barrel was proof-fired in 1937, and the first complete equipment was tested in 1938 and put into service in March 1939 as the K12(V). The Army was quite pleased with the performance; it fired a 107.5kg shell to a maximum range of 115,000 metres (71.46 miles), thus out-performing the Paris Gun. But it was less pleased with the performance of jacking the gun mounting up and down between each shot, and asked Krupp if something could be done about it. Krupp therefore did some further research into the application of hydraulic balancing rams under the gun cradle and found that it was possible to operate these at much higher pressures than had been previously thought practical. The barrel could thus be shifted forward in the cradle and balanced, and so provide sufficient space behind the breech to permit the full recoil stroke without striking the ground and without having to jack the structure up. The mounting was then redesigned accordingly and a second gun built as the K12(N) and issued in the summer of 1940. No more were ever made.

Both guns were issued to Eisenbahn Batterie 701, and the K12(V) was taken down to the French coast and directed against England. Several shells landed in the Dover area, but the greatest range attained appears to have been with a round which fell at Rainham, near Chatham in Kent, which was 88km (55 miles) from the nearest point on the French coast.

It is of interest, and illustrative of the problems confronting technical intelligence specialists, to read the summary of a report, written in February 1941, on the fragments found at Rainham:

> 'The examination of fragments of a German long-range shell which fell at Rainham, Kent, has shown the probable calibre of the gun to be 22cm. It is possible, however, that the calibre may be of the lower and more standard size of 21cm, the apparent value of 22cm being due to the general expansion of the shell body prior to fracture.
>
> 'The shell is of a special "rifled" design in the sense that undercut and nearly longitudinal slots are machined in the external surface to accommodate soft iron skids which are machined to engage with the rifling of the gun and serve as the driving band of the shell.
>
> 'The shell weight computed for a diameter of 22cm is in the order of 235lb, including 33lb of high explosive. The shell walls are rather thinner than might have been anticipated but this is offset by the fact that the material of the shell body was a good quality alloy steel (containing chromium, molybdenum and vanadium) heat-treated to give a yield point exceeding 50 tons per square inch. Muzzle velocity of the shell is probably not less than 4,000ft/sec. Shells of similar calibre have been fired into south-east coastal areas, as also have shells of still larger calibre (11 or 12 inches).'

The actual figures, determined after the war, were 21cm calibre, 237lb weight and 4,922ft/sec muzzle velocity, indicating a fairly accurate piece of deduction from a few rusty scraps of steel.

One gun was captured by the Allies in Holland in 1945 and subjected to a very close examination. The general opinion of the British experts was the same as that of the Krupp engineers who designed and built the weapon: as a practical gun it was nonsense, but as a technical exercise and ballistic research tool it was invaluable. But at 1,500,000 Reichsmarks it was an expensive tool.

Small shells for big guns

One of the constant demands of gunners is for longer range from their guns. This gives two benefits. Firstly, if you have a longer range than your opponent you can site your guns further back, out of his reach, and bombard him with little fear of retaliation. (Or at least, you could before the days of air superiority.) Secondly, a longer range means that for a given arc of fire your gun can command a much greater area: a gun with a 90-degree arc of fire and a maximum range of 10,000 yards can command an area of about 6.4 square miles. A gun with a maximum range of 20,000 yards can command just over 25 square miles of territory.

There are various ways to obtain more range; lengthen the barrel so that the propelling gases have more time in which to work, or increase the propelling charge, or make the shell lighter. But they all carry some sort of penalty. Lengthening the barrel enough to provide a worthwhile increase in range will produce an unwieldy monster of a gun; increasing the propelling charge will soon cause the chamber pressure to exceed the limits for which the gun was designed; and a lighter shell may move faster initially but will lack 'carrying power' because of the unfavourable ratio between weight and diameter, and thus the range increase will not be very significant.

In the 1930s a French designer called Edgar Brandt, who had made something of a name for himself by developing infantry mortars, began looking at ways of improving the range of current French field artillery. After running through the obvious options he began looking at other ideas and eventually hit on the 'discarding sabot'. The reasoning behind this idea runs like this: for any given calibre of gun there is an optimum weight of shell which is governed by its 'ballistic coefficient', which, roughly speaking, is the ratio of weight to diameter expressed as w/d^3. If you make the shell heavier you will lose velocity; if you make it lighter you will gain in velocity but lose in carrying power or momentum. But to gain velocity in the bore it is advantageous to have a light shell since it accelerates faster. What you need is a shell which is light so as to gain velocity in the bore but, at the same time, has the optimum w/d^3 value. Which, on the face of it, seems impossible.

What Brandt did was to take a standard 75mm gun shell, which had a good w/d ratio, and fit it with two belts or 'sabots' of 105mm calibre, and then load it into a 105mm gun and fire a 105mm cartridge behind it. Because it was much lighter than the normal full-calibre 105mm shell it left the bore with a much greater velocity. And once it left the bore the two sabots were detached and discarded, leaving the 75mm shell (of good flight characteristics) being propelled at a much higher velocity than any 75mm gun could have launched it and therefore going to a much greater range.

Brandt had got about this far with his experiments when war broke out in 1939. Many ordnance engineers knew about his activities, as a result of which his workshop in Paris was high on the German visiting list once they had completed their occupation of France, and much of his research work and notes were appropriated and taken back to Germany. Krupp and Rheinmetall, and some smaller firms, took up the challenge and began work on sabot designs. The remarkable thing is that all the work appears to have been devoted to improvements in velocity and range; there do not seem to have been any significant attempts at improving velocity for the purpose of defeating hard targets, the direction in which British research was directed, though this may have been due to the critical shortage of tungsten.

Some of the most interesting work was done by a Professor Haack, who appears to have worked with Krupp, Röchling and perhaps Rheinmetall on various designs. Haack's aim was slightly different from that of other designers; he saw the sabot system as a means of getting what he called his 'ideal projectile' into reality. Haack's ideal projectile was one with a shape best calculated for passing through the air, and this equates to a finely tapering head, a short curved body and a tapering rear section culminating in a rounded base. This gave the ideal airflow over the shell body and the minimum drag at the rear end. There was, of course, a catch in it; such a shape would be almost impossible to fire from a gun with any accuracy, because the constantly curving body meant that there was no parallel-walled surface to ride in the bore and give stability to the shell. As a result, Haack had never had the opportunity to demonstrate the superior flight characteristics of his pet theory. But now the sabot provided what his shell didn't have – an interface with the gun barrel. By supporting the base and nose of his shell in discarding sabots he could get the thing up to speed in the gun bore and then throw away the supports at the muzzle to leave his ideal projectile travelling with perfect stability. This led to some interesting results in experimental firings; not only was there an improvement in performance by virtue of the sabot principle, there was an additional improvement thanks to the perfect aerodynamic shape of Haack's ideal projectile.

Projectile design, though, is not simply a matter of external shape. Internal matters such as filling it with explosive, what explosive to use, and fitting it with a suitable fuze all come into it, as do more mundane things like what grade of metal to employ and how much and how complicated the actual manufacturing processes of casting and machining will have to be. And in these areas the ideal projectile proved to be a good deal less than ideal, for it would demand new fuze designs, new filling techniques and new manufacturing processes, all of which added up to economic problems. The only practical solution was a compromise; a not-so-ideal projectile which might lose a little of the potential performance (though it would still be an improvement on the normal full-calibre projectile for a given gun) but which would be an easier article to manufacture.

The results covered a broad field of ideas. The two fundamental questions in the design of discarding sabot projectiles are the nature of the sabot and the method of making it separate cleanly at the muzzle without disturbing the flight of the sub-projectile, and the German designs illustrated several different solutions. A common feature, though, was the selection of the sub-projectile; almost every designer went 'one size down' for his sub-projectile. Thus, if he was designing for a 105mm weapon, he used an 88mm shell; for a 15cm weapon, a 12.8cm shell and so forth. Gun calibres are not chosen haphazardly; they generally move in a more or less orderly progression, the shell weight roughly doubling at every increase. I say 'roughly' because frequently the perfect mathematical solution – that is exactly doubling the weight of shell – causes ballistic mismatches, and a slight adjustment one way or the other has to be made to achieve stability or accuracy. So that dropping one calibre to find the sub-projectile was quite a logical way of going about things, since it at least meant that the designer began with a shell which was known to be practical. As it was now going to be launched at a somewhat higher velocity than the original designer had planned, there might be some fine-tuning to do, but that would be all.

Two fields of sabot design were rather unusual; those intended to improve the performance of anti-aircraft and naval guns. Unusual because anti-aircraft guns are often sited near centres of population, and since what goes up must come down, the dangers from the sabots discarded during the first few hundred feet of flight would constitute a considerable hazard to the gun detachments and the local population. Unusual because no navy, before or since, appears to have evinced much enthusiasm for sabot projectiles in order to increase the range of its guns. Indeed, the naval design is particularly interesting since it introduced the 'pot sabot' before anyone else. In this design the sub-projectile was a 12.8cm shell enclosed in a steel cylinder which was of 15.2cm calibre and carried the usual sort of driving band. The shell base sat in a central recess in the bottom of the cylinder, which extended to about two-thirds of the height of the shell. It was then retained in place by a three-piece ring attached to the cylinder by shearable pins. The result resembled a house-plant in a pot, hence the term

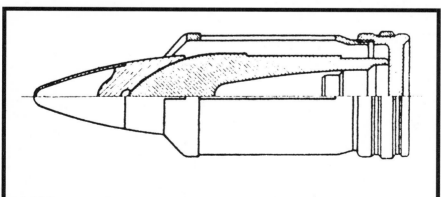

A 15.2cm pot sabot armour-piercing naval shell. The sabot was designed with planes of weakness which split in the gun barrel but remained in place to support the shell until discarded at the muzzle.

'pot sabot'.

On firing the three-piece ring was jarred by the initial acceleration and sheared its locking pins, but was retained in place because of the gun barrel surrounding it. The entire projectile weighed less that a standard 15.2cm shell, and therefore exited the muzzle at a higher velocity, where-upon the three parts of the ring flew off because of centrifugal force, and the air passing into the pot slowed it down and drew it off the shell, leaving the 12.8cm shell to fly to the target. There are no figures available for the performance, but it would be reasonable to expect an increase in range of at least 30 per cent over the standard 15.2cm shell.

Anti-aircraft sabot projectiles came in a number of shapes and sizes, but most of the work appears to have been done for the 10.5cm *Flak 38* and *39* guns, using 8.8cm flak shells as the sub-projectiles. One of the better designs used a 10.5cm base attached to the 8.8cm shell simply by friction, together with a three-piece ring at the shoulder of the shell. The base was formed so as to leave a space between the bottom of the shell and the base piece itself, and the base-piece had a small hole in it. When the shell was fired the gas from the propellant charge passed through this hole and filled the space at high pressure. As the shell left the muzzle and came into normal atmospheric pressure, this high pressure simply blew the base off the shell. At the same time the three-piece ring broke into its three parts by centrifugal force and was flung aside.

Another ingenious design, which was to have a resurgence many years later, had a similar base but instead of a three-piece ring at the shoulder had three stub wings of airfoil section sticking out so that they rested on the gun bore when loaded and supported the nose of the shell. On leaving the muzzle the base unit was discarded but the wings stayed in place; being streamlined they added little drag, but their airfoil section gave the shell extra lift and thus a secondary increase in range to add to that already achieved by the sabot principle. This idea was revived in the 1970s by the late Dr Gerald Bull for his Extended Range Full Bore 155mm shells.

Rocket artillery

When the German Army Weapons Bureau set up the rocket experimental station at Kummersdorf West in 1929, its avowed purpose was 'to study the performance and principle of the solid-propellant rocket and to develop a light, cheap weapon, easy to produce, which would fire a concentration of rockets carrying the heaviest charge possible against targets of limited area within 3 to 5 miles.' (Dornberger: *V-2*). This it did, but after 1931, when Captain (as he then was) Dornberger was sent there charged with the study of liquid-propellant rockets, that side of the story has tended to dominate the history books, and the development of solid-fuel rockets has been more or less forgotten. Which is unfortunate because, working quietly away in the background, this side of the business produced some exceedingly practical weapons, and doubly unfortunate because, blinded by the high-tech missiles and other gadgetry, the Allied investigators tended to neglect these more primitive designs and consequently we know far less about their development.

The first successful weapon to come out of Kummersdorf was the 15cm *Nebelwerfer*, literally 'smoke-thrower'. It was well named, for not only did it throw smoke physically, it also threw psychological smoke. The term *werfer* had always applied to mortars, and still did, and using it for a device intended to launch rockets was a masterly stroke, since anyone hearing about it would immediately assume it was just another trench mortar, armed with smoke bombs. Most armies in the early 1930s had specialist smoke troops armed with mortars, for screening infantry movements, so the name *Nebelwerfer* rang no alarm bells with anyone.

'Solid rocket propellant' was simply a grandiose name for ordinary nitro-cellulose smokeless propellant powder, as used with all German artillery and small arms, and the first task for the Experimental Station was to develop suitable forms of this substance. By dissolving the propellant into a solvent it could be turned into a form which could be extruded or moulded into various shapes and sizes which would (because propellant burns only on its exposed surface) allow control of the time and rate of burning and hence the thrust and duration of a rocket.

Next came the form of the rocket itself, and how it was to be stabilised. And remember, the object was not simply to get a rocket to fly, it was to get a rocket to fly '3 to 5 miles' and with reasonable accuracy and consistency, and carry 'the highest charge possible' of high explosive, and, of course, the end result had to be something which would stand up to active service in the field, be simple to operate and repair, firing ammunition which was safe to transport and shoot.

Passing over the multitude of experimental rockets fired, the final design proved to be a 'tractor' rocket, spin-stabilised. The complete projectile weighed 76.6lb (34.8kg) and was 36.4 inches (924mm) long. The forward section was a cylinder with a 15cm diameter ballistic cap on the front and an expanded skirt, also 15cm diameter, at the rear. Inside this were seven sticks of propellant powder and an ignition system, and the rear end of the tube carried, inside the skirt, 26 venturi jets inclined at 14 degrees to the axis of the motor body. The area inside this ring of venturis was screw threaded, and into this was screwed the shell, a simple tube filled with 5.4lb (2.47kg) of TNT and a base fuze.

The weapon which fired this device was the 15cm *Nebelwerfer 41*, a simple cluster of six open-ended barrels mounted on the two-wheeled, split-trail carriage of the 3.7cm *Pak 36* anti-tank gun. To operate it was simplicity itself. It was laid and pointed like a gun; the rocket unit had an electric igniter plugged into one of the venturis, with its connecting wire trailing alongside the shell portion, and was loaded into the rear end of the open barrel. The six sets of igniter leads were plugged into a distribution circuit, the crew stepped clear, and electric current was applied by means of a magneto. The rockets fired sequentially, so that the blast of one did not upset the flight of any others, in ten seconds, and the crew stepped in to reload. The maximum range was 6,900 metres (4.2 miles, nicely inside the specified requirement) and the accuracy was quite good. It became the German Army's standard ground rocket launcher, being introduced into service in June 1941 with the first troops who invaded Russia and remaining in service until the end of the war.

On the theory that if a large rocket is good, a larger one will be better, Kummersdorf West next developed a 21cm HE rocket, known as the 21cm *Wurfgranate Sprengstoff*. This resembled an artillery shell in outline, and reversed the order of things which had been made in the 15cm model, putting the high explosive head at the front and the rocket motor in the rear. This was probably decided on empirically, as a result of trials; what works in one calibre does not necessarily work in another, and in this case the pusher rocket produced the better answer. It was also, one suspects, rather easier to manufacture. The tapering nose of the round carried a filling of 10kg (22.4lb) of amatol, while the parallel-walled body was the motor, loaded with seven sticks of propellant each weighing about 2.5kg. The base was closed by a venturi block which had 22 venturis on a six-inch circle, each angled at 16 degrees so that as well as giving thrust, they also gave spin to stabilise the rocket in flight. The whole thing was 49.5 inches (1.25m) long and weighed 242lb (109.8kg); it had a maximum range of 7,850 metres. The launcher was much the same as the 15cm model, but with only five barrels.

The last of the three original designs was the 30cm *Wurfkorper Sprengstoff*, weighing in at 277lb (125kg) and 46.5 inches (1.18m) long, with a maximum range of 4,550 metres. It differed from the previous designs in having a large egg-like 66kg warhead loaded with amatol, screwed into the base of which was a thinner, tubular motor unit with six 2.5kg sticks of propellant and an electrical igniter. This was closed at the rear end by a plate with 18 venturi jets inclined at 12 degrees so as to provide spin and thrust at the same time. The launcher for this weapon was a simple steel framework in which the rockets lay and were given the necessary direction as they ignited; this was carried on a two-wheeled trailer, with little or no pretensions to being a gun carriage.

More designs, in 28cm and 32cm, resembling the 30cm pattern, were later developed, and various simple single-rocket launchers were also issued. The ultimate solution was a framework which could be erected in minutes, and on to which one of the larger rockets, in its transport crate, could be placed. It was then fired, straight out of the crate; it was hard to get simpler than that .

This group of rockets formed a useful accretion to the field artillery and probably saw most of their service on the Eastern Front (where, of course, they were confronted with the 'Stalin Organ', the Soviet free-flight rocket). But one last design was to come, this time from Rheinmetall-Borsig, in the shape of *Rheinbote*.

Rheinbote was the solid-propellant solution to the long-range artillery requirement, a four-stage device in which three boosters fired in turn, each being discarded when it burned out and ignited the next stage, the third booster igniting the sustainer rocket in the section carrying the warhead. The high explosive warhead weighed 40kg, the rocket reached a maximum speed of Mach 5.55 (almost 6,000km/hr) and it had a maximum range of 218km (135 miles). Launching was performed from a simple rail on either a converted 8.8cm gun carriage or a modified V-2 transport wagon. Some 220 of these were fired into Antwerp in November 1944, but in the long run it has to be said that they were a very complicated and expensive method of getting a 40kg warhead on to a target.

Probably the last, and certainly the most impressive of the rocket weapons was the *Sturmtiger* 38cm Rocket Launcher 61, a highly modified Tiger tank. The body was built up into a boxy superstructure, in the front face of which was a short-barrelled weapon resembling a large mortar. It was, in fact, a breech-loaded rocket launcher. Many attempts had been made to produce a breech-loaded rocket launcher with a closed breech, but all had hitherto failed. The rocket blast, confined inside a gun barrel, rebounds from the breech-block face and sets up sporadic high pressures inside the bore which can, variously, either burst the gun, deform the rocket body, or, at best, severely upset the flight characteristics due to the rush of gas bursting out behind the rocket as it leaves the muzzle.

All this was avoided with the *Sturmtiger*; the barrel had a double wall, and vents in this wall at the muzzle led back to ports alongside the breech block, in the chamber. When the rocket ignited the blast was directed into these ports and thus allowed to escape from the muzzle vents. There was no rebound and the rocket was allowed to depart under the pressure of its own blast and nothing else. It weighed 345kg and had a maximum range of 5,650 metres with, apparently, quite commendable accuracy. It was developed in early 1943, largely as a result of the Sebastopol campaign where the need for a short-range demolition weapon capable of dealing out heavy blows against strongpoints had been felt. Ten equipments were built during the second half of 1944 and they were thereafter employed in various engagements.

Perhaps the last word on this equipment came from a British officer who submitted a report on a visit made to a number of research establishments in Germany in August 1945;

'We were taken to see a tank 20ft x 12ft mounting a 38cm rocket howitzer. This throws a 700lb projectile 6,000 yards, presumably for concrete busting. Understood to carry 8 projectiles. A REME officer had been told by a general to fire it, but had, with considerable wisdom, found that this was not practicable.'

The Röchling shell

The development of this projectile began in the early 1930s as a private venture by the Röchling Eisen- und Stahlwerke of Düsseldorf; it was designed for one task only – to defeat concrete fortifications.

Anti-concrete shells – *betongranate* – have a long history in continental Europe, because until 1940 virtually every border was lined with fortifications. The French had their Maginot Line, the Germans their Siegfried Line, the Czechs, Poles, Hungarians, Russians, Belgians, Dutch... they all had forts and barriers and ditches, but most of all they had forts. And the most modern of these forts were sunk into the ground, with several metres of earth above a thick reinforced concrete structure. No ordinary shell would succeed against this; even a delay fuze would merely allow the shell to burrow into the earth and then detonate relatively harmlessly as it struck the concrete. And, in all probability, the concrete it struck would not be the actual fort but a separate thick layer of concrete set in sand as a 'burster shield' expressly for the purpose of bursting such shells before they reached the main structure.

Anti-concrete shells were, in many respects, similar to anti-armour shells; hollow projectiles with a hardened steel nose and a relatively small filling of high explosive in a cavity in the rear end of the shell, and fitted with a base fuze. The shape of the nose was generally more blunt that that needed to defeat armour, the hardness of the tip slightly less and the amount of high explosive slightly greater, but that was the only difference. On striking the heavy tip would smash into the concrete and the fuze, initiated by the sudden shock of arrival, would have a pre-set delay which allowed the shell to burrow well into the concrete before detonating. It would be unlikely to pass completely through a typical fortress roof – which could be as much as 10 metres thick – but it would certainly blow a massive crater into the concrete and weaken the structure, so that a sufficient number of such shells arriving on the roof would, sooner or later, achieve penetration.

Röchling considered that the anti-concrete shell as it was known in 1930 was inefficient; it was based upon penetration theories which were out of date and the company had a better idea. A long, thin, but heavy projectile would concentrate its mass into a much smaller area than the diameter of a conventional shell and thus do a better job of penetrating. The only drawback to this idea was that it is impossible to stabilise a long, thin and heavy shell by spinning it, and the preferred weapon for anti-fortification work was the 21cm howitzer, a conventionally rifled weapon.

What finally evolved, after many experiments and false starts, was a long thin projectile with a discarding sabot band at the shoulder and a second sabot in the shape of a pot at the rear. Inside the pot, and wrapped around the tail of the shell, were four flexible fins which sprang out as the pot was blown off by air drag as the shell left the gun. The forward sabot was also discarded after leaving the muzzle. Having been fired from a conventionally rifled gun the shell was spinning as it left the muzzle, but the expanded fins soon damped this down to a slow roll and the projectile was kept point-foremost by the action of the fins.

Once perfected the performance of this projectile against concrete bore out Röchling's promises; it was staggeringly effective. It was too late into service to see any employment during the 1940 campaign in France, and in any case there was no particular attempt made to defeat the Maginot Line. But after the campaign was over a number of French and Belgian forts were experimentally bombarded and this showed that these shells would pass through the earth cover, through the concrete burster plates, through the concrete roof of the fort, through the interior spaces, through the floor and then detonate in the ground beneath. Indeed, the performance was so effective that when the *HWA* reported the results to Hitler, he ordered that no Röchling shells would be used except upon his own personal authority, lest the secrets of the design be discovered by an enemy if a shell happened to malfunction and not detonate. And since few officers were anxious to draw attention to themselves, few applications were made and fewer authorised. As a result, the Röchling shell saw very little use throughout the war.

Other aspects of ammunition design

There is an old gunmakers' truism to the effect that the easiest way to improve the performance of a gun is to leave it alone and improve the ammunition, and the Germans certainly proved the correctness of this during the war. Much of this work was similar to development being carried out on the Allied side – for example, the development of sabot projectiles (though for different purposes) – but much of it was original thought on the part of the Germans, and much of that laid the foundations for a great deal of advanced ammunition developed in various countries in later years.

Anti-tank ammunition had a high development priority, which increased after the invasion of Russia and the discovery that the Soviets had tanks which were superior to those of Germany. The Germans had been among the first to see the advantage of using tungsten, and they had adopted it, as we have seen, for their taper-bore guns and also for their conventional anti-tank guns in the shape of their *Panzergranate 40* or 'arrowhead shot'. But the shortage and eventual disappearance of tungsten as an ammunition component made them look in other directions.

The shaped charge, or hollow charge – *hohladung* in German – had been known for many years, and a few ordnance engineers had tried to put it to some practical warlike use during the First World War with no success. In the immediate postwar years more engineers played with it and in 1938 two entrepreneurs named Matthias and Mohaupt announced that they had developed a 'new and powerful explosive' which would penetrate armour plate, that they would hold a demonstration near Zürich, and that representatives of all European armies were invited to attend, preferably carrying cheque-books.

The representatives duly attended, the demonstration took place, and holes were indeed blown through armour plate, though not without a good deal of mystery and sleight-of-hand on the part of the demonstrators to avoid showing exactly what was happening. They then invited bids for their secret. Unfortunately for them the various armies had been smart enough to send ordnance engineers to see the demonstration, and these men were smart enough to realise that what they had seen was a successful application of the shaped charge – or 'Monroe Effect' as it was then known, after its discoverer – and that if these two mysterious figures could make it work, then an ordnance engineer ought to be able to repeat the trick. And they all shot off back to their laboratories and set about producing a working shaped-charge munition, leaving Matthias and Mohaupt empty-handed.

Germany won the race, producing a demolition charge late in 1939. This was the easiest of all shaped-charge devices to produce once the basic design had been settled. It was simply a bee-hive shaped canister filled with explosive and supported on three legs. The bottom of the bee-hive was hollowed out in a hemisphere and lined with copper. A detonator and a length of fuze went into the top of the bee-hive. And like all good munition designs it was simple and effective because it had been designed with one specific requirement firmly in view; it had to blow holes through the armoured turrets of forts. All you had to do was get on to the fort, place this device on top of the gun turret, ignite the fuze and stand clear. When the explosive detonated, the hemispherical cavity 'focussed' the blast into a fine, fast-moving jet of explosive gas and molten copper which simply drove through the armour steel and into the gun-room below. What came through the hole was a blast of flame and a slug of metal, plus a good deal of metal debris blown off the interior of the armour around the hole. It did no good at all to the gunnery equipment inside the turret, nor to the gunners. And all this was put to the test in May 1940 on the attack on the Eben Emael fort in Belgium, the hinge of the Belgian defences and a spot which the Germans simply had to take so that their forces could cross the Albert Canal.

The operation against Eben Emael would hardly have been impossible without this 'secret weapon', but it was certainly one of the most secret operations carried out by the Germans and it was not generally known until some years after the war exactly how it had been done. The story released for public consumption was full of heroic actions by infantry pioneer troops who paddled rubber boats across the canal in the face of withering gunfire to fight their way into the fortress… good, stirring stuff. But entirely untrue. The fort was taken by glider-borne troops who landed on top of it and blew in the gun turrets with shaped charges. The infantry pioneers paddled across next day, the remains of the gliders were removed before any unauthorised person could see them, the glider troops were whisked away, and there was Eben Emael, captured by the valiant *Wehrmacht*. And in the general confusion of those days nobody really bothered to question the official version.

The shaped-charge designers, meanwhile, had moved on; they were now developing artillery shells capable of penetrating armour by the force of the shaped charge, rather than the kinetic energy of the projectile which, hitherto, had been the only conceivable method of using a gun against armour. There appeared to be three fundamental factors in the design of shell; firstly, the charge had to be detonated some distance away from the armour in order to allow space for the jet of explosive gas and molten metal to form itself and achieve the desired velocity – about 25,000 feet per second (7,600m/sec), secondly it seemed that the optimum shape for the recess in the front of the charge was a cone, rather than a hemisphere, and thirdly the explosive had to be detonated at the rear end, away from the cone, so that the moving detonation wave did the necessary shaping of the charge as it passed over the cone.

All this, of course, was being discovered by other nations as well; at least, those nations which had attended the Zürich demonstration and thus had their researchers stimulated. Britain moved very quickly and had a shaped-charge rifle grenade in service by the summer of 1940 and was working on artillery shells, the USA was also at work, and the Russians were probably working, although their subsequent designs suggest that they took a short cut and copied captured German shaped-charge ammunition for most of the war years. But sooner or later they all discovered the same phenomenon: if you fired a stationary shaped charge at a piece of armour you got a deep, narrow hole. If you fired a spinning shaped charge at the same piece of armour you got a wider and much less deep hole. The reason was that the centrifugal forces acting on the jet dispersed it so that it was less finely focussed and thus working over a greater area when it struck the target. As far as the British were concerned, that was enough; they gave up working on shaped-charge shells, except for one equipment (the 3.7-inch mountain howitzer) which had no hope of ever firing a solid projectile at a velocity likely even to dent armour. For the rest, they got solid shot or nothing.

The Germans, though, were more persistent and, perhaps, more ready to look at unconventional solutions. There are three ways to stabilise an elongated projectile: spin, fins or drag – the bullet, the arrow and the spear are the three basic examples. So if spin was not acceptable, then the next to be considered was fins. Here the wind-tunnel at Peenemünde came in useful; most of the aerodynamic testing for the V-weapons had been done and the Peenemünde scientists were only too happy to exercise their minds on something fresh. One fundamental discovery was that the conventional form of fin, as used on mortar bombs, in which the fins were the same diameter as the body of the projectile, was virtually useless in stabilising a low-trajectory projectile moving at supersonic speed. The fins had to get well out into the airstream to have any useful effect.

Röchling had made the same discovery empirically while developing its anti-concrete shell, using flexible fins which wrapped around the shell body and were able to spring out, assisted by centrifugal force, as they left the muzzle, and similar wrap-around fins were to be used on the *Panzerfaust* shoulder-fired anti-tank weapon. But this was only suitable at low pressures and velocities. High pressures and velocities invariably damaged the fins, either in the bore or after leaving the gun, principally because in order to be flexible enough to wrap around the shell body they were too flimsy to withstand the air pressures at high speeds. One solution was to put calibre-sized fins on an elongated boom which positioned them well back behind the body of the shell and thus into the area where the airstream converged after passing over the shell. It was aerodynamically attractive, but not practical to have the fins filling up the chamber of the gun where the cartridge was supposed to be, so that idea was soon discarded.

Eventually the 'jack-knife' fin was perfected. The rear end of the shell was formed into a stem, at the end of which it returned to full diameter and carried a driving band. On the front edge of the full diameter section four blades were hinged so that they were normally folded forward to lie alongside the stem, where they were held by springs. For the passage up the bore the fins were confined into the space around the stem but, as soon as the shell left the muzzle, the blades were flung outward by spin and held at right-angles to the axis of the shell, with most of their surface well out in the airstream. The driving band on the base of this tail unit was, in fact, a mere sealing band; it was not locked to the shell and could rotate freely, so that although it bit into the rifling and thus sealed the propelling gas behind it, it only passed a small amount of spin to the shell, largely through friction. This amount of spin was enough to ensure the blades opened on leaving the muzzle, but once the blades had extended, their resistance to the air soon damped out most of what spin there was, leaving the projectile with no more than a comparatively slow roll which had no effect upon the shaped-charge jet.

Unfortunately the perfection of this design was only completed shortly before the war ended, and few projectiles of the 'jack-knife' pattern ever reached service. The design has never been duplicated since, although the individual features of the jack-knife fins and the slipping driving band have

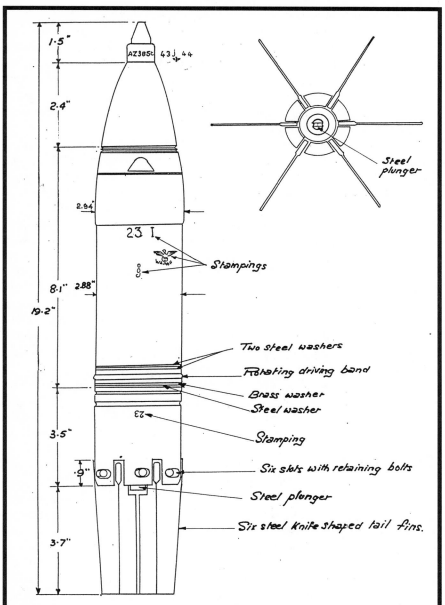

An alternative design of finned shaped-charge shell for a 7.5cm gun. In this model the fins trail behind the body and are flung out by the centrifugal force provided by the small amount of spin transmitted to the shell even though the 'driving' band is on roller bearings. Once these fins were extended the air pressure would damp out most of this residual spin. The steel plunger in the base also aided in pushing the fins out, since its inertia caused it to press back on the fins as the shell accelerated.

appeared on a variety of explosive munitions since 1945.

So, for the duration of the war, the German shaped-charge shells fired from guns were spun, and if the results were less than optimum they were still sufficiently good to justify the retention of the shells in service. But another idea presented itself as a method of extending the life of guns which were otherwise outclassed. The 37mm *Pak 36* anti-tank gun, for example, was formidable enough in 1936, but by 1942 it was of very little use against anything more than a light tank or an armoured car. To permit it to remain in service and do some useful work, it was provided with a 'spigot bomb' shaped-charge projectile which could deal with virtually anything on tracks. The 3.7cm *Steilgranate 41* consisted of a large shaped-charge warhead about six inches in diameter, with a long tail rod. Around this tail rod was a sleeve carrying four fins. The dimensions of this device were such that when the tail rod was slipped into the muzzle of the 3.7cm *Pak 36* gun, the sleeve and fins fitted snugly around the barrel and the warhead was in front of the muzzle.

A special cartridge was provided and the sights suitably adapted, and the projectile could be fired with adequate accuracy up to a practical range of about 300 metres or an absolute maximum range of about 800 metres. The warhead contained 2.42kg (5.34lb) of a TNT/hexogen composition and could blow a sizeable hole through 180mm of armour plate at any range, which was quite sparkling performance for 1942. This device saw quite a lot of use; but a similar design for the 5cm *Pak 38* appears to have been rather less successful. It had the same performance but its shape had to be different; the sleeve had to be the same diameter as the warhead in order to pass over the muzzle brake of the gun, and it appears that the result was not as accurate as the 3.7cm version. At any rate it seems to have seen less use and was certainly less commonly found.

(It is amusing to note that in July 1941 Lieutenant Colonel Blacker, the originator of the Blacker Bombard and the PIAT, suggested a similar stick bomb for the 25-pounder field gun. He was instantly rebuffed by the Ordnance Board, who said, 'The proposal to use a 25-pounder gun and carriage as a mounting for a Bombard is considered to be a prostitution of the proper function of the equipment.')

By the early part of 1944 the anti-tank weapon question was becoming critical. The number of anti-tank weapons in a division had increased steadily since 1939 as the numbers of enemy tanks had increased, and their size and power had increased in step with the size and armour thickness of the opposing tanks. But the limit of conventional anti-tank guns had almost been reached – and was reached, before 1944 was out, in the 12.8cm *Pak 44* gun – whilst the only alternative appeared to be hand-held weapons such as the *Panzerfaust* (a primitive recoilless gun) and the *Panzerschreck* (a copy of the American Bazooka rocket-launcher). What was needed, it was felt, was a lightweight anti-tank gun using shaped-charge technology to provide a lethal projectile. Recoilless guns were suggested, but the army was reluctant to accept this solution unless it was compelled to; recoilless guns were too hungry for propellant (four-fifths of the propelling charge was used up in the rearward blast from the venturi) and the demand for propellant powder was fast approaching the maximum possible output of Germany's explosives industry. So something which didn't eat propellant was preferable to something which wolfed it down. Rheinmetall-Borsig, which appears never to have been short of good ideas, took up the challenge and decided to apply an entirely new ballistic principle that it had been developing for some time. This was the 'High and Low Pressure System' (*Hoch-und-Niederdruck System*) in which the high pressure from the explosion of the cartridge was confined in a relatively heavy breech section and was then allowed to bleed gradually (comparatively speaking) into the lightweight barrel at a lower pressure in order to drive the projectile. This gave the ballistic advantages of regularity and consistent burning which accrue from high pressure, together with a more gentle acceleration and a longer-sustained propulsive effort from the 'bleeding-in' of the propulsive gases at low pressure.

The gun developed for this system was fairly conventional in form; its principal feature was an exceptionally light smoothbore barrel and a substantial, if simple, sliding block breech. The carriage was exceptionally light, using torsion bar suspension, a cradle in the form of a lightweight cage with the recoil cylinders of drawn tubular steel inside, much lighter than the conventional bored-out block of steel, and with an ingenious barrel balancing spring made out of laminated plates. Unfortunately it was too light to withstand either firing or travelling for very long and had to be redesigned into a more conventional form. But, in the event, quite a number of these new guns were simply mounted on old 5cm *Pak 38* gun carriages in order to get them into the field.

The heart of this gun lay in the ammunition, which was highly unorthodox. The complete round was a fixed unit, cartridge and projectile being loaded in one piece. The steel cartridge case was that of the standard 10.5cm *leFH 18* field howitzer and carried the normal percussion primer and a charge of 360 grams of standard diglycol powder. The mouth of the case was closed by a heavy iron plate, about 15mm thick, pierced with eight venturi-like holes. In the centre of this plate was a steel spigot. The projectile was a standard 8.1cm high explosive mortar bomb body modified to carry a shaped charge which was capable of defeating 140mm of armour. The tail boom of this bomb was hollow and in its normal use was where the primary propelling cartridge was fitted. But in this application the tail remained empty and was fitted over the spigot standing up from the cartridge closing disc. It was then retained by drilling a hole through tail unit and spigot and inserting a pin designed to shear at a pressure of 550kg/cm^2.

The round was loaded into the gun in the normal way and fired. The

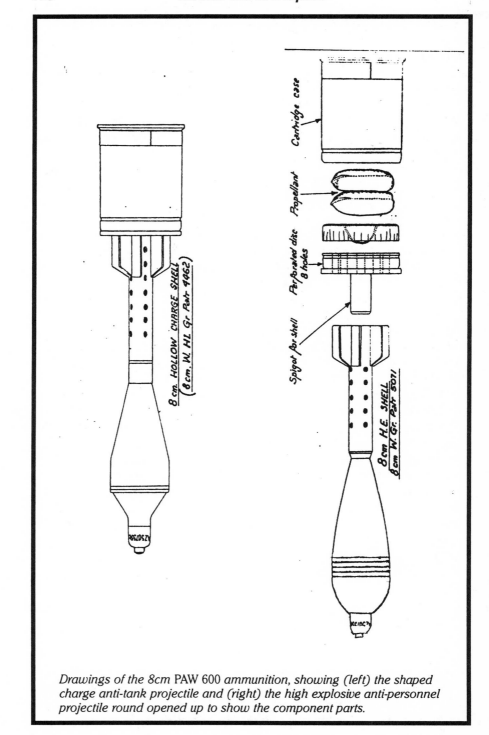

Drawings of the 8cm PAW 600 ammunition, showing (left) the shaped charge anti-tank projectile and (right) the high explosive anti-personnel projectile round opened up to show the component parts.

charge exploded inside the cartridge case and the pressure was retained there because the heavy iron plate was positioned behind a step in the barrel and could not move. The explosion generated a pressure of about 1000kg/cm^2 (just over 6 tons/in^2) which then passed through the holes in the closing plate and began building up pressure behind the projectile. Once that pressure reached 550 kg/cm^2 the holding pin sheared and the projectile was released, reaching a velocity at the muzzle of about 520m/sec (1,705ft/sec) and having a maximum accurate range of about 750 metres. This may not sound much but it was all that was required in the close-range anti-tank business, and it was a good deal better for the soldier than the 30–50 metres to be expected of the *Panzerfaust*, for instance. A second round of ammunition, using a standard service HE mortar bomb, was designed for general anti-personnel use and was said to give a maximum range of about 6,000 metres, but it is doubtful if any of this ammunition was ever issued; this gun was primarily for anti-tank shooting, and at that stage of the war there would have been no urgency about providing the alternative ammunition.

Production of this *Panzer Abwehr Werfer 600* (*PAW 600*), which was later re-named the *Panzer Wurf Kanone 8H63* (*PWK 8H63*) under a new system which I doubt if half the German Army ever heard about before the war ended, began in December 1944 and about 250 guns were made before production stopped in March 1945. Several were captured by the Allies but the principle was more or less ignored for several years after the war. It was eventually adopted by the Americans for their 40mm grenade launchers, by the British for an anti-submarine mortar, and by the Soviets for a 73mm armoured car gun. The Krupp company, which had collaborated with Rheinmetall-Borsig in the gun design, also developed an 8cm prototype, and when the war ended was working on an improved model in 10.5cm calibre (the 10.5cm *PAW 1000* or *PWK 10H64*) which could defeat 200mm of armour.

The Sea War

It was the war at sea which first revealed some of the results of German pre-war research. Probably the first surprise for Britain was the liberal use of magnetic mines, but since the Royal Navy had been experimenting with these off and on since the First World War they could hardly be called revolutionary, although the steps needed to counter them involved some hard and fast work. The action against the *Graf Spee* off the River Plate also revealed that the German Navy was in possession of radar. At that time virtu-ally all British radar effort was directed towards air defence, and the discovery that the Germans were using it as a naval gunnery aiming device showed that the British could not afford to sit on their hands in the assumption that the radar they had at the beginning of the war would see them through to the end.

But Germany's greatest sea warfare threat came from the submarine, and it was in this field that much of its naval research was directed. Great strides were made in the development of the hydrogen-peroxide motor and the well-known *Schnorkel* which allowed a U-Boat to remain submerged for much longer periods than had ever been possible before, and this led to much greater difficulties in detecting them. But the new engine was only just coming into service as the war ended, and for the U-Boats actually in service, the greatest problem was defying detection by the various devices which the British and American naval and air forces were using.

One evasive device which came into use was *Bold* or *Pillenwerfer*, a per-forated canister containing a chemical mixture based on calcium carbide. When released into the water the chemicals reacted to produce a gas, which in turn produced a thick cloud of fine bubbles which formed a dense screen which reflected the Asdic (or Sonar) signal and gave a spurious indi-cation of the U-boat's position. This effectively 'blinded' the Asdic or Sonar detection equipment of the Allied sub-hunters and allowed the U-Boat to make its escape.

It was better, of course, if the U-Boat could have some warning of the approach of Allied vessels long before they were a danger and thus avoid the uncertainty of relying on *Bold*. For this purpose the U-Boats were issued with a remarkable flying machine, the Foch-Achgelis FA 330 *Bachstelze*. This resembled a helicopter, but was in fact an unpowered 'rotor kite' which could be towed on a line behind the U-Boat, at about 350 ft–400 ft above the sea. An observer in the kite had a much wider view of the surrounding area than was available to the occupants of the U-Boat conning tower, and he could see the approach of ships long before the ships could detect either him or the U-Boat. Whenever the U-Boat surfaced for battery charging or cruising by day, the kite was manned and flown, and was highly successful as a means of detecting convoys or other likely targets. Once something was seen, the kite could be rapidly winched down, dismantled and stowed away, and the submarine could then submerge and take whatever action was necessary. Should an aircraft appear and leave little time for winching, the pilot of the kite could pull an emergency lever which jettisoned the rotor blades and actuated a parachute; by undoing his seat belt, he then allowed the useless fuselage to fall away while he floated down. About 200 of these kites were built but experience soon showed that they were only practicable in areas where Allied air patrols were rare, and thus found most of their application in the South Atlantic and Indian Ocean. Moreover a rough sea could easily prevent their being launched, and for these reasons the use of *Bachstelze* in the North Atlantic was quickly abandoned.

A rather more ambitious extension of this idea was to carry a small float-plane in the submarine which could be stowed away in pieces, rapidly put together when needed and used for reconnaissance. Such a plane was built, the Arado 231, which could be stripped down to fit inside a six-foot canister on the U-Boat's after-deck. It had a top speed of just over 100mph and a reconnaissance range of almost 300 miles, but when some were supplied to U-Boats for trials it was found that the business of getting the plane onto the deck, and later stripping it down and stowing it, was only feasible when the sea was perfectly calm. With anything more than a slight chop, the job was virtually impossible, and U-Boat commanders were understandably reluctant to linger on the surface while their crews wrestled with a collapsible aeroplane. The Arado was replaced by the *Bachstelze* kite, which was almost as effective.

Another offensive-defensive device was the *Wasseresel* which was a dummy U-Boat conning tower stuffed with high explosive. This, it was proposed, would be towed along the surface by the submerged U-Boat in order to fool Allied warships into thinking it was the genuine U-Boat. Whereupon, it was hoped, they would sail full steam ahead in an attempt to ram, and blow themselves up. There is no record of this plan ever succeeding, probably because it appears that it was rarely – if ever – used. U-Boat captains were not keen to go into action carrying a ton or so of high explosive strapped to their decks, and when they were being hunted, they didn't like being held back, with their approximate position and course advertised to their enemies, by the *Wasseresel* being towed at the end of its long line. Unofficial reports seem to show that most of the few which were issued were 'accidentally lost at sea' shortly after leaving harbour.

Torpedoes

The principal weapon of the U-Boat was the torpedo, but the torpedo in its simple form had a number of disadvantages. One was its lack of speed. A long-range torpedo might take four or five minutes to reach a target, whereas a gun shell would do the same trip in four or five seconds. This meant that the target could move, zig-zag or dodge before the torpedo got to it; a second drawback proved to be that once the torpedo was launched from the submarine, no correction was possible in order to make it hit the target. Another defect was that the exhaust from the torpedo engine left a trail of bubbles in the water, and this, combined with the slow speed, gave even more advantage to the target. To try and overcome some of these disadvantages, a variety of torpedo projects were developed in Germany, some of which succeeded and some of which did not.

One of the best was the development by Junkers of a highly efficient engine which would propel a torpedo at 40 knots, cutting the travel time substantially and thus giving the target less chance of manoeuvring out of danger. The Junkers Jumo KM 8 engine was a brilliant technical achievement, consuming its own exhaust gases so as not to leave a telltale trail in the water, it was a 4.5-litre V-8 which developed 425 horsepower. This may sound incredible, but it must be remembered that submarine torpedoes were up to 30 feet in length and weighed about two tons, and needed a highly efficient engine to produce workable speeds. However, development of the motor took a long time, and because of problems with priorities for material and difficulties in setting up manufacture it never got into production.

The other method of trying to overcome some of the drawbacks was to design a torpedo which would, after launching, actually hunt for its target, using some form of detector. The most obvious effects from the target which lent themselves to detection were the magnetic field of the ship and the noise it made, either by its engines or by the beat of the propeller, in the water. The magnetic field was first explored by fitting magnetic-detecting fuzes which would detonate the torpedo underneath the target, thus having the same effect as a mine, but the steps taken by the Allied navies to proof their ships against magnetic mines also proofed them against magnetic torpedoes, so that idea had to be abandoned. But it was impossible to get rid of the noise, and by the middle of the war most U-Boats were equipped with the *Falke* torpedo fitted with the *Zaunkönig* acoustic homing device. This picked up the noise of the ship and steered the torpedo towards it and was remarkably successful until the Royal Navy realised what sort of a weapon they had to deal with. Very rapidly the British produced an incredibly simple antidote – two lengths of steel pipe towed behind the ship. These clashed together and set up such a noise that the torpedo homed on them instead of the ship.

The German Navy responded with *Zaunkönig II*, an improved version which, it was hoped, would be able to sort out the noise of the decoy from the noise of the ship and home on the correct target, but a few adjustments to the noise-maker produced such a medley of tones and rhythms that the selective circuits of the new model were completely defeated and the torpedo still homed on the pipes.

In order to improve the chances of hitting, particularly in convoy attacks, torpedoes known as *FAT*, equipped with pattern steering devices were introduced. These would leave the submarine on a set course but after a short time would begin to make pre-set turns. It was hoped that by this means a torpedo fired straight into the middle of a convoy, without aiming at a particular ship, would eventually turn in such a fashion as to come up against a target. This went into service in 1943 and was followed by a second type, known as *LUT*, which accelerated in the straight stretches between turns and also had a variety of patterns, one of which could be pre-selected before firing. Another steerable device allowed the angle of turn to be pre-set, so that the submarine did not need to be pointed at its target to launch the torpedo. It could be launched at an angle and would then turn and settle on a direct course.

Probably the development along these lines which appeared to have the greatest chance of success was the *Schnee-Orgel*, an array of six torpedo-tubes fitted into late model U-Boats and aligned so that the torpedoes, when fired in a salvo, would spread out to cover a 10 minute arc (one sixth of a degree) and thus, again, would be almost certain to hit something in a convoy no matter how hasty the aim. Fortunately for the Allied convoys, very few of these arrays were built before the war ended.

New U-Boats

However, the most promising of the German secret weapons at sea was the Type XXI U-Boat. This introduced many revolutionary ideas, and incorporated many new developments, including the *Schnorkel*, a streamlined hull, vastly increased battery capacity and rapid reloading for the torpedo-tubes. Technical difficulties meant that the first of them, *U.2511*, did not put to sea operationally until a week before the German surrender, but she was able to evade with ease the British hunter-killer groups she encountered, and claimed to have made a totally undetected dummy run on a British cruiser before returning to her base in Germany in time to surrender. Had production difficulties been overcome, the Type XXI might have made a significant impact; even so, it profoundly influenced all post-war submarine design.

Fast attack craft

Turning now from the high seas, a tactic which attracted a good deal of favour in the German Navy was the possibility of dashing into Allied harbours with fast boats and there either torpedoing or otherwise wrecking as much of the moored shipping as possible. One of the first ideas in this line was *Linse*, a remote-controlled E-Boat capable of 35 knots and carrying a 400kg demolition charge of high explosive in the stern. The theory was that this could be launched from a parent ship out at sea and guided into a harbour, brought up against a moored warship and then detonated by remote control. Some trials were done, but the principal objection seemed to be that, even at 35 knots, it was still highly likely to be blown up before it ever got to its target, either by shore defence guns or by the guns on the ships in harbour.

More speed was the answer to this, and 'Tornado' was designed. This was little more than a deck holding together two ex-sea-plane floats, with the pulse-jet motor of a V-1 missile on top to push it through the water. A 700kg demolition charge was carried in the nose, and the device (it could hardly be called a boat) could be remote-controlled as the *Linse*, or it could be steered by a pilot who, when close to the target, locked the controls and dived overboard in the hope of being picked up later by a rescue boat. This was somewhat faster than *Linse*, and it also carried a much more powerful charge, but there were difficulties about getting a supply of V-1 motors. Since all the available production was booked for use in the V-1 missiles, and since by that time the V-1 campaign was under way, no diversion of V-1 components for any other programme was permitted.

In no way daunted, the developers went off and, just before the war ended, came back with *Schlitten* ('Sledge'), which was a hydroplane propelled by a Ford V-8 engine. This could reach a speed of 65 knots, carried the same 700kg warhead as Tornado, and could either be remote-controlled or piloted. It looked as if the designers had got it right this time, but the end of the war prevented the beast from being tried out.

Midget submarines

A more practical method of dealing with enemy ships at anchor was the midget submarine or piloted torpedo; the terms tend to be used interchangeably in German documents. There was a lot more interest in this field than is generally supposed. There were a number of occasions when Royal Navy midget submarines were used during the war, but it is less well known that the Germans, Italians and Japanese all had midget submarines of one sort or another either in service or in the design stage before the war broke out. The first German project of this type was *Hecht* ('Pike'), little more than a piloted torpedo with a detachable warhead. Over 50 of these were built, but they were mainly used as experimental and training vehicles. *Hecht* was powered by an electric motor driven by batteries, which had neither power nor endurance sufficient for operational work. As a result, an improved model powered by a petrol engine was produced under the name of *Neger* ('Negro'). This also changed the design by placing the engine and pilot in one tubular hull, such that the pilot had his head and shoulders above the waterline while a 'proper' torpedo was slung beneath and could have its motor started and be launched by the pilot at will. While *Neger* was satisfactory from the mechanical point of view, it had a drawback in that the pilot had to breathe pure oxygen, and this tended to restrict his activities since there was a time limit on oxygen breathing.

So *Neger* was modified to use a recycling air supply, and became known as *Molch* ('Salamander'). Several of these models seem to have been used in late 1944 and early 1945 against Allied shipping in the approaches to Antwerp, but they were not generally successful. *Molch* was shortly superseded by an improved design called *Marder* ('Marten') which was much the same as *Molch* but could be completely submerged for short periods, allowing the pilot to make the major portion of his run awash and then submerge to close in on his target. To allow this, the propulsion system reverted to electric motors, but they were more powerful than those fitted to the original *Hecht* series

With a certain amount of experience with these small piloted torpedoes behind them, the designers now became more ambitious and decided to produce a midget submarine, one which totally enclosed the crew rather than having them riding on top. The first model to be produced was called *Hai* ('Shark'); it was a slender fish-like body which carried one man and was propelled by a petrol engine to give an underwater speed of over 20 knots, a most remarkable performance. It was capable of staying submerged for up to sixty hours stationary, and could travel submerged at top speed for two hours. While it was hardly a practical vessel – it carried no armament, for example, nor was there room for any – but as a test-bed it was highly advantageous, and it was remarkably successful for a first try.

With this experience to guide them, the next model was a more warlike device. Called *Biber* ('Beaver') it was 19ft long, displaced three tons and carried two standard torpedoes slung alongside the hull. Originally a one-man affair, the later models allowed a two-man crew to be carried, and a number of these craft were used with success in the Scheldt estuary and also against Russian coastal shipping off Murmansk.

Finally came *Seehund* ('Seal') a 15-tonner which carried two torpedoes and had a two-man crew. This could move at 8 knots on the surface or 6 knots submerged, and with auxiliary fuel tanks attached to the outside (which could be jettisoned when empty) it had a range of 500 miles. Development of the *Seehund* was completed in 1944, and in January 1945 they went into action, first in the Scheldt estuary and then according to German sources, against shipping in the Thames estuary and off Margate. Unfortunately, because of the dislocation in German reports due to the end of the war no definite details of any success they may have had off the English coast has ever been forthcoming, though it is known that they were responsible for the sinking of one or two vessels in the Scheldt.

Nuclear and Chemical Warfare

The nuclear bomb

When one bears in mind that nuclear fission was discovered by a German physicist (Otto Hahn, who later received the Nobel prize for his discovery) and that Germany probably had a higher concentration of first-class physicists than any other country in the 1930s, it seems remarkable that no German nuclear bomb ever appeared. There are various theories which have been advanced from time to time to explain this; that the German scientists were too stupid to see what was under their noses, that they saw what was needed but got their sums wrong, that they refused point-blank to work on such a device, that they 'went through the motions' but were careful not to produce any results... there are more than enough reasons on offer. But it seems that the real reasons are somewhat complex and demand an understanding of the scientific mentality, particularly the German scientific mentality, which obtained in that period, something which is frequently absent from the analysis.

Professors in pre-war Germany were held in very high esteem; from several accounts it seems that even the most belligerent Nazi official shuffled his feet when confronted with one. And those with Nobel Prizes or other official acclaim were absolutely incontrovertible; what they said was so, and they saw no need to explain themselves to lesser mortals. As a result, their utterances were frequently enigmatic. One of the basic problems besetting the German nuclear programme would appear to be the inability of the scientists to express themselves clearly and simply to the non-scientists. Indeed, some of them appear to have been unable to explain themselves to each other with any degree of clarity. Time and again in the various accounts produced in postwar years by German scientists and others, we see cases where Herr Professor A and Herr Doktor B have had a conversation, and, in subsequent reports or letters, make it clear that both went away thinking the other had said something entirely different. Worse; in some cases they went away thinking that they themselves had said something entirely different. And a good example of the inability to communicate with the non-scientist was a series of lectures given in Berlin early in 1942 at which the prospect of a nuclear bomb was to be aired. Had the titles of any of the papers used the word 'bomb' there might have been an interested non-technical audience; as it was, with titles such as 'Absorption Resonance' and 'The Theoretical Basis for Energy Production from Uranium Fission', the military and political heads they hoped to impress stayed away in droves. The trumpets sounded uncertain notes and nobody heeded the call to battle.

The German nuclear programme, if it can be called such, began shortly before the outbreak of war. At that time there was still a vigorous interchange of information between scientists of all countries, and thus the properties of the atom and the possibilities raised by its fission were widely discussed among the international community of physicists. To the few who understood these things it was apparent that there were two possibilities which stood out; the development of power by means of the heat of a controlled nuclear reaction, and the development of explosive power by the energy released in an uncontrolled nuclear reaction. But as the 1930s progressed, the Nazi policy of anti-Semitism was operated with increasing viciousness and rigour and far-seeing Jews began leaving Germany. Many of the more eminent scientists were Jewish and numbers of them found posts in Britain and the USA in which to exercise their talents. Moreover, the official Nazi line was to decry any Jewish achievement, and thus even the mention of Einstein's Theory of Relativity could bring official displeasure down on any lecturer unwise enough to refer to it.

However, and to their credit, the German scientific community was not noticeably anti-Semitic; most of the Gentiles had been tutored by Jews at some time and their academic relationship and respect remained. So that when the Jews left Germany most of them remained in correspondence with their old companions. And those, on both sides, who had been working on the fringe of nuclear physics, a rare speciality in those days, kept each other informed of what they and others were doing, what progress was being made, and what might be possible. It did not, in those days, have any appearance of being sensitive information, and, for those who understood it, it was an all-consuming passion which simply had to be discussed with others in the field in order to foment new ideas and select new directions for study.

In December 1938 Hahn and Fritz Strassmann demonstrated the fission of uranium 235. The news spread rapidly around the scientific world, and even the non-scientific press was moved to speculate upon the possible use of such energy in a bomb, though most people who read the story probably considered it about as fanciful as anything H.G. Wells had written. Other scientists followed up this research, and several German scientists wrote to various branches of the German government, drawing their attention to the possibilities in this discovery. Throughout 1939 the Army Weapons Office organised a series of meetings and conferences at which the military met the scientists and tried to discuss the possibilities and the probabilities. So far as the Army was concerned, what it boiled down to was that a highly technical scientific phenomenon (fission) had been demonstrated, but the rest of it was pure theory, much of it expressed in barely comprehensible mathematics. There had been no experiments, such as constructing an atomic pile, to carry the theories any further forward; there was no guarantee even that such an experiment might not end in a colossal disaster. Scientists were willing to suggest and prophesy, but they were very short on positive information.

In October 1939 the Weapons Office finally drew up a list of experimental work which the scientists suggested must be done in order to produce some answers upon which to construct more questions, and parcelled out this list to six scientific centres. The ultimate questions which had to be answered were, 'Is it possible to build a nuclear reactor which will produce material with which a military weapon can be constructed? And if it is possible, how long will it take and what will it require in terms of money, men and equipment?'

By the end of 1941 sufficient experimental work had been done to permit the assembly of a report, which was duly submitted to the Weapons Office. In summary, it considered that a reactor could and should be built, and it should be able to produce fissionable material. But turning that material into a bomb was a distant prospect which relied upon a great deal more experimentation being carried out as and when the reactor was built. The reactor proposed would use heavy water as the moderator (to slow down the neutrons and thus enable them to be captured). There were alternative methods of constructing an atomic pile, but since heavy water was available from Norway, it was the obvious course to choose.

By this time one man had appeared as the general voice of the German physicists, Professor Werner Heisenberg, winner of the Nobel Prize for Physics in 1933. Heisenberg had spent the summer of 1939 in the USA; with the war clouds gathering over Europe he had been urged by many friends to stay there, but he insisted upon returning. His country was going to war, and his place was in Germany. Many writers and commentators have since been unable, or so it seems, to understand this. Heisenberg claimed not to be a Nazi adherent, so why should he go back to Germany? It seems that the simple proposition that Heisenberg was a patriot, and put his country first, is incapable of being understood. No soldier would see any problem here; a soldier defends his country, not whatever political party happened to be in power when he enlisted, and Heisenberg's view would appear to have been the same. (And before you parrot 'Patriotism is the last resort of the scoundrel' remember that at the time Dr Johnson was defining scoundrels, not patriotism.)

So Heisenberg returned to Germany, and in spite of running up against the SS for his adherence to 'Jewish physics' was able to pursue his research. His attainments placed him, fairly naturally, at the head of the physicist community and in the spring of 1942 he became Director of the Kaiser Wilhelm Institute for Physics in Dahlem.

By this time about five separate bodies were pursuing the atomic pile project, each with a different theory of how it should be constructed, the physics of which need not detain us. Moreover, since all five were under different organisations, there was, again, the element of compartmented secrecy, so that only occasionally did one body discover what the others were doing or what results they were obtaining. Heisenberg appears to have worked this system to his advantage for, from his few statements on the subject in post-war years, he, and one or two others, seem to have decided upon their course of action. They would continue experimenting, but at no great speed. Whilst they were fairly sure a bomb could be made, it was obviously something which would take a long time and a vast industrial effort, and this provided them with an excellent reason for spinning out their work. But the crux of the matter was that few of the scientists were prepared to deliver the technology into Hitler's hands, for fear of what he might do with it. Defending Germany was one thing; giving Hitler an atomic bomb to further his dreams of world domination was something entirely different.

The equivocation came to a head in June 1942 when Speer, recently appointed as Minister of Munitions, organised a meeting of physicists with himself and his military and technical entourage, a meeting which came about simply because General Fromm, chief of the Weapons Office, had mentioned to Speer that some scientists were working on the prospects of a nuclear bomb. But the lectures through which Speer sat appeared to be mathematical dissertations on smashing the atom, on a mysterious 'uranium machine' (the atomic pile) and on the difficulties of scientific research in wartime. Eventually, Speer appears to have lost patience and asked Heisenberg bluntly how nuclear physics might be applied to the production of a bomb. According to Speer's memoirs, Heisenberg replied that, whilst they knew, theoretically, that such a weapon could be made, the practical application of that theory and the construction of a bomb could take years. Pressed further he opined that the Americans might, just, produce such a bomb by 1945, if indeed they were working on one at all.

Nevertheless, Speer was willing to put up money and provide facilities if the scientists actually thought they had a sporting chance of producing a bomb within a reasonable period of time. When he put this proposition forward and asked how much would be needed, he was somewhat taken aback to have 40,000 Reichsmarks suggested as a suitable sum; this was the sort of money a second-class university might budget for its chemistry department for a year. After much persuasion, the scientific budget was raised to about 350,000RM, and this, as much as anything else, convinced Speer that there was nothing of wartime value to be expected from nuclear physics and that the scientists themselves were convinced that far more basic research had to be done before anything practical could be contemplated. In his own words, when further questions later that year were answered by the suggestion that three or four years of work were needed,

'We scuttled the project to develop an atomic bomb.' Thereafter all official work was directed towards the development of a nuclear reactor capable of producing power.

Two atomic piles were eventually built, one near Hechingen, which used heavy water, and one at Erfurt, which was a 'low temperature reactor' also using heavy water. Neither achieved the desired chain reaction, largely because their size and content were insufficient. It has since been argued that because both were 'obviously' unlikely to function, they must, therefore, have been built for some other purpose, and that purpose must have been the production of radioactive material for use in an explosive bomb. This seems to me to be arguing from hindsight; to the German scientists of 1944/45, nothing was very obvious, and, more to the point, they were labouring against grave material disadvantages.

The supply of heavy water was limited, since the principal source in Norway had been destroyed by Allied bombing and the final shipment by sabotage; and those researchers who did have some of it were very careful to keep it under their hands, even to the degree of denying its existence to any possible rivals. The supply of pure graphite, required as a reflector, was also limited, since the ability to manufacture it had been severely curtailed by Allied bombing; and the available quantity of uranium, well that was limited, too, by what could be refined from stocks of ore found in Belgium in 1940 and from ore mined in small quantities from a source in Bohemia. No matter how much the scientists knew or understood, or thought they knew or understood, about nuclear science in 1944, no amount of knowledge was going to get round those basic facts. Add to that the other indisputable fact, that in 1943–45 German industry simply could not have achieved anything like the scale of the comparable American effort without it being detected and bombed flat within weeks, and I think it safe to say that the production of a nuclear weapon by Nazi Germany was never a practical proposition.

This is not to say that it was not feared by the Allies; they were never sure of what the Germans might be up to inside their laboratories, and the formation of the Alsos mission and its hotfoot pursuit of the advancing American forces in search of clues to nuclear research is evidence enough of that. Dr Samuel Goudsmit, who was the physicist heading the Alsos mission, was dismissive of the German work as soon as he saw the atomic pile at Hechingen, and from then on castigated the German scientists as ignorant and unscientific. But Goudsmit's testimony must be filtered through two screens; firstly his association with the American atomic programme and the American way of doing things, which predisposed him to sneer at anything indicative of less effort, and secondly the fact that his parents, who had remained in Holland when Goudsmit went to the USA before the war, were sent to a concentration camp and there killed in February 1943. For reasons never satisfactorily explained, Goudsmit held this against

Heisenberg personally, since it appeared that a Dutch scientist had written to Heisenberg to enlist his aid in getting the Goudsmits released; though it also appears that Heisenberg never received the letter until after both Goudsmits were dead, and in any case, was himself walking a knife-edge with the SS and was far from being likely to be able to influence its operations in the slightest manner.

Whatever; Goudsmit is an unreliable witness when it comes to reporting objectively on the German nuclear programme.

In 1943 the Army Weapons Office, having read the various papers produced by the different parties in the atomic research programme, asked a biophysical laboratory to look into the possible applications of radioactivity to weapons. From this has arisen the theory that the German Army was looking towards a conventional high explosive bomb (or rocket warhead) with an outer casing filled with radioactive dust, so that upon detonating the warhead the dust would be distributed around the point of burst and act as a radiological poison. Some work appears to have been done on this by a team of physicists working under the auspices of the German Post Office (which held a broad brief for scientific research) but the whole thing then tends to slide off into a mysterious area of conspiracy theory involving a secret U-Boat cargo, dispatched to Japan but captured and spirited away by the Americans. There certainly was a U-Boat, *U.234*, which had been sent off to take a variety of weapons and weapon drawings to Japan, and it was taken by the Americans, and its cargo was taken away for examination. But precisely what was in that cargo has never been revealed. And until it is, I prefer to reserve judgement on the question of radioactive weapons. One thing which argues against the idea is that if the Germans were not willing to use nerve gas, which was a technology and a tactic which they completely understood, I cannot see that they would be willing to use what amounted to much the same sort of weapon, but with technology and tactics they certainly did not understand.

Chemical warfare

Germany originated chemical warfare in February 1915 by firing 15cm shells charged with xylyl bromide against the Russian Army. However, the designers had overlooked the fact that in the sub-zero temperatures of the Polish winter the xylyl bromide would freeze solid in the shells and thus fail to vapourise and have the desired lachrymatory effect. Their next attempt, using chlorine gas released from cylinders near Ypres in April 1915, was more effective, but again failed tactically because the German Army was unprepared for its immediate success and failed to follow up and assault the gap in the Allied front in sufficient strength. From these rather inauspicious beginnings, gas warfare became a major feature of both the Western and Eastern Fronts in the First World War. Contrary to popular opinion, it was not a mass killer; the best available figures relating to gas casualties give a total of 91,198 dead and 1,205,655 non-fatally wounded. The best available figure of the total number of battle deaths in the First World War is 8,555,290, and of wounded 21,199,467. Putting these together we have gas causing about 1.07 percent of battle deaths and about 5.69 percent of wounded, for a total expenditure of some 125,000 tons of gas.

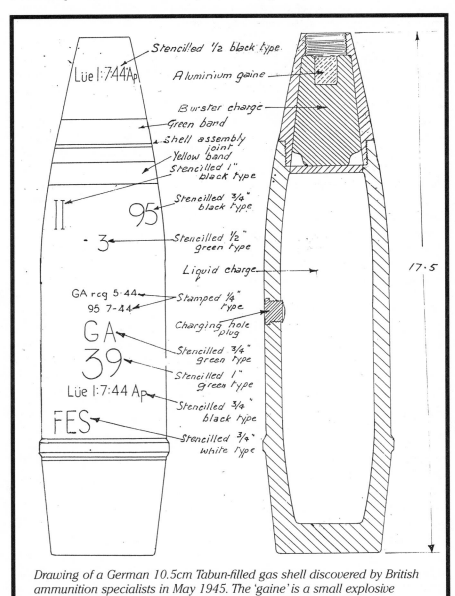

Drawing of a German 10.5cm Tabun-filled gas shell discovered by British ammunition specialists in May 1945. The 'gaine' is a small explosive charge which relays detonation from the fuze to the burster charge.

Looked at in the light of cold figures, chemical warfare thus appears to be non-cost-effective; but what the cold figures fail to take into account is the psychological and nuisance value of gas, which is considerable, as was recently seen in the Gulf War. The knowledge or even suspicion, that an adversary might use gas is enough to drive armies into prodigies of effort in order to provide their troops with protection; gas masks, gas-proof clothing, decontamination equipment, medical resources, personal anti-gas injections, salves and pills without end. The task of advancing under fire, or serving a gun, or doing anything at all warlike under a summer sun, wrapped in an impervious suit and breathing through a restrictive mask, is physically demanding and ultimately exhausting. The slightest whiff of a strange substance is enough to set gas alarms sounding and men climbing into anti-gas equipment, and it virtually brings an army to a standstill.

So irrespective of its lethal capabilities, chemical warfare is a useful tactical weapon. But there was so much revulsion in the 1920s and 1930s against the use of gas that it became universally outlawed. Not that this prevented the Italians using it against the Abyssinians, or the Japanese from using it against the Chinese; they were a long way from Geneva and nobody took much notice. (Why there should have been such revulsion is something I have never understood; for some reason or other the higher thinkers of the world appear to believe that it is perfectly acceptable for a soldier to be disembowelled by a shell fragment, but not for him to be asphyxiated. The soldier fails to see the difference.)

Outlawed or not, if gas existed there was always the chance that it would be used, and as a result all the major nations studied gas warfare. All, of course, were quick to point out that they were merely studying the defensive aspects in case some nefarious outlaw should use it against them, but in truth it is very difficult to study how to defend against any weapon if you don't know how the weapon works or what its effects may be. The only way to know that is to possess the weapon and try it out. And therefore research into gas warfare continued, at a relatively low level, throughout the inter-war years.

In 1919 the standard war gases were phosgene, chlorine, mustard, Lewisite, and various arsenical smokes and tear gases. Of these, phosgene was the standard by which the effectiveness of any lethal gas was measured, mustard was important because of its ability to attack the skin and its persistence, and Lewisite (invented in the USA in 1918) was untried in war but claimed to be the most lethal gas yet developed. During the subsequent years several compounds were tested but, apart from refining mustard gas and making it rather easier to handle in filling factories, little advance was made in Britain or the USA. Little advance was made in Germany either, in the deliberate search for war gases, but, as is often the case, research in another direction suddenly produced a surprise.

The German population was growing in the 1930s, and feeding them was

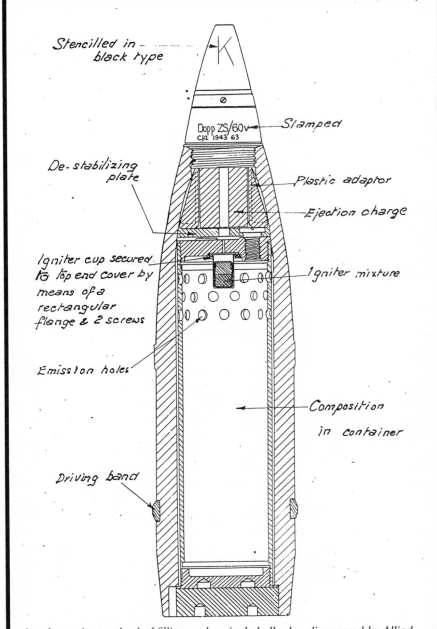

An alternative method of filling a chemical shell, also discovered by Allied searches in May 1945. This carries a canister of arsenical compound which is ignited by the time fuze and ejection charge, and is then ejected through the base of the shell by blowing out the baseplate. The canister falls to the ground and emits lethal arsenical smoke.

a vital matter. Farmers demanded better insecticides and weed-killers, and chemists began searching for them. After exhausting all the 'natural' substances which had been used for years, they began looking into synthesising chemicals which would attack the weeds but leave the crops alone. This led a Dr Gerhard Schräder to conduct research into organo-phosphorus compounds, and he discovered a substance called ethyl-dimethyl-amido-phosphor-cyanidate. This proved to be a highly efficient insecticide; and on further examination it suggested itself as an equally efficient war gas. Further development took place and eventually it was put into production as 'Tabun', and a special factory, the *Anorganawerke*, was built near Dyhernfurth in Silesia (now Brzeg Dolny, Poland), a few miles from Breslau (now Wroclaw).

The production engineering problems of converting the laboratory reaction into a workable and safe manufacturing process were considerable, but by 1942 the factory was in operation with a planned eventual production capability of 1,000 tons of Tabun per month. Some 15,000 tons are believed to have been produced before the advancing Red Army over-ran Dyhernfurth (and promptly dismantled the factory and shipped it, and its contents, back into Soviet Russia without telling the rest of the Allies anything about it).

Since the organo-phosphorus area appeared to hold more promise, more research took place, and in 1938 another composition was adopted for military use. This was isopropyl methyl-phosphoro-fluoridate, now called 'Sarin' and discovered by the same team that found Tabun. Plans for production were drawn up, but Sarin was a great deal more difficult to manufacture than Tabun, and although a pilot plant had been built at the Anorganawerk, and had turned out a small quantity of Sarin, no production for service use ever took place.

Finally, in 1944, pinacolyl methyl-phosphoro-fluoridate, called 'Soman', was discovered, a compound considerably more lethal than the earlier pair, but which was still in the laboratory stage when the war ended.

The Western Allies, though, knew nothing of this. Their first intimation that something nasty was lurking in German ammunition depots came when a party of British Army ammunition specialists examined a recently-captured dump in Germany in April 1945. Included in the stocks of various kinds of ammunition was a large quantity of 10.5cm howitzer shells marked with a single green ring and the letters 'GA'. Some unrecorded hero examined these items and reported that,

'The chemical filling is dark brown with a sweetish smell of chloro-benzene... it is a new type of filling containing 20 per cent chloro-benzene and an arsenic derivative which is under investigation. It is not vesicant but somewhat poisonous by penetration through the skin... and is relatively persistent.'

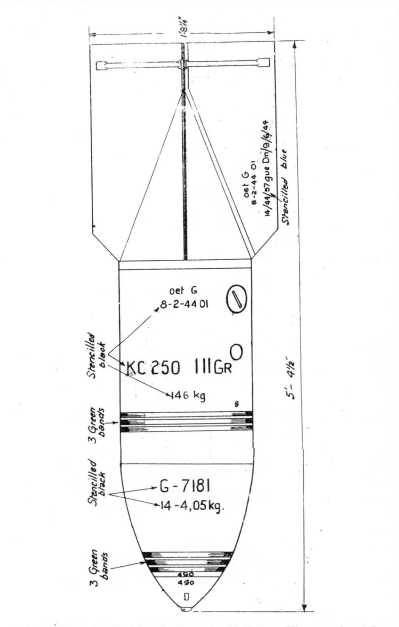

A nominal 250kg chemical bomb charged with Tabun. (The actual weight was 146kg, but its physical size placed it in the 250kg class for storage.) Of interest in the various markings are '14-4,05kg' which tells the type and weight of the explosive burster, and 'Dn 9/6/44' which gives the place and date of final filling and assembly.

Eventually about half a million shells and over 100,000 aircraft bombs charged with this substance were discovered in dumps scattered throughout Germany, although, according to some reports, the aircraft bombs were not intended to be dropped, but had simply been filled up in order to use up the stock of gas produced at Dyhernfurth before the factory was abandoned to the advancing Russians. After analysing the mysterious dark brown liquid, which was, of course, Tabun, the Allied chemists were astonished. When they later discovered Soman and Sarin, they were horrified. These, they said, were agents up to thirty times more lethal than phosgene and, moreover, agents against which there seemed to be little or no defence. They were given the generic name of 'nerve gases'.

These 'G Agents', a term derived from the original German notation of GA and GB for Tabun and Soman, work on the human body by an entirely different method from previous war gases. The early gases attacked the lungs and respiratory system, or they were systemic poisons ingested through the skin. The G agents operate against the nervous system. The functioning of the body depends entirely upon the nervous system transmitting impulses, and these impulses lead to the formation of a compound called acetylcholine at the nerve junctions. Acetylcholine is then neutralised by a second compound called cholinesterase which, by its action on the acetylcholine, 'cancels' the impulse on the nerve path and leaves the system open to receive a fresh signal. The G agent attacks the cholinesterase, converting it into something entirely different, a compound which does not have the cancelling effect on the acetylcholine. As a result, the nerve junction remains blocked and fresh signals cannot pass. The body's functions are no longer under the brain's control. The effects run from a streaming nose through difficult breathing, distortion of vision, nausea, vomiting, involuntary micturition and defecation, to convulsions, coma and eventual death.

This catalogue of symptoms is induced either by inhaling the fumes or by contact with the liquid, and the sequence of events is extremely quick. In a lethal concentration, Soman can cause death within one or two minutes, and the others are equally rapid. The astonishing thing is that even though these effects were known by the late 1940s the production of organo-phosphates as insecticides and weed-killers has continued, to the detriment of the health of countless agricultural workers, and we now have the so-called 'Gulf War Syndrome' and the recent discovery in Kurdistan that the G agents appear to be causing genetic mutations in children born to survivors of G agent attack.

The question therefore arises of why the Germans never, even in their most desperate last defence, used these agents? Two suggestions have been made. The first is that Hitler, from his experience of gas warfare in World War One, firmly resisted its use except as a response to any Allied use of gas. The second is similar, that the Germans were reluctant to use the nerve agents because they had not found any method of defence against them or antidote to them. This second reason is tied to the fact that Britain was also carrying out research into insecticides and weed-killers in order to boost farm production during the war and, in order to deny such information to the enemy on economic grounds, placed a ban on printing scientific papers dealing with organo-phosphates. Even during war, scientific journals circulated around the world, and, via neutral countries, the belligerents were able to watch what was being reported by other belligerents. And the sudden cessation and subsequent absence of any papers on the organophosphates in British scientific publications pointed, so far as the Germans were concerned, to one thing only – that the British had discovered the G agents. And if the British had discovered them, then Germany would be faced with them should they initiate chemical warfare. And they had no antidote.

(If this sounds far-fetched, consider the following: in the late 1930s there was a great deal of work done in Britain on the use of infra-red to detect aircraft, a study which was later dropped once radar became viable. But, because of this study, there were quite a few scientific papers published on aspects of infra-red detection. This was picked up by the Germans, who immediately assumed that the British would be using infra-red equipment for night operations, and they went to a great deal of trouble and expense to develop a small, hand-held infra-red detector for issue to front line troops so that they could immediately discover whether infra-red light was being directed against them. The British never used infra-red illumination until the later stages of the war, when it was introduced simply as a night-driving aid for vehicles.)

Biological warfare

Biological warfare was another of the frightening prospects being bandied about in the 1930s, with newspaper stories of germ-laden bombs being dropped by fleets of aircraft, presumably when they were not occupied in dropping gas bombs. But biological warfare appears to have been a long way down towards the bottom of the German priority list. The great defect of biological warfare is that it tends to be colour-blind and cannot distinguish between different uniforms, nor does it recognise national borders. For a continental nation, therefore, biological weapons are distinctly two-edged, and they can turn round very easily to destroy their owners. It was quite feasible for the Japanese to experiment with biological weapons in Manchuria, for there was little or no danger of it rebounding against insular Japan, but for Germany to attempt to use a biological agent against, say, the Russians, invited the spread of disease back into Germany.

This is not to say that, as with gas, research into biological weapons was not carried out. It certainly was, and by Allied as well as Axis countries, but in this case I think it safe to say that the defensive aspect far outweighed the offensive. Countries were generally more concerned with countering the threat than actually instigating such warfare themselves. Germany made a particular study of aerosol technology, basing the work on that of a Belgian pioneer in the subject, Professor Dautrebande, and applied the findings to methods of dispersing both war gases and biological agents, but never turned the experiments into practical devices for use in the field. There are also suggestions that chemical and biological agents were tested on concentration camp inmates, but the reports of these are somewhat inconsistent and the results, described in nauseating detail, do not appear to bear any relationship to the effects to be expected from war gases or germ warfare, and must be discounted.

APPENDIX 1

The Special List

On 1 January 1945 the Army Weapons Office prepared a 'Special List' of ammunition manufacturing projects which were then authorised and in progress. This list was recovered after the war but there was no explanatory text with it, and many of the projects mentioned have never been satisfactorily resolved; by the time Allied investigators found this list and went to make enquiries at the various factories, vital personnel had disappeared, documents had vanished, and equipment was spirited away, looted or simply destroyed. Moreover, of course, some of the projects may have been terminated some time before the war ended, leaving no trace behind them.

For what it may be worth to researchers and students, and for the interest of others, the list is reproduced here, mysteries and all. Where additional explanation has been thought necessary it is added in [square brackets]. The only editing has been to remove a column indicating the Armaments Inspectorate district in which the factory was, and to correct one or two obvious misprints. If it does nothing else, it certainly reveals the range of the manufacturing and development programme and the variety of munitions devices under development.

Company/Place	Product
Rheinmetall-Borsig, Breslau/Hundsfeld	1. Electric impact nose and base fuzes
	2. Ditto; free from materials in short supply
	3. Control and energy devices
	4. Ignition equipment and test gear
Rheinmetall-Borsig, Sömmerda	1. Impact fuzes for HDP
	2. Impact fuze AZ 1Rh
	3. Fuzes for 38cm Stü Mrs [SP assault rocket projector]
	4. Impact fuze *Gerät 040* [54cm *Karl* SP howitzer]
	5. Nose fuze for rocket shells RG60 and RG61
	6. Base fuze for HDP
	7. Mechanical impact fuze for A4 rocket
	8. Base fuze 5127/1 for piercing shell
	9. Combustion time fuze for 8cm illuminating mortar bomb
	10. Cartridge primer c/12
	11. Cartridge primer c/22
	12. Tracers without screw-threads
	13. Tracers pressed into shell base
Rheinmetall-Borsig, Gispersleben	1. 8cm mortar bomb for 8cm *PAW 600*
	2. 7.62cm jumping mine for the jumping mine thrower

  3. Hollow charge shell for *Gerät 040*
  4. 8cm hollow charge mortar shell 4462
  5. 10cm anti-tank mortar shell Rh
  6. 24cm HE shell for K3Vz [splined shells for a deep grooved version of the standard 24cm heavy gun]
  7. 10cm hollow charge anti-tank shell *PAW 1000*
  8. Threaded sheaths and fuze bodies from welded tubes
  9. 10.5cm HE shell TS [*Triebspiegel* – 'sabot']
  10. 10.5cm TS incendiary shrapnel
  11. 12.8cm HE shell TS
  12. 12.8/10.5cm TS incendiary shrapnel
  13. 12.8/7.5cm HE shell TS
  14. 4/21cm HE shell 41 [For taper-bore version of the 24cm K3 heavy gun]

Fasterstoff und Spinnerei Fürstenberg AG, Fürstenberg, Mecklenburg

  1. 28/12cm *Peenemünde Pfeilgeschosse* [for K5(E)]
  2. 15cm Tromsdorff shell for 15cm K18 gun
  3. 15cm vaned high capacity shell 70kg, for sFH 18
  4. 21cm vaned high capacity shell for 21cm How 18
  5. 28cm Tromsdorff shell for K5(E)

Wittkowitzer Bergbau, Mährisch-Ostrau.

  1. 28/12cm *Peenemünde Pfeilgeschosse* [for K5(E)]
  2. 15cm vaned high capacity shell for heavy infantry gun sIG 33
  3. 12.2/10.5cm hollow charge TS shell
  4. 15cm hollow charge shell 39 with mine fins
  5. 32/12cm *PPG* [for trials in a French 32cm gun]
  6. 24/12cm *PPG* for K3 smoothbore gun

Skoda Works, Pilsen.

  1. 15cm fin-stabilised long shell
  2. 21cm mortar shell for *Ladungswerfer* [spigot mortar]
  3. 21cm mortar shell 'Glas' for Mortar 42
  4. Long range shell, Skoda pattern, for sFH 18
  5. Long range shell for assault howitzer 34
  6. Long range shell for leFH 18 howitzer
  7. 30.5cm spin-stabilised high capacity shell for 30.5cm howitzer 42
  8. Light long range shell with suction cup [?]
  9. 30.5cm HE shell for Skoda howitzer
  10. 30.5cm anti-concrete shell for Skoda howitzer
  11. 10cm hollow charge shell with folding fins
  12. 15cm shell Gr 35 with folding fins
  13. Long range shell for medium field howitzer mFH (Skoda) 5141
  14. 10.5/8.8cm sabot HE shell for leFH 18
  15. 12cm illuminating mortar bomb for GrW 12
  16. 10.5cm fin-stabilised long shell
  17. 15cm fin-stabilised long shell
  18. Cartridge case for 10.7cm gun K352(f), coiled steel type C case [for captured French field guns]

19. Cartridge case for 30.5cm Italian howitzer 640
20. Coiled case corresponding to solid steel case 6345St
21. Ersatz manufacture of long cartridge cases
22. Coiled cartridge case for 8cm tank gun KwK 36
23. Fuze Dopp.Z.s/60(t) [combustion time fuze, Czech]
24. Rolled iron driving bands for 24cm shell Gr 35 for 24cm Czech gun cmK(t)

Brünner Waffenwerke, Prague/Waschowitz

1. Cartridge case for 10.7cm gun K352(r), Type C, coiled steel case. [Russian 107mm field gun]
2. Coiled steel cartridge case for Italian 30.5cm how.
3. Improvement of the 7.92mm proof ammunition s.S., and conversion to iron-cored semi-AP S.m.E
4. Development of pressure barrel for proof-firing of 7.62mm Patr 43
5. Coiled cartridge case for 8.8cm tank gun KwK 36
6. Coiled cartridge case based on solid steel case 6354

Brandenburger Eisenwerke, Brandeburg/Havel

1. Molybdenum-free armour plates.

Polte, Magdeburg

1. Development of lead-free rifle bullets
2. All-steel cartridge case for 12.8cm anti-tank gun
3. Cartridge case, special construction, 4AKH 21347
4. Cartridge case 5345Dt, shortened to 680mm
5. Development of the *Matter* explosive bullet
6. Development of the *Prinz Albrecht* explosive bullet
7. Development of the explosive rifle bullet Sprenggeschoss 43 *Prinz Albrecht*
8. Development of the explosive pistol bullet Sprenggeschoss '08 *Prinz Albrecht*
9. Development of rifle bullet 43 with tracer with reduced lead content.
10. 2cm piercing tracer shell free from chromium
11. Electric igniters for cartridges SmE
12. Electric igniters for 2cm AP practice cartridges
13. Electric igniters for 2cm HE practice cartridges
14. Increase in efficiency of hollow charge munitions.

Hugo Schneider, Leipzig

1. Cartridge case 6358 built-up type D
2. Cartridge case 6216 Type D
3. Steel cartridge case, special type.
4. Primer c/12 substitute
5. Simplified HE rifle grenade

Hessische Industriewerke, Horne-Westfalen

1. 28/12cm PPG for smoothbore K5(E) gun
2. 24/12cm PPG for smooth-bore K3 gun
3. 32/12cm PPG for French 32cm gun
4. 15cm Röchling shell 42 for sFH18 howitzer
5. 15cm Röchling shell for 15cm gun K18

Fried. Krupp, Essen	1. Long range shell for 10.5cm leFH 18
	2. 12.8cm HE shell L/5.0 for 12.8cm gun K81
	3. Base fuze for PPG
	4. Molybdenum-free armour plate
	5. 15cm high capacity HE shell for sIG 33 infantry gun
	6. 21cm high capacity shell for 21cm Mrs 18 howitzer
	7. 30.5cm high capacity shell for howitzer 42
	8. 8.8/7.0cm HE shell TS for 8.8cm Flak 18 and 41
	9. 10.5cm TS HE shell for Flak gun
	10. 10.5/8.8cm TS HE shell for the new Flak barrel.
	11. 12.8/7.5cm TS HE shell for Flak gun
	12. 15/12cm TS HE shell (new sub-calibre)
	13. 10cm HE mortar bomb for tank mortar
	14. 12cm illuminating mortar shell for GrW 42
	15. 10.5cm high velocity piercing shell
	16. 12.8cm high velocity piercing shell
	17. 17cm piercing shell PsGr 43; increase in efficiency
	18. 10.5/5.5cm high velocity piercing sabot shell
	19. 10.5/6.5cm high velocity piercing sabot shell
	20. 12.8/7.5cm high velocity piercing sabot shell
	21. 10cm hollow-charge mortar shell for tank mortar
	22. 21cm Tromsdorff shell for 21cm gun K18
	23. Piercing shell with reduced air resistance
	24. 42cm HE shell for Skoda howitzer 42
Dynamit AG, Troisdorf-bei-Köln	1. Detonator 49; fitting with delay
	2. Exploders made from plastic explosive
	3. Waterproof igniter for hollow-charge S Mine
	4. Delay for detonator of Tellermine 42
	5. Development of special polystyrene for fixing fuzes.
Dynamit AG, Duneburg	1. Reduction of smoke from propellants
	2. Lignin powder
	3. Manufactured of nitrocellulose by direct nitration of wood (sawdust, wood pulp)
	4. Ammonpulver (smokeless powder with ammonium nitrate incorporated)
Gebr. Junghans, Schrammberg	1. Time and percussion fuze Dopp Z s/60v
	2. J-Feder (clockwork demolition delay igniter) 504
Wasag, Reinsdorf	1. Ranging HE filling for 17cm gun K39
	2. Ranging HE filling for 21cm shell Gr 18
	3. 17cm illuminating shell for Navy
	4. Development of HE mixtures making more use of Hexogen
	5. Hollow charge for *Gerät 041*; cast filling
	6. Internal ballistic research for weapon with high fire density (*Feuerfolge*)
	7. Reduction of smoke from propellants
	8. Seven-hole propellant

9. Increase of velocity for 7.5cm PAK 40 gun
10. Lignin propellant
11. Nitrocellulose by direct nitration of wood
12. Paper and pulp impregnated with ammonium nitrate
13. Pot Mine 4931
14. Tracers pressed into the base of the shell
15. HE charges for *Gerät 041* [54cm *Karl* SP howitzer]
16. Rifle anti-tank grenade with extra propellant
17. Thermoplastic explosive charge
18. Illuminating shell with increased duration of light.

Deutsche Sprengchemie, Torgelow

1. Seven-hole propellant

Richard Dietsch, Geyer/Erzegebirge

1. Primers c/22 without materials in short supply
2. Increase in ignition strength of gun cartridges
3. Reinforced cartridge cases of 'Dn' pulp for 7.5cm field gun 85
4. Watertight and airtight cartridge bags

Deutsche Waffen-und-Munitionsfabrik AG, Lübeck/Schlutup

1. Increased efficiency of hollow-charge munitions
2. Development of spark chronographs
3. 100 volt electric detonators
4. Low voltage electric detonators
5. Lead-free rifle bullet development
6. Lead-free rifle bullet Patr 43 development
7. Lead-free 7.65mm pistol bullet development
8. Hollow charge shells with light casing
9. HE shell cartridge for signal pistol, time fuzed
10. 26mm signal pistol cartridge
11. Propellant for 7.92mm rifle cartridge with bullet not containing materials in short supply
12. 5.6mm rifle cartridge with steel caps [.22 Long Rifle]
13. 7.5cm shell *Gr 38 Hl/C mit Klappleitwerk* [hollow-charge shell with spring-out fins]
14. 7.5cm hollow-charge shell *Gr 38 Hl* with sintered iron insert.
15. Tracers pressed into base of shell
16. 9.4cm projectile for *Nebelwerfer*
17. 7.5cm hollow-charge shell with over-calibre fins
18. Development of HE rifle grenade *Prinz Albrecht*
19. Development of HE rifle projectile for 7.92mm Sturmgewehr 43 *Prinz Albrecht*
20. Development of HE pistol projectile 9mm Pist '08, *Prinz Albrecht*
21. Development of apparatus for measurement of velocity and time of flight
22. Spark cinematography and the development of apparatus as necessary
23. X-Ray cinematography investigations

24. Flame thrower 44 a and b
25. Single shot flame thrower FmW 46
26. Large flame thrower apparatus for tanks
27. Improved type of flame thrower Abw FmW 42
28. Testing for cracks in piercing shells
29. Increase in muzzle velocity of 7.5cm piercing shell *Panzergranate 40* for 7.5cm PAK
30. Increase of the muzzle impulse in lead-free pistol bullets
31. Chemical and physical investigations into propellants

Th. Bergmann & Co., Welton/Mark

1. Illuminating shells *Leuchttöpf*
2. Impact fuze AZ 5092, development of AZ 5075
3. Impact fuze 5097, all-ways fuze for rifle grenade
4. Cartridge Primer c/22 in steel
5. Tracers with delayed ignition
6. Tracers without screw-threads
7. Tracers pressed into the base of shells
8. Anti-tank rifle grenade with extra propellant
9. Practice rifle HE grenade
10. Rifle propaganda grenade
11. Cartridge primer c/22 without scarce materials

Zeiss-Ikon AG, Dresden

1. Impact fuze AZ5091, development of AZ 5075
2. Maximum pressure apparatus
3. Accelerometer for drop tests
4. Apparatus for measuring the intensity of smoke from propellant powders.

Siemens & Halske, Simonsstadt

1. Velocity and time of flight measuring apparatus
2. Development of the magneto-elastic pressure box.

Gustloff-werke, Sühl/Thüringen

1. Improvement of hollow-charge munitions

Gustloff-werke, Hirtenberg N.D.

1. Development of lead-free rifle bullets
2. Development of observation bullet *Beobachtung Geschoss* with reduced amount of lead
3. Rifle projectile with fuze, Gew Gesch mZ

AEH Zählerfabriken, Berlin

1. Electric induction impact fuze
2. Electric fuze for hollow-charges
3. Maximum pressure apparatus
4. Electric percussion arrangement for fuze E Zdr AEG
5. Electric impact fuzes with & without delay
6. Anchored mines, rocket-propelled

Deutsche Edelstahlwerke, Dortmund/Aplerbeck

1. Small shot-firing machines [blasting magnetos]
2. Electrical impulse generator
3. 8cm mortar bomb of malleable cast iron
4. 12cm mortar bomb WGr 5055(h) for GrW 42

Sachsenwerke,
Radenerg

1. Electrical bomb fuze El Z 66
2. Chemical long-delay fuze [for demolitions]

Stock & Co,
Berlin-Stolberg

1. 10.5/5.5cm TS piercing shell for high velocity
2. 10.5/6.5cm TS piercing shell for high velocity
3. 12.8/7.5cm TS piercing shell for high velocity
4. 5.5cm piercing shell for *Gerät 58* Flak gun

SGW Döhlen,
Freital/Sachsen

1. 12.8cm piercing shell, high velocity
2. 12.8cm piercing shell for tank gun KwK L/55
3. Economies in alloys used in piercing shells

Niedersachsen AG,
Spenge, Krs. Herford

1. Long range shell for leFH 18 (Haack's profile)
2. 10.5/8.8cm TS HE shell for leFH 18
3. 10.5/8.8cm TS HE shell for Flak 39
4. 10.5/8.8cm TS HE Shell for new Flak gun
5. 12.8/7.5cm TS HE Shell for Flak 39 with altered rifling
6. 15cm TS HE shell TS5091
7. 15/12cm TS HE shell
8. 5.5cm piercing shell Psgr 43 for *Gerät 58* Flak
9. 12.8cm piercing shell for tank gun KwK L/55
10. 15cm piercing shell for direct fire
11. 10.5/7.5cm TS piercing shell for leFH 18
12. 10.5/5.5cm TS piercing shell for high velocity
13. 12.8/8.8cm TS piercing shell for tank gun KwK L/55
14. 12.8/8.8cm TS piercing shell for 12.8cm PAK 81
15. 15/8.8cm TS piercing shell, simplified
16. 12.8cm piercing shell *Pzgr 41* for PAK 81 with barrel extension
17. 10.5cm hollow-charge shell with sabot
18. 12.2cm hollow-charge shell for Russian howitzer 396
19. 12.8cm hollow-charge shell for PAK 81
20. 12.2cm hollow-charge shell with sabot
21. 15cm hollow-charge shell *Gr 39* with spring-out fins
22. 24/12cm PPG for K3 smoothbore gun
23. 10.5cm finned high capacity HE shell (*Flügelminen granate*) for leFH 18
24. 10.5cm incendiary shrapnel with sabot for Flak 38
25. 12.8/10.5mm TS incendiary shrapnel for Flak 40.
26. 15cm finned high capacity HE shell with flash tube
27. Sabots from synthetic resin
28. Economy of alloys in piercing shells
29. Piercing shells with reduced air resistance

APPENDIX 2

German Code Names

The following list includes every known German special equipment code name, including many which are not mentioned in the body of the book, such as radars and target detection devices. Entries named in **bold type** are more fully explained in the text. Entries noted as being 'for unspecified missile' were generally being developed in broad detail, leaving the fine-tuning to a specific missile for a later date.

Note, too, that some of these words were in common use for well-known conventional weapons; *Marder* was also a self-propelled anti-tank gun; *Uhu* was also a night-fighter.

Adlergerät	An infra-red telescope for the detection of aircraft by the emissions from bomber exhausts and used to direct searchlights. Used in some quantity in the early part of the war as a substitute for radar.
Amsel	Acoustic target-seeking device for torpedoes. Using a microphone circuit it was intended to pick up and lock on to the target's propeller noise.
Ansbach	Fire control system for anti-aircraft batteries based on the *Mannheim* radar but with a remote display to permit the operator to be in a bomb-proof bunker. About 30 were in use in 1945.
Archimedes	Passive acoustic homing head developed by Telefunken for the *Enzian* missile.
Armin	Infra-red target detector for missiles.
A-Stoff	Liquid oxygen.
Bachstelze	A towed rotor-kite used as a reconnaissance and early warning spotter for U-Boats.
Bad	Acoustic proximity fuze under development by the Graf Zeppelin Institute.
Baldrian	Acoustic homing head for torpedoes developed by Telefunken.
Balkon	A sound-locating system for U-Boat use, enabling the U-Boat to detect screw noises of targets or enemy warships. A form of Sonar.
Bayreuth	Intended to be a fire control radar set for anti-aircraft guns operating in the 25m band. Development stopped in 1944 in favour of a set working in the 9cm band.
B-IV	General name covering a series of remote-controlled demolition vehicles, similar in principle to, but much larger

than, the better- known *Goliath* (qv). The vehicle was tracked, and had normal driving controls so that it could be manually driven close to its operational site. The driver then got out and the vehicle was then remotely controlled by radio. It carried a 550kg charge of explosive in a box on the front and was driven up to the obstacle where the box was dropped. The vehicle was then reversed, turned, and driven back to the controller, after which the explosive was detonated by radio control. In practice the dropping linkage usual stuck and the vehicle was destroyed in the explosion.

BAZ-55A	Acoustic bomb fuze by Rheinmetall-Borsig.
Beethoven	A 'piggy-back' composite aircraft similar to *Mistel*, but using 'war-weary' bomber aircraft as the weapon.
Berlin	Tactical control and early warning radar set for gunnery and fighter control, using a plan position indicator which gave a map-like display of the defensive sector.
Biber	A one-man U-Boat which carried two torpedoes.
Blaulicht	Active radar homing device for missiles.
Blitz	Arado 234 reconnaissance bomber.
Bold	Anti-detection device used by U-Boats. Also called *Pillenwerfer*.
Bombersage	A recoilless 30mm gun battery mounted behind the pilot of a fighter aircraft and firing upwards against enemy bombers.
Brabant	Guidance system for air defence missiles using radar to track target and missile, and a *Kogge-Brigg* radio link.
Brigg	18-channel super-regenerative radio receiver used with various missile guidance systems.
B-Stoff	Mixture of hydrazine hydrate (92%) and water (8%) used as rocket fuel in conjunction with *A-Stoff*.
Bulldogge	Active radar homing device for air defence missiles.
Burgund	Missile guidance system using optical target and missile tracking and a *Strassburg-Kehl* radio command link for air defence missiles.
Butterblüme	This began as an infra-red airborne interception equipment but later turned into a mapping device for locating ground targets by heat radiation from chimneys, locomotives, vehicle engines and so on. The development model was ready for flight testing as the war ended. A forerunner of today's 'thermal imaging'.
Bv 143	Blohm & Voss flying torpedo.
Bv 226	Blohm & Voss air-to-air or air-to-sea missile project.
Bv 246	A winged glide bomb similar to FX 1400 but of better aerodynamic shape. Fitted with the *Radieschen* (qv) guidance system it was intended for use against Allied Loran navigational radio stations.
Claudia	An acoustic detection system of which little is known. It is

	believed to have been an advanced form of sound-locating system for use by anti-aircraft command as a method of by-passing radar jamming.
Colberg	Radio command guidance receiver used with the *Griefswalde* transmitter. Developed as a back-up in case the *Stassburg-Kehl* system proved a failure.
Colmar	Radio command guidance receiver used with the *Kehl* transmitter for controlling the Hs298 missile.
C-Stoff	50/50 mixture of hydrazine hydrate and methanol. Used as rocket fuel in conjunction with hydrogen peroxide.
Dackel	(1) Active radar homing device for missiles.
	(2) Name given to the T3d torpedo, a pattern-running type with a speed of 9 knots and a range of 62km.
Dogge	Acoustic homing device proposed for use with the X-4 missile.
Donau-60	An infra-red target detection system for the control of coast artillery guns, in which four thermal sensors were deployed along the coast some 4km–5km apart, each being a paraboloid mirror with a bolometer detector at the focal point. Each would detect and give a bearing to a ship target, locating it by the heat of the funnels. These bearings were then transmitted to a central plotting station which correlated the data and issued firing orders to the guns. Zeiss made between 20 and 30 of these per month during 1939–40 and installations were made at several places.
Doppellinse	Infra-red homing device for missiles under development by AEG.
Dortmund-Duisburg	Wire-guidance system proposed for the *Fritz-X* or Hs 293 missiles. Under development in 1944–45 and the ancestor of all subsequent wire-guidance systems.
Düka-88	An 8.8cm recoilless gun (*Düsenkanone*) mounted in an aircraft.
Duren-Dettmold	Another wire-guidance system, similar to *Dortmund-Duisburg* but using pulsed direct current signals instead of audio-frequency alternating current signals.
Düppel	The German name for 'Window', half-wavelength strips of metallised paper dropped from aircraft to jam radar sets. The name comes from the location, in Denmark, of the first German tests of the idea in January 1943.
Düsseldorf-Dettmold	Another wire-guidance system for the X-4 missile, differing from *Duren-Dettmold* only in small circuit details.
ElKu	Name derived from 'Elektro-Akoustik' and applied to the *Paplitz* (qv) proximity fuze.
Elsass	Radio command guidance system for missiles, using radar for target acquisition, a *Rüse* transponder for tracking the missile, and a *Strassburg-Kehl* radio link for transmission of commands. Three versions were designed for use with

Wasserfall, *Schmetterling/Enzian* and *Rheintochter* missiles.

Elsass-Lothringen	A radar command guidance system based on *Elsass* but with the addition of a television camera in the missile to permit the operator to have visual command of the final part of the missile's flight.
Emden	Infra-red homing device for missiles under development by AEG.
Enzian	Messerschmitt ground-to-air missile.
Egerland	Tactical and fire control radar set, the first German set to operate in the 9cm band. First installation was in Berlin in January 1945; 1000 were ordered but only two were ever made. Consisted of two co-ordinated radar sets, *Kulmbach* for detecting targets and *Marbach* for controlling gunfire.
Eidechse	A multi-band tuning attachment for air defence radar sets so that frequencies could be quickly changed in the face of electronic jamming. Installation began in late 1944 and by the end of the war almost all *Mannheim* and *Wurzburg* radars had been fitted.
Emil	A fine range-measuring device added to *Wurzburg* radar sets to improve their range measurement accuracy when used to control anti-aircraft gunfire.
Erdstuka	Rocket-assisted 1800kg armour-piercing bomb used by Stuka dive-bombers against hard targets.
Eva	An infra-red early warning device for anti-aircraft defences, intended to detect the heat from bomber engines and exhausts.
Falke	(1) Video camera unit for missile guidance. By Löwe-Opta of Berlin, it used a spiral scan but was dropped in favour of *Tonne* (qv). (2) Type T 4 naval acoustic-homing torpedo; 20 knots, 8km range, and the first of its type.
Falter	An infra-red airborne interception device which also acted as a warning device if pilots were being scanned by an enemy infra-red detector.
FAT	*Feder-Apparat-Torpedo*. A steering attachment which could be fitted to the standard G7 torpedoes and which steered the torpedo on an erratic course with regular reverse turns so as to hunt through a convoy or formation of ships.
Feuerlilie	Sounding rocket used for aerodynamic research.
Fi 103	Fieseler factory title for *FZG 76* or V1 flying bomb.
Flamingo	An infra-red warning device, intended to replace *Kormoran* (qv).
Flatter	Television homing system for unspecified missile.
Fliegerfaust	9-barrel shoulder fired air defence rocket launcher.
Fliegerschreck	An air defence rocket development by Rheinmetall-Borsig.
Flitzer	Proposed infra-red guidance system for air defence missiles.

Flugkorper	Alternative name for Bv 246.
Föhn	Multiple air defence rocket launcher.
Förstersonde	Rocket-boosted anti-tank bomb dropped from aircraft.
Franken	Radio command guidance system for missiles using optical tracking of both missile and target and a *Kogge-Brigg* radio link.
Fregatte	Command guidance receiver for air defence missiles, similar to *Brigg* but of the super-heterodyne type to work with *Kogge* or *Kai* transmitters.
Freya	Standard German early warning radar set, and the first to be developed. Work began in 1936 by the Gema company. By 1939 over 100 sets were in operation.
Friedensengel	Blohm & Voss LT 10 glide torpedo.
Fritz-X	Alternative name for FX 1400 (qv).
Froschauge	An infra-red warning device for aircraft, indicating to the pilot that he was being tracked by an infra-red search device. It proved to be totally useless and was quickly abandoned.
F-Stoff	Titanium tetrachloride, used as a smoke-producing agent in various munitions.
Fuchs	Radio proximity fuze intended for use in Hs 117, Hs 298 and other missiles, by AEG Berlin, it had a transmitter in the nose of the missile and a receiver to detect the reflected signal. Production was supposed to begin in January 1945 but it is doubtful if any were made.
Fühler	Infra-red homing device for air defence missiles under development by Uhrentechnik GmbH.
FX 1400	Guided glide bomb, controlled by an observer in the aircraft which dropped it.
FZG 76	*Flakzielgerät 76*; official title for the V-1 flying bomb.
G7P	Proposal for an electrically-propelled torpedo using new types of battery to develop 30 knots and 10km range.
Gebogenerlauf	Curved-barrel attachment for the Machine Pistol 44 (later known as the Assault Rifle 44) to permit firing round corners. Similar to *Krummlauf* (qv).
Geier	Name given to a projected active homing torpedo.
Gerät 104	35cm calibre recoilless gun mounted in an aircraft.
Gleit Torpedo	Alternative name for Hs 295 (qv).
Glühwurmchen	Infra-red homing device for air defence missiles under development by Rheinmetall-Borsig.
Goldammer	Anti-jamming circuitry for attachment to radar sets to defeat 'Window' jamming.
Goldbutt	Small peroxide turbine torpedo for use by midget submarines.
Goldfisch	Small peroxide-turbine torpedo for use by midget submarines.
Goliath	A remote-controlled small tracked vehicle carrying a charge

of 75kg of TNT and originally driven by two batteries. Controlled electrically via a cable which it paid out behind it, the device was driven up to an obstacle, or pillbox and there detonated. It had limited range and power and was replaced by a version using a small Zundapp petrol engine, which improved matters.

Grasmücke	Radar homing head for unspecified missile.
Greif	Heinkel 177 heavy bomber.
Greifswalde	FM radio control transmitter for missile guidance systems, to work with the *Colberg* receiver.
GT-1200	Anti-ship missile by Henschel.
Hagelkorn	Alternative name for Bv 246.
Hai	One-man midget submarine.
Hamburg	(1) Infra-red homing head for use with the Bv 143 flying torpedo.
	(2) Name applied in some Luftwaffe reports to the Allied 'Window' jamming measure, because of its initial use in a raid on Hamburg.
Hamburg B	A proposed air defence missile with infra-red homing.
Hammer	Short-range anti-tank gun under development by Rheinmetall-Borsig as the war ended. It used a smooth-bore barrel and the projectile had a pear-shaped tail boom with fins. The interface between the tail boom and the gun barrel formed a venturi through which the propellant gases flowed and drove the projectile from the bore in the manner of a rocket. Also called *Panzertodt*.
Hansa	Infra-red homing device for missiles.
Harfe	Upward firing battery of 20mm gun barrels similar to *Bombersage* (qv). It never got past the design stage.
Hawaii	Developed from the *HV-Gerät* (qv) in 1944, a radio beam-rider missile guidance system. *Hawaii 1* used VHF radio and controlled in one dimension only, for use by ground stations; *Hawaii 2* used UHF radio and controlled in two planes, for use by airborne controllers. It never passed the design stage.
Hecht	This name appears in connection with three entirely different devices, none of which appear to have got beyond the project stage:
	(1) An anti-aircraft free rocket project.
	(2) A propulsion unit for a rocket-boosted glide bomb.
	(3) A midget U-Boat carrying one torpedo under the keel.
HeP 1077	Factory designator for *Julia* (qv).
Hohentwiel	An air-to-surface radar for the detection of ships. It was intended to mount it in bombers to aid night attacks but it had not passed its development trials when the war ended.
Hs 117	Henschel anti-aircraft missile, also called *Schmetterling*.
Hs 293	Heschel rocket-boosted glide bomb.

Hs 294	Henschel controlled glide bomb.
Hs 295	Henschel gliding torpedo air-to-sea missile.
Hs 296	Henschel armour-piercing guided glide bomb.
Hs 297	Henschel factory name for *FZG 76*.
Hs 298	Henschel air-to-air missile.
HV-Gerät	Radio beam riding guidance system proposed for air defence missiles and later for the A4 rocket, A conical-scan radar was pointed at the target and the missile measured its deviation from the centre of the beam and corrected itself to fly in constant alignment with the beam axis. Development was stopped in 1941, to be revived later as *Hawaii* (qv).
Igel	Infra-red homing head for unspecified missile.
Ingolin	Name used by the Walter company for concentrated hydrogen peroxide used as a rocket fuel.
Isegrimm	An electromagnetic proximity fuse developed by the Ernst Orlich Institute of Danzig. Relied on the inductive effect of the target to produce the proximity reaction. The project ran into difficulties and was later abandoned because the earth's magnetic field interfered with operation.
Jagdschloss	A tactical control radar set used in anti-aircraft divisional headquarters, having a range of 120km. Fifty of these sets were in use by 1945.
Jägerfaust	Vertical-firing recoilless gun battery. When the war ended 12 Me 163 jet fighters fitted with *Jägerfaust* were ready for use at Brandeis airfield near Leipzig but were grounded due to lack of fuel.
Julia	Heinkel project for a piloted rocket-propelled aircraft similar in concept to *Natter*.
Kai	A command guidance radio transmitter similar to *Kehl* but in the decimetric wavelength. Used in conjunction with *Brigg* or *Fregatte* receivers.
Kakadu	Radio proximity fuze developed by Donaulandische GmbH of Vienna. 3,000 are said to have been made for the Hs 293 missile and they performed well, relying upon the Doppler effect of the signal reflected from the target.
Kampf	Rheinmetall anti-aircraft missile project. Little known, since it started in November 1944 and was abandoned in February 1945.
Karussel	An infra-red homing head for use with *Wasserfall*, under development in 1945.
Kassel	A remote-controlled fire control radar for anti-aircraft guns, mechanically similar to *Ansbach* but operating in the 25m band. It was planned but was abandoned in 1943 when centimetric radar became possible.
Kater Gerät	A hand-held infra-red detector for front-line troops to warn them of observation by infra-red devices. It was widely issued in 1939–40 but fell into disuse because no Allied troops were

	using infra-red devices at that time.
Katzenauge	Another infra-red detector for ground troops, much the same as *Kater Gerät*.
K-Butt	Peroxide-turbine torpedo, 45 knots, 3.3km range; 60 produced for use by midget submarines.
Kehl	Radio command guidance transmitter for missile control, used with the *Strassburg* receiver.
Kerze	Optical tracking device for air defence missiles.
Kirschkern	Code name given to the *FZG 76* flying bomb during its development.
K-Laus	Sometimes called Klaus; an anti-jamming attachment for radar sets to defeat Allied 'Window' jamming. It was based on band-pass filtering of the Doppler shift frequencies so as to admit only signals between 200 and 700 cycles. About 50 were in place by early 1945, and it was probably the most effective of the many anti-jamming devices.
Klippfisch	Peroxide-engined torpedo, tested in 1942.
Knickebein	Guidance device used to assist navigation of bomber aircraft attacking England. Two radio beams were directed from stations on the continent so as to intersect over the target area. The aircraft would find one beam and then follow it to the intersection and then release their bombs. The system was open to electronic jamming, which was duly performed by the British, after which the system was abandoned.
Knüppel	Optical tracker used with the *Burgund* system of missile control.
Kogge	Radio command guidance transmitter used in conjunction with the *Brigg* receiver and operating in the decimetric wavelength to reduce the possibility of detection and jamming. In prototype stage at the war's end.
Kolberg	Radio receiver for a proposed missile guidance system for *Fritz-X* and Hs 293. Developed by Lorenz, it only appeared in prototype form.
Korfu	An anti-aircraft gun control radar.
Kormoran	An infra-red early-warning detector for anti-aircraft defence. Its development was dropped in favour of *Flamingo*.
Kottbus	An infra-red homing device for missiles.
Kran	A guidance transmitter to be used on the X-4 missile in conjunction with the *Walzenbrigg* receiver.
Kranich	An acoustic fuze developed by Ruhrstahl AG of Brackwede. Probably the best of all German proximity fuze designs.
Krebs	Infra-red missile guidance system under development by AEG in 1945.
Kreuzotter	Type T 3e torpedo; 20knots, 8km range, used by *Molch* and *Seehund* midget submarines.
Krummlauf	A curved barrel attachment for rifles or sub-machine guns to

permit firing out of the side ports of a tank or armoured personnel carrier at troops close to the vehicle, or for firing around corners. The curved extension was drilled with holes to bleed off some of the propellant gas and reduce the velocity during the change of direction.

Kugelblitz — (1) A radio proximity fuze for the *Rheintochter* missile, developed by Patent Verwertungs Gesellschaft of Salzburg. It worked on the Doppler shift principle.

Kuhglocke — Electrostatic proximity fuze developed by Rheinmetall-Borsig, It utilised the electrostatic charge on an aircraft arising from the ionised exhaust gases. Intended for use in air defence missiles it never got beyond the prototype stage.

Kuhglockchen — As the name suggests, a smaller version of *Kuhglocke* for use in anti-aircraft gun shells. This appears to be the only German proximity fuze design for use with conventional artillery, but it never got off the drawing board.

Kulmbach — An illuminating and tactical control radar set with Plan Position Indicator, used in the *Egerland* system to survey an area and then to 'put on' the gun control radar when a target was found. Operational in Berlin in early 1945, only two were made.

Kurier — A high-speed 'squirt' transmitting system used by U-Boats for communication with their home bases. The apparatus consisted of a number of dials which could be set with basic information such as identification number, latitude, longitude, time and other information. Once communication was established the Kurier was switched on and all the pre-set information was sent at very high speed in a burst of pulses. The dual object was to make the transmission difficult to decipher and also to expose the U-Boat to radio direction-finding for as short a time as possible.

Kurmark — A radio transmitter operating in the radar frequencies and sending out nothing but imitation radar signals in order to mislead Allied jamming devices. It had been designed as an anti-aircraft gun control radar but the arrival of centimetric radar made it obsolete before it could be issued, and the transmitter unit was converted into this anti-jamming role.

Kurt — Spherical, rocket-boosted aircraft bomb broadly copied from the British bomb used against the Ruhr dams.

Kurzzeitsperre — Rocket and cable barrage for the defence of airfields.

Lerche — Guidance system for torpedoes which could be operator controlled or switched to a passive homing system. Still in the experimental stage when the war ended.

Licht — Radio command guidance system for unspecified missile.

Lichtenstein — An airborne radar for night fighters; the first successful German set of this type, it entered service in August 1943.

Linse — (1) Infra-red homing device for missiles.

	(2) A remote-controlled motor-boat carrying a 400kg explosive demolition charge.
Lohengrin	Radio command guidance system for use with Hs 117 missile. It used optical tracking of both target and missile and radio commands by means of a *Kogge-Brigg* radio link.
Lotte	Infra-red proximity fuze for an unspecified missile which was abandoned when it proved impossible to develop a seeker cell sensitive enough to give the desired proximity range.
LT 1000	Luft-Torpedo (air dropped), peroxide-turbine propulsion; 50 knots, 5.5km range.
LT 1500	Luft-Torpedo (air-dropped), jet propulsion;. 40 knots, 2.2km range.
Lübeck	One of a series of metric-wavelength radar sets proposed for anti-aircraft fire control, development of which was abandoned in 1943 in favour of centimetric wavelength radars.
Luchs	Acoustic homing device for an unspecified air defence missile.
LUT	A variation of *FAT* (qv), a random steering device for torpedoes which had more variations in pattern than did *FAT*, but was only coming into service as the war ended.
M-5	Oxygen-piston-engined torpedo; 40 knots, 26km range, large warhead.
Madrid	Infra-red homing head for the *Enzian* missile, developed by Kepka of Vienna.
Mainz ·	Anti-aircraft fire control radar intended as a replacement for *Wurzburg D*, but which proved to be particularly susceptible to jamming. Production was stopped after about 40 had been made.
Malsi	A data conversion set for anti-aircraft batteries which allowed target data derived in one location to be transmitted to another battery up to 5km distant, and be automatically converted to gun data applicable to the new location. This allowed a battery which was jammed to receive data from a nearby battery with a radar on a different frequency which was not jammed.
Mannheim	An anti-aircraft fire control radar, development of which began in 1940 but was shelved by the 'one-year ban'. It was later revived and the first set tested in January 1942. Issues for service began early in 1943.
Mannheim Riese	A combination of elements from the *Wurzburg* and *Mannheim* radar sets, characterised by the enormous antenna required in order to develop a fine beam to be used for controlling the *Wasserfall* missile. Only four were made.
Marabu	(1) Radio proximity fuze for Hs 117, Hs 298, *Rheintochter* and *Wasserfall* missiles. Developed by Siemens-Halske under sub-contract from Rheinmetall-Borsig, it was to have a 40m

operating range, but it never got as far as firing trials.

(2) Alternative name used by the German Navy for *Seehund*.

Marbach	A gun control radar for anti-aircraft defence. A part of the *Egerland* system, it was 'put on' to its target by the *Kulmbach* radar set and then tracked the target while relaying pointing data to the guns.
Marder	(1) A radio proximity fuze development by the Ernst Orlich Institute of Danzig. A ground radio sent a signal which was reflected off the target and picked up by a ground receiver which then triggered a second transmitter to send a signal to the fuze to detonate it. It probably seemed like a good idea at the time…
	(2) A piloted torpedo capable of complete submersion for short distances.
Marga	This appears to have been a project for a recoilless grenade launcher which had a brief life around July/August 1944 before being abandoned.
Matter	An explosive 7.92mm rifle bullet for observation and target marking under development in 1945 by Polte of Magdeburg.
Max	Rheinmetall-Borsig anti-ship missile project cancelled in 1941.
Maximilian	Radar homing device for missiles, developed by Blaupunkt. Three version existed: *Max A* was an active homer with its own transmitter and receiver; *Max B* was a passive homer responding to the radar emissions from Allied bombers, and *Maximilian* was a passive homer which detected the reflections of the radar which was tracking the target. None ever reached production.
Meise	Acoustic proximity fuze developed by Neumann & Borm, Berlin, and using a resonant microphone to pick up the noise of the aircraft propeller.
Messina	Radio transponder for use in missile guidance systems.
Mimose	Infra-red homing device for missiles.
Mistel	Guided Ju 88 bomber filled with explosive and controlled by another aircraft as a flying bomb.
Molch	A one-man U-Boat carrying two torpedoes.
Mondfisch	Coast defence (land-based) torpedo using a peroxide jet propulsion system.
Moritz	A semi-active radar homing device for *Enzian* missiles. A continuous-wave transmitter on the ground 'illuminated' the target, and the reflected signal was picked up by the missile. The Doppler shift frequency was used to determine the range and direction of the target, and the missile then steered itself towards it. It proved, however, that there was a strong likelihood of *Moritz* homing in on the transmitter rather than the target, and development was abandoned.
Mosaik	A radio signal system relying on the use of very short

scrambled groups of pulses for jam-proof control of missiles. The intention was that only the correct circuitry in the missile's receiver would be able to translate the signals into commands and the random application of jamming would be ignored. The project was under development from 1943 to 1945 without much success, though a similar system was later used by the US Army to control its Corporal missile.

Mosel
An infra-red target detector used for coast-watching and direction of coast artillery gunfire. Tests showed that this particular design was unsuited to this application and the equipment was withdrawn and scrapped.

Möwe
Guided air defence rocket for ships; abandoned in 1944.

Mücke
An infra-red airborne telescope for warning of infra-red observation by the enemy and also for the detection of aircraft by night. In experimental stages only.

Münchausen
A 54cm recoilless airborne gun, similar to *Gerät 104* (qv).

Myrol
A solution of methyl nitrate in methanol and other solvents, used as a liquid explosive or as a component of other explosives, and proposed for use as a rocket fuel. Extremely sensitive, it appears to have been the subject of much experimental work but saw very little practical application.

Natter
Piloted, rocket-propelled fighter aircraft.

Naxos
Airborne receiver which homed on to British H2S radar emissions from aircraft.

Neger
A one-man piloted torpedo carrier.

Netzhaut
Infra-red homing device for missiles.

Nipolit
A solid propellant explosive based on diethyline glycol dinitrate (DEGDN) which is relatively inert and has considerable mechanical strength, allowing it to be shaped and formed into, for example, hand grenades which did not require any metal casing.

Nürnberg
Anti-jamming circuitry for addition to various types of radar set to overcome electronic jamming.

Nusskracker
A free-rocket development for air defence, of which only fragmentary mentions have been discovered.

Oberon
A sighting and fire control system under development by Rheinmetall-Borsig and Askaniawerke, for use with the various upward-firing gun batteries proposed for use by fighter aircraft.

Obi
An infra-red searchlight control device. By detecting bomber exhausts it was hoped to be able to align the searchlight before switching it on, but its detection ability never reached the required standards of range and accuracy, and it was dropped in favour of radar control in 1943.

Ofen
An infra-red survey and mapping equipment carried in an aircraft. It was hoped that this would enable mapping and navigation to be done at night, relying upon the heat

emission from houses, factories and vehicles, but it had barely reached the development stage by the end of the war. Another ancestor of today's thermal imaging.

Ofenröhr
Soldiers' name for the 8.8cm anti-tank rocket launcher copied from the American Bazooka. Officially called *Panzerschreck*.

Orchestra
An automatic electronic coordinate and data converter for anti-aircraft batteries. Similar to *Malsi* but electronic instead of hand-operated, it would convert data from one site to up to eight other sites up to 10km away. The only installation known was in the air defences of Stettin.

Ortler
Radio transponder for missile command systems, under development by Medek und Schörner GmbH.

Ostmark
Proposed design of centimetric radar set for the control of light anti-aircraft guns. Development was abandoned in favour of *Rettin* (qv).

Panzerblitz
Air-to-ground rocket under development by Deutsche Waffen & Munitionswerke in 1945, to be used by Hs 132 jet aircraft against tanks.

Panzertodt
Alternative name for *Hammer* (qv).

Papagei
Radio command guidance system for unspecified missile.

Paplitz
An infra-red proximity fuze for a variety of missiles, including Wasserfall and Hs 117. It was developed by the Elektro-Akoustik Institute (ELAK) at Namslau and then at Kiel and also known as 'ElKu'. It operated by detecting the heat emission from aircraft engines and exhausts. Flight tests in March 1945 proved that it worked, but it could only be used at night because of interference from solar radiation in daylight, and thus it was never put into production.

Parsifal
A radio command guidance system for Hs 117 using optical target and missile tracking with radio commands by a *Kehl-Colmar* link.

Peter-X
A guided glide bomb under development by Ruhrstahl but which appears to have been abandoned in late 1944.

Pfau
An acoustic homing head for torpedoes, capable of detecting and homing on to the noise of ship propellers. It was produced in small numbers and appears to have been used with some success in the final months of the war.

Pfiefenkopf
Anti-tank guided missile using television guidance under development in 1945.

Pfeil
Dornier 335 twin-engined fighter.

Pillenwerfer
Alternative name for *Bold* (qv).

Pinscher
Radio proximity fuze for use on missiles or bombs, developed by the Ernst Orlich Institut of Danzig. It used separate receiving and transmitting elements and relied upon the strength of the reflected signal to trigger the firing circuit. One model was made in October 1944 by the

Reichsrundfunk GmbH of Poznan and four more in November, after which no more were made. A simpler model, *Pinscher D*, was proposed but not made.

Pinsel	Alternative name for *Pfiefenkopf*.
PiO	Another name for *Zossen* (qv).
Pirat	Glide bomb reportedly under development in 1945 by Rheinmetall-Borsig.
Pistole	A photo-electric proximity fuze for missiles, using a light source in the missile which was reflected back from the target to trigger the fuze. This project gradually merged into that for *Wassermaus* (qv) and *Pistole* eventually died.
Potsdam Gerät	A copy of the British Sten Gun, down to the British proof and inspection marks. They were intended for use by 'stay-behind' parties of guerrillas, 'Werewolves' and other patriotic bands expected to resist Allied occupation of Germany. About 25,000 were made by Mauserwerke in late 1944 and early 1945. Without metallurgic examination it is impossible to distinguish these weapons from the British-made article.
Potsdam L	An infra-red thermionic camera used in an airborne interception device. Although only in the experimental stage it proved very successful, but it was too late to be further developed before the war ended.
Pudel	An acoustic homing head for a modified version of X-4. Eight were made but flight tests had not been completed when the war ended. The effective detection range was expected to be in the region of one kilometre.
Püppchen	Small wheeled anti-tank gun firing the 8.8cm rocket used with *Panzerschreck*.
R4M	Air-to-air free rocket for use by Me 262 jet fighters, *Natter* and similar air interceptors.
Radieschen	A radio homing device for the FX 1400 guided bomb.
Rastatt	A proposed metric wavelength radar for anti-aircraft gun control, abandoned in favour of a centimetric design in 1943.
Reichenberg	Piloted V-1 missile project.
Reise-Gustav	Anti-jamming equipment installed in *Wurzburg-Reise* radar sets to combat 'Window' jamming.
Reiss-Laus	Anti-jamming equipment for installation in anti-aircraft fire control radar sets to overcome 'Window' jamming.
Rettin	A centimetric waveband fire control radar set for light anti-aircraft guns. Only one experimental model was made, and tests were never completed.
Rheinbote	Long range surface-to-surface multi-stage free-flight rocket for artillery use. Some 200 were fired against Antwerp in 1945.
Rheingau	A proposed metre-band fire control radar, abandoned in favour of a centimetric design in 1943.

Rheingold	A control unit for the *Wasserfall* missile forming part of the *Elsass* control system. It consisted of a radio guidance transmitter combined with a *Wurzburg* radar set for tracking the missile in flight. It also worked with the *Rüse* transponder to measure the roll attitude of the missile in flight.
Rheinland	Radio command guidance system for missiles.
Rheintochter	Rheinmetall-Borsig ground-to-air missile.
Rotterdam	The German name for the British H2S centimetric radar set, so-called because the first such set to fall into their hands came from a British bomber which crashed near Rotterdam in January 1943.
Rotkäppchen	Wire-guided anti-tank missile under development by Ruhrstahl.
Roulette	An infra-red proximity fuze under development by Brinckmann of Gera; the idea was dropped in 1944 in favour of more promising designs.
RSK 1000	Alternative title for *Kurzzeitsperre* (qv).
Rüse	Name derived from *Rück-sender* – 'return transmitter' – this was a transponder device for use in tracking missiles by emitting a distinctive signal when interrogated from the ground.
Salamander	Heinkel 162 jet fighter.
Salbei	Mixture of nitric acid and 5%–10% sulphuric acid, used as the oxygen carrier with *Tonka* (qv) as a rocket fuel.
Sammellinse	An infra-red navigation device for bombers. By using the heat emissions from the ground it would display a map on a cathode-ray tube. In development stage only.
Sarin	Nerve gas now generally known as GB.
Sauerkirsche	Radio command guidance system for missiles.
Schliebelaus	Anti-jamming equipment for anti-aircraft fire control radars to counter electronic jamming. Development stage only.
Schlitten	Remote-controlled hydroplane carrying a demolition charge.
Schnee-Orgel	A battery of torpedo tubes to be fitted to late-model U-Boats and capable of firing salvoes with a ten-degree spread.
Schnee-Wittchen	Blohm & Voss LT 11 glide torpedo.
Schwalbe	An infra-red target detector for naval use. Marginally successful and used in small numbers.
Seedorf	A television receiver used by the controller of a guided glide bomb. It was used with *Tonne* in controlling the Hs 293 missile, giving the operator a view of the target as seen by the approaching missile The screen measured 57mm x 82mm and had a 224-line scan.
Schildbutt	Peroxide-turbine torpedo; 45 knots, 15km range.
Schornsteinfeger	A radar camouflage material, consisting of a thick bituminous paint heavily loaded with carbon. When applied in thickness carefully calculated in relation to the radar

frequency the arriving signal would be trapped within the dielectric material and its return energy damped out. An early attempt at 'stealth' technology.

Seehund (1) An infra-red telescope for naval use. It had two roles, firstly signalling, where the sender used in infra-red lamp, and secondly for U-Boat use for detecting Allied aircraft using infra-red searchlights, which the German navy thought were in use for detecting U-Boats by night. Developed early in the war and in use by 1941.

(2) A midget U-Boat crewed by two men and carrying two torpedoes.

Seetakt Naval search radar for shipboard use developed by the Gema company in 1936 and installed in various warships by 1939.

Sieglinde An acoustic detection device for air defence, essentially the old- fashioned sound locator modernised. Under development late in 1944 as a possible back-up device to radar in the face of Allied electronic jamming.

Soman The third of the original nerve gases, discovered in 1944.

Sonne Proposed missile guidance system in which a radio in the missile interrogated two or more ground transmitters in order to fix its position.

Spanner A name used to cover a number of infra-red developments. *Spanner* proper was an airborne intercept equipment; a small number was made but it was not used after 1942. The name was then applied to a driver's vision monocular for driving vehicles in the dark, using infra-red guide lamps on the roadside. This became known as *Spanner FG-1250*. A third model, *Spanner FG-1221* was then developed, this being a periscope viewer for tanks equipped with an infra-red driving light called *Uhu*.

Spatz An infra-red coast-watching equipment for detecting ships at night by funnel radiation. One development model was built and tested but the idea was then abandoned in favour of radar.

Sperre An infra-red warning device used to detect Allied infra-red driving lights or searchlights.

Spinne Wire-guided torpedo fired from land installations for coastal defence. It ran at 30 knots and had a range of 3.2km.

Springbok A pilotless aircraft produced for use as a target during the development of various air defence missiles.

Sprotte A television camera for use in air defence missile guidance and developed by Fernseh GmbH. It was never tested.

Steinbarsch Peroxide-turbine torpedo; 50 knots, 7km range, 100 produced for service.

Steinbock Anti-tank guided missile with infra-red homing, generally similar to *Pinsel*. Never got beyond the design stage.

Steinbutt Peroxide-turbine engined torpedo; 45 knots, 8.7km range, 100

	produced for service.
Steinfisch	Peroxide-turbine engined torpedo; design cancelled, replaced by *Steinbutt*.
Steinwal	Peroxide-turbine long range torpedo; 45 knots, 24km range. Development not completed.
Stendal	An anti-jamming apparatus for attachment to *Wurzburg* radars, developed by Telefunken in April 1942,
Stilpyramid	A radar homing unit intended for use in glide bombs or missiles. It would lock on the radio or radar emissions from Allied aircraft and direct the missile to the aircraft. It was still under development when the war ended.
Stimmgabel	An acoustic proximity fuze, similar to *Kranich*, but for use in a parachute-retarded bomb to be dropped into bomber formations from high-altitude defenders. Under development by the Graf Zeppelin Research Institute, field tests had been made which proved the principle but there were no plans for production.
Stör	Optical target seeker for unspecified missile.
Strahlungsperre	Another infra-red coast watching apparatus, produced early in the war for harbour defence. It was abandoned in 1942 as the small angle of view meant poor coverage of the target area unless an uneconomical number of devices was deployed.
Strassburg	An 18-channel super-heterodyne radio receiver used in the *Strassburg-Kehl* command guidance link for FX 1400, Hs 293 and other projects.
Strassfurt	Radio guidance system under development by Rundfunk AG, to be used in the *Enzian* missile.
Stuttgart	Radio telemetry system used with *Feuerlilie 55* rocket.
SV-Stoff	Mixture of nitric acid and nitrogen dioxide, more commonly called Red Fuming Nitric Acid (RFNA), used in rocket fuels.
Tabun	Nerve gas, now generally known as GA. The original nerve gas, discovered in 1936.
Taifun	Free-flight air defence rocket.
Tastlaus	Anti-jamming attachment for fire control radars to defeat electronic jamming. Introduce in November 1944 to replace *Wurzlaus*.
Taunus	Anti-jamming attachment for fire control radars to defeat 'Window' jamming.
Tetan	Tetranitromethane; a liquid waste product of the manufacture of TNT, used as a component of various experimental explosives developed after 1943 in order to compensate for shortages of raw materials for conventional explosives. Also called *X-Stoff*.
Tonka	Mixture of aniline, monoethylaniline, dimethylaniline. gasoline, naphtha, triethylamine and isohexylamine, used in conjunction with nitric acid as a rocket fuel. There were a

number of slightly differing formulae, identified as *Tonka 93*, *Tonka 250* etc.

Tonne — A television target-seeking camera used on Hs 293 glide bombs. Developed by Blaupunkt; 1000 ordered in 1944, but later cancelled and the project abandoned.

Tornado — (1) A free-flight air defence rocket.

(2) A demolition boat built up from the floats of a Junkers 52 seaplane and the motor from an *FZG 76* missile, and carrying a 700kg explosive charge.

Traute — Acoustic homing head for unspecified missile.

Trichter — Radio proximity fuze for air-to-air blast bombs to be dropped into Allied bomber formations. Under development by Blaupunkt from August 1944, one laboratory model had been field tested.

T-Stoff — Concentrated hydrogen peroxide. Used as an oxygen carrier in various rocket fuels, and, reacting with sodium permanganate, as a steam generator for the turbine pumps in the V-2 missile and for torpedo engines.

Uhu — An infra-red driving light developed for use on tanks and other vehicles, used in conjunction with *Spanner FG-1221*.

Urechse — A multi-band tuning attachment for fire control radars, to allow rapid changes of frequency and thus outwit electronic jamming. Installation began late in 1944 and about 50 sets had been equipped by the end of the war.

Vampir — An infra-red driving aid, similar to *Spanner*, using a detector scope to pick out infra-red guide lamps at the roadside. In this role it became *Vampir FG-1229*. Later the optics were adapted for use as a rifle night sight as *Vampir ZG-1229*.

Vesuv — Acoustic homing head for unspecified missile.

Victoria — Radio command guidance system for unspecified missile.

Visol — General name for rocket fuels made from vinylethyl ether mixed with aniline or alcohol, and hypergolic (self-igniting) when put in contact with nitric acid.

Volksjäger — Popular name for the He 162 *Salamander* fighter.

Walter — An infra-red viewing device made by Leitz of Wetzlar, using an f/0.8 lens of 75mm focal length, quite an achievement for 1939.

Walzenbrigg — Radio command guidance receiver intended for the X-4 air-to-air missile. It was small enough to fit into the wing-tip pods in place of the spools used for the wire-guided version.

Wärmebold — An infra-red emitter intended to give out a swamping signal so that enemy detection devices would be unable to pick out individual targets because of an overall floodlighting effect. It did not prove successful.

Wasseresel — A dummy U-Boat conning tower packed with explosives and mounted on a float.

Wasserfall	Radio-controlled, supersonic, guided air defence missile.
Wassermann	A early warning radar set for anti-aircraft fire command.
Wassermaus	An active photo-electric proximity fuze proposed for the *Wasserfall* missile, this consisted of a transmitter emitting flashes of light and a photo-electric receiver which measured the intensity of the reflected flashes and triggered the fuze when this reached a pre-set level.
Wespe	An 'Identification, Friend or Foe' (IFF) transponder to be carried in aircraft or missiles. When interrogated by a ground radar the *Wespe* would transmit a signal which would modify the image on the radar screen and positively identify the signal as being friendly.
Widder	Infra-red homing head for unspecified missile, under development by AEG in 1945.
Wiesel	Radio proximity fuze for missiles or air-to-air bombs under development by the Ernst Orlich Institut of Danzig. Used a very recondite system of detection (the *Huth-Kuhn* oscillator) which most authorities consider was unlikely ever to have worked.
Windhund	A radar homing device working in the 3cm band and intended to home missiles on to Allied aircraft by locking on to their radar signals. It was to be used with supersonic missiles in order to cater for the case where the Allied operator switched off his radar when he detected a missile approaching. Under development but never reached the stage of a working model.
Wischer	Radio command guidance system for unspecified missile.
Wismar	Anti-jamming equipment for fire control radars to counter electronic jamming.
Wurzburg	An early warning and fire control radar set. One of the first German designs it began development by Telefunken in 1936. There were several variant models:
Wurzburg A	In production April 1940; 200 made.
Wurzburg B	Adaptation of an experimental infra-red equipment to a *Wurzburg A* radar as a possible counter to 'Window' jamming for daylight fire control. Was unable to penetrate heavy cloud and was abandoned.
Wurzburg C	Development began February 1940; used lobe-switching to determine target height. Production began in 1940 and 1,000 were made.
Wurzburg D	A *Wurzburg C* modified to provide more accurate range measurement. Produced from August 1941 and became the standard AA fire control set, over 2,500 being operational in April 1945.
Wurzburg-Riese	A standard *Wurzburg D* improved by the use of a much larger antenna array. Originally for the ground control of fighter aircraft it was later adopted for anti-aircraft fire control and

for the control of air defence missiles.

Wurzburg-Riese-G	*Wurzburg Riese* radar set improved by the addition of a *Freya* set as an aid for setting-on to specific targets and to assist range determination during jamming.
Wurzlaus	An anti-jamming modification to all *Wurzburg* radars to counter 'Window' jamming, installed during July and August 1943.
X-4	Wire guided air-to-air missile.
X-7	Wire-guided anti-tank missile.
X-Stoff	Another name for *Tetran* (qv).
Zaunbutt	Peroxide-turbine torpedo with homing head.
Zaunkönig	Acoustic homing head for torpedoes. The name was also applied to the T 5 torpedo (25 knots, 6.2km range) which used this head exclusively.
Zaunkönig 2	Improved version of the T 5 torpedo, similar performance.
Zirkel	A beam-riding guidance system for missiles which in addition to guiding the missile also measured distance and velocity in order to compute and execute its own combustion shut-off signal. Individual components of this system had been tested, but the system as a whole was never built.
Zitterrochen	Henschel missile model with delta wings, developed for wind tunnel experiments into supersonic flight.
Zossen	A fire control system containing a photo-electric cell and a light source, controlling an upward-firing gun battery in a fighter aircraft. Developed by AEG at Neustadt, it was first tested in mid-1944 and further development was still in progress when the war ended.
Z-Salz	Name given to calcium or sodium permanganates used as oxidising components of rocket propellants in which *T-Stoff* (qv) was the combustible component.
Z-Stoff	Aqueous solution of calcium permanganate (*Z-Stoff C*) or sodium permanganate (*Z-Stoff K*) used as an catalyst in rocket fuels to assist the decomposition of hydrogen peroxide.
Zunder-19	A proximity bomb fuze for the 250kg aerial bomb, to give a burst height of 25 to 30 metres above the ground. Under development by Rheinmetall-Borsig from 1937 onwards, the contract was cancelled in 1943 but the company continued working on it until 1944 before finally giving it up.

Index

Case Selection in the United States Supreme Court

Doris Marie Provine

Case Selection

in the United States Supreme Court

The University of Chicago Press
Chicago and London

The University of Chicago Press, Chicago 60637
The University of Chicago Press, Ltd., London

Library of Congress Cataloging in Publication Data

Provine, Doris Marie.
    Case selection in the United States Supreme Court.

    Includes bibliographical references and index.
    1. United States. Supreme Court.   2. Judicial
review—United States.   3. Judicial process—United
States.   I. Title.
KF8742.P76   347′.73′263   79-25967
ISBN   0-226-68468-7

DORIS MARIE PROVINE is assistant professor of
political science, Maxwell School of Citizenship
and Public Affairs, Syracuse University.

To my parents   Charles Richard
and Edith Koegle Long

Contents

Acknowledgments

Many persons were generous and supportive as I worked on this book, but I am especially grateful for the assistance of David Danelski, who was helpful at every stage of research, from first inspiration to final product. I also appreciate the considerable efforts of Roger Cramton, Peter Katzenstein, Theodore Lowi, and Lawrence Baum, all of whom read my work and offered careful and detailed suggestions for revision. William Provine was also an important contributor, providing intellectual, financial, and emotional support throughout the project. I owe these kind and generous men a substantial scholarly debt.

Others have also made the task of research and writing much easier. Michael Barkun, a colleague, and Allen Snyder, a former clerk for Justices Harlan and Rehnquist, each read the completed manuscript and gave me their suggestions, which I have incorporated. S. Sidney Ulmer kept me up to date with his frequent articles concerning case selection. I have benefited from his writings and his friendly advice. Finally, I am grateful for the assistance of a number of librarians. The staffs of the Cornell Law Library, the Bentley Historical Library of the University of Michigan, and the Manuscript Division of the Library of Congress provided me friendly, useful, and frequently time-consuming assistance, for which I am very grateful.

Bob Woodward and Scott Armstrong's *The Brethren* appeared when this book was in page proofs. Consequently, I was unable to incorporate references to it.

Introduction

We have no more right to decline the exercise of jurisdiction which is given than to usurp that which is not given. The one or the other would be treason to the constitution.
John Marshall (1821)

The responsibility of the Supreme Court to undertake decision in cases satisfying jurisdictional requirements has changed dramatically since John Marshall was chief justice. The Judiciary Act of 1925, which remains in effect, put the question of review almost entirely within the discretion of the Supreme Court.[1] With that law, most cases became reviewable only by the discretionary writ of certiorari. The Court retains some formally obligatory jurisdiction, but even this small proportion of its work has taken on discretionary characteristics as the caseload has grown increasingly burdensome.[2] The typical issue the Supreme Court faces now is not whether the Court has jurisdiction to decide but whether it will choose to decide a case on the merits.

The decision to decide has become more and more crucial because the capacity of the Court to hear and resolve cases has not kept pace with the increasing volume of petitions. The Court currently turns down more than 90 percent of the petitions which fulfill jurisdictional requirements.[3] This amounts to about three thousand five hundred refusals to review each term. While the Court claims that case selection is not decision on the merits, the denial of review is the end of the road for most petitioners on the issues raised. The case-selection process, therefore, has immense practical importance for litigants.

Case selection in a period of crowded dockets also has practical importance for the Court. Discretionary case selection permits the Court to decide for itself the degree to

1

which it will become involved in confrontations among the various branches and levels of government. Similarly, case selection provides the justices with the opportunity to decide whether cases brought by the government or those brought against it will most often be resolved on the merits. Case selection thus permits Supreme Court justices to determine the relationship of the Court to the other branches of the national government and to the state and local governments.

The press of cases before the Supreme Court also allows it to explore a broad range of subject matter. The Court can either sample quite evenly from the array of cases brought to it, or it can establish criteria which will provide easier access to adjudication for some groups in our society than for others. In short, because of its broad discretion to set its own agenda, the Court is no longer the passive institution "with neither force nor will but merely judgment" described by Hamilton in *The Federalist Papers*.[4] Case selection, therefore, provides a good indication of the decision-making priorities of the Supreme Court and of the influence of groups on those priorities.

In settling upon the cases it will resolve on the merits, the Supreme Court helps shape political discourse in our society. Case selection has this effect because the decisions of the Court on the merits constitute a highly visible and much-discussed part of our political life. Litigants, of course, are well aware of the capacity of the Court to affect public attitudes. Those who seek to influence political discourse through litigation may even prize the opportunity to be heard in the Supreme Court as much as winning on the merits.

The prominence of the Supreme Court means that its case-selection decisions will either add to or detract from its public image. Although the possibility of refusing decision can protect the Court from being compelled to issue a politically damaging decision on the merits, this opportunity for sidestepping conflict must be exercised with circumspection. If the Court is popularly perceived to be ducking important issues by denying review, its reservoir of popular acceptance may suffer. Another problem raised by avoiding controversial issues is that the refusal to hear a case is often equated by the public with Supreme Court approval of the lower court's decision.

Although the almost unbounded power of the Court to select cases can lead to difficulties in controversial cases, case-selection discretion probably enhances the diffuse support enjoyed by the Supreme Court. The absence of standards helps preserve the Court's image among laypersons as an available source of relief for legal wrongs.

Despite the political significance of case selection, the standards the Court applies in deciding whether or not to take up a case on the merits are obscure. The Court's single published guide to its criteria in case selection is Rule 19 of the Supreme Court Rules.[5] This "rule," only a few sentences long, merely cites "the character of reasons which will be considered" in the review decision. Conflicts among lower courts and "important federal questions" are the principal grounds for review mentioned in Rule 19. The Court has not released any official commentary on this vague rule, and the justices have failed to give it precise meaning through interpretations in published decisions. Consequently, when the Court declines to hear a case, the only certain thing, as Justice Frankfurter often said, is that the case did not garner the four affirmative votes necessary for review.

Although some members of the Court publish dissents from denials of review, these opinions provide an uncertain gauge of the Court's thinking.[6] The publication of a dissent from a denial does not even indicate that the dissenter was the only justice to vote for review in the case. Others may vote for review but may not want to state their views publicly. As Justice Rutledge explained to his friend Justice Murphy, in declining to join him in a dissent:

> I entirely agree with your views . . . but I have not so far noted a dissent from actions on cert. I have not finally made up my own mind as to whether my inclination is to continue as I have heretofore. Hence, I reluctantly have concluded not to join formally with you, though my whole heart and mind are in accord with your views.[7]

The secrecy with which the Court shrouds case selection has important political implications. One consequence of the absence of published votes and opinions is that the justices cannot be held accountable for negative review decisions. They are not even bound by an obligation to follow precedent or any other easily understood criterion in their voting.

Secrecy in case selection also affects litigants, who differ in their capacity to deduce probable review criteria from the pattern of grants and denials and the Court's meager guidelines on review criteria. Not surprisingly, those with petitioning expertise and experience tend to benefit from the obscurity of standards for review. Since the advent of discretionary review, the federal government, represented by the Solicitor General, has been the principal beneficiary of the Court's secretive approach to case selection. The cases selected for review by the Solicitor General have always been decided on the merits much oftener than those of other petitioners.

The evidence available on how the Supreme Court decides what cases to take up on the merits is almost entirely indirect, much of it consisting of the docket books of Harold H. Burton, who sat on the Court from the 1945 through the 1957 terms. Burton used his docket books to record the vote in each case that came before the Court while he was a justice. A careful and precise man, Burton kept accurate, exhaustive records. He saved nearly every document he received as a justice, including memos from the chief justice, personal notes, and the materials his clerks provided him. In addition, Burton kept a diary, in which he recorded his daily activities. Burton deposited these materials in the library of Congress, where they are available to the public for scholarly work. No other justice has made as many Court documents public, and since the advent of discretionary review, none except Burton has released case-selection records.[8] Burton's papers are, therefore, an invaluable resource for understanding case selection in the Supreme Court.

Burton's Court records did not, however, become available until after his death in 1965. Scholarly research on case selection proceeded in the absence of these materials, some of the most frequently cited articles having been written before 1965. In their speculations about the case-selection process, these writers relied on the published record of grants and denials or on differences among justices on the merits.

Some of these authors focused on the inadequacy of Rule 19 as a description of case-selection criteria. In a series of articles on the 1949–52 terms, Fowler Harper and various coauthors analyzed the cases the Court declined to review in order to show that some had more legal significance than the cases the Court did agree to hear.[9] Others challenged Rule 19 by examining denials in specific areas of law. Jerome Hanus, working with certain criminal-procedure cases, and Stephen Earp, using sovereign-immunity petitions, each argued that case selection is sometimes used to avoid difficult issues or to make policy indirectly.[10] Chapter 2 in the analysis to follow uses case-selection memoranda and voting records to assess the willingness of the Court to use case selection to avoid difficult cases.

Joseph Tanenhaus and three coauthors used the published record of grants and denials for a somewhat different purpose.[11] These authors attempted to show how Supreme Court justices actually proceed in separating the cases they review from the much larger number they reject annually. These authors hypothesized that the heavy caseload forces the justices to rely on certain salient characteristics about petitions in making case-selection decisions. Only cases with characteristics that indicate their importance are examined with care. The authors attempted to deduce these cues from the pattern of grants and denials. Chapter 3 tests their reconstruction of the case-selection process with actual voting records.

Only one scholar has attempted to deduce individual votes in case selection without actual voting records. Glendon Schubert, in two related articles, used game theory propositions and voting patterns on the merits to speculate about how various justices voted.[12] Schubert focused on the decisions of the Court in Federal Employers' Liability Act cases, on which the justices divided sharply regarding review. He contended that some justices make their case-selection decisions to maximize their power to achieve their policy preferences on the merits. Chapter 5 uses case-selection voting data on the same cases Schubert considered in order to examine his power-centered theory of case selection.

Surprisingly, only one scholar, Sidney Ulmer, has mined the Burton materials to consider judicial motivation in case selection.[13] In a series of articles Ulmer argues that disagreement in case selection and disagreement on the merits are strongly related, both resting on attitudinal differences among the justices.[14] Lawrence Baum, using analogous voting data from the California Supreme Court, came to a similar conclusion about the interrelatedness of case-selection decisions and decisions in fully considered cases.[15] Both men suggest that judges tend to vote for review when their policy preferences conflict with decisions reached in the lower courts. Chapter 4 examines their argument for the primacy of political preferences in case selection.

The analysis in the chapters to follow supports the major premise underlying the work of all of these authors: that subjective considerations lie at the heart of case selection. My study differs from previous research, however, in hypothesizing that the justices' perceptions of a judge's role and of the Supreme Court's role in our judicial system significantly limit the range of case-selection behavior that the justices might otherwise exhibit.[16] I suggest here that a high degree of consensus exists within the Court, both about the role of the judge and about the role of the Supreme Court as the forum of last resort in our complex federal system. During the Burton period, this consensus on the role of the Court was evident from the significant percentage of unanimous votes to review in cases concerning the jurisdictional boundaries between the various layers of government and in cases brought by certain petitioners: the federal government, labor unions, and those claiming infringements of civil rights and liberties.

When the justices disagree in case selection, I will argue, they reflect differences in how they weigh the fundamental responsibilities of the Court against the circumstances of actual cases, as well as differences in how they view the merits of the claims that petitioners make for relief. The Burton materials suggest that the merits are frequently a source of disunity in case selection because Supreme Court justices differ in the extent to which they consider the lower-court outcome relevant to case selection. The justices also differ, of course, on the merits themselves. The tendency of the justices to take their perceptions of the merits into account in voting for review thus provides a double source of disagreement in case selection.

The evidence from the Burton period suggests, however, that the tendency of a justice to take the merits into account in case selection has important limits. Contrary to what Schubert thought, none of the Burton-period justices was so anxious to see his preferences for one outcome over another become law that he routinely voted in case selection to advance that objective. The justices neither combined in subgroups in case selection to "win" on the merits nor voted individually in a way that would indicate particular sensitivity to probable outcome on the merits. Shared judicial beliefs about the type of behavior appropriate to a judge appear to prevent Supreme Court justices from simply voting their policy preferences in case selection.

The importance of the judicial role as a limitation upon the expression of personal preferences is a familiar theme in fully considered cases. Judges often claim to be bound by the norm that they must act according to the law and proper procedures, not according to their feelings. The moving statement of Justice Blackmun in the landmark death-penalty case, *Furman v. Georgia,* is illustrative:

> Cases such as these provide for me an excruciating agony of the spirit. I yield to no one in the depth of my distaste, antipathy, and indeed, abhorrence, for the death penalty, with all its aspects of physical distress and fear and of moral judgment exercised by finite minds. That distaste is buttressed by a belief that capital

punishment serves no useful purpose that can be demonstrated. For me, it violates childhood's training and life's experiences, and is not compatible with the philosophical convictions I have been able to develop. It is antagonistic to any sense of "reverence for life." Were I a legislator, I would vote against the death penalty for the policy reasons argued by counsel for the respective petitioners and expressed and adopted in the several opinions filed by the Justices who vote to reverse these judgments.[17]

The analysis of case-selection voting that follows supports Blackmun's statement. A justice's conceptions of the judicial role and the Supreme Court's role appear to be key elements in his decision making. But role perceptions and preferences for one outcome over another are probably more entwined with each other than Blackmun implies. Nevertheless, it seems worthwhile to conceptualize role perceptions as an intervening variable between the policy preferences of the justices and their case-selection votes. To fail to take this mediating variable into account is to ignore a crucial dimension of judicial decision making.

One The Case-Selection Process

For decades, more requests for review have come to the United States Supreme Court than it could possibly grant. The annual influx of cases involves certiorari petitions, jurisdictional statements, briefs opposing review, bulky records of lower-court actions, and miscellaneous motions, responses, and correspondence. To maintain a feasible workload the Court must sift through these materials and reject most requests for assistance. Although the work of selecting cases has always been considerable, it has grown more burdensome in recent years as lower-court litigation and the tendency to appeal have increased. By 1975, the Court was receiving about four thousand review requests annually, more than twice as many as it recieved only two decades earlier.[1]

Although the number of requests for relief has increased markedly over time, the Court's capacity to resolve disputes has remained fairly constant. The Court seems to have the capacity to hear and decide with opinion between one hundred and two hundred cases every year.[2] The Court can also decide cases without hearing and without opinion, but even with this abbreviated consideration it can accept only a small proportion of the cases brought to it. With the growing number of petitions before the Court, the proportion of granted cases has necessarily decreased. It stands now at about 5 percent.

Congress and Case Selection

Under the Constitution, Congress has the responsibility to determine the appellate jurisdiction of the United States

Supreme Court. Congressional legislation has established two routes for full appellate review: certiorari and appeal.[3] The certiorari route, which permits the Court unfettered discretion in determining which cases deserve review, is the primary basis for case selection. Cases that come within the Court's appeals jurisdiction, on the other hand, now constitute less than 10 percent of the caseload. Technically, they must be disposed of on the merits if they fulfill jurisdictional requirements.

The Development of Discretionary Jurisdiction

Periodically throughout its history the Court has voiced complaints about its workload. Congress has usually responded with legislation directed at relieving the burden. During most of the nineteenth century, however, congressional response to workload problems was piecemeal and dilatory: Court terms were lengthened, the number of justices was increased, and circuit duties were reduced.[4]

Finally, in 1891, Congress acted forcefully to insulate the Supreme Court from the burden of appeals.[5] Congress created nine intermediate federal courts, which, with two additions, correspond to the present U.S. courts of appeal. Congress also restricted somewhat the right of appeal to the Supreme Court, making some categories of cases decided by the new courts reviewable only upon issuance of a writ of certiorari by the Supreme Court. The Court's use of the writ of certiorari is an artifact of early English law.[6] The writ historically was an order issued to an inferior body to call up the records of a case to the higher tribunal. In United States law it refers to a court's wholly discretionary decision whether or not to take up a case on the merits.

The Court did not immediately exploit the potential of discretionary jurisdiction. The justices granted only two writs between 1891 and 1893.[7] Soon, however, the Court grew more comfortable with its new power, and the grant rate for the next three decades settled at about 16 percent. At the same time, Congress continued to whittle away at the categories of cases that the Court was required to review. Despite these changes, over 80 percent of the incoming cases still tapped the Court's obligatory jurisdiction, and this burden prevented the Court from keeping current with its docket.[8] By the end of World War I, the Court had fallen more than a year behind schedule.[9]

Congress acted to remedy the situation with the Judiciary Act of 1925, which drastically reduced the Court's obligatory appellate responsibilities.[10] Congress accomplished this reduction in the workload of the Court by greatly increasing its discretionary certiorari jurisdiction. This major reformulation of the Court's appelate jurisdiction remains in effect today.

The justices themselves wrote the 1925 legislation, and a delegation from the Court, led by Chief Justice Taft, energetically lobbied in its behalf.[11] It was appropriately nicknamed the "Judges' Bill." The increased discretionary jurisdiction proposed by the justices promised to relieve the Court of the necessity of turning to Congress every time the caseload increased. Because Congress had often been insensitive in the past to the Court's problems in managing its work, the justices must have been eager for more complete independence. As Chief Justice Taft confided to a friend in 1924:

> A man cannot do all the work there is to do, and if
> Congress refuses to furnish the means by which our
> Court can keep us [abreast] we shall just have to let the
> work sag. We could do the work if Congress would give
> us an extended jurisdiction in certiorari. In that way we
> could eliminate a lot of cases that do not deserve the
> time that we have to spend on them.[12]

The justices' campaign for the Judges' Bill dwelt upon the emerging role of the Court as a forum for settling issues of general importance to the nation. The justices stressed that they could not at the same time act as a court of last resort for disappointed litigants:

> Cases ought to stop after two Federal Courts have
> passed upon them, unless they are of particular im-
> portance or unless they involve something more than
> the mere rights of the litigants and concern the public.[13]

This argument has continued to be attractive to Supreme Court justices. The belief that the Supreme Court should not function primarily as an appellate court for correcting lower court errors constitutes an important element in the modern Court's conception of itself, as will be seen more clearly later.

The extent to which Congress, when it adopted the Judges' Bill, agreed with this conception of the Court's proper role is unclear. The House of Representatives approved the proposed legislation "like an uninformed and indifferent ratifying body, manifesting no awareness that it was passing a bill involving really great changes in the disposition of federal legislation."[14] Only one senator seriously challenged the bill, which passed easily on February 13, 1925.

Soon after Congress acted, Frankfurter and Landis, the leading experts on Supreme Court jurisdictional issues, predicted that the 1925 legislation would mark the beginning of "a new chapter in the history of the federal judiciary."[15] In their view, the grant of wide discretion to select cases for decision was a needed innovation, although one that had some inherent disadvantages. One problem was the work involved in deciding what to decide:

> Petitions for certiorari will steadily increase. This means a growing absorption of the Court's time not in the adjudication of cases and the writing of opinions, but in determining whether cases should be adjudicated.[16]

This increasing number of petitions would, they predicted, eventually force Congress to revise jurisdictional boundaries again:

> The Act of February 13, 1925, will be no more permanent than was its most recent predecessor, the Circuit Courts of Appeals Act. If anything, changes in the future are likely to be more rapid than they have been in the past because the accelerated business pace of the country is reflected in the pace of the business of the courts.[17]

Although these writers were correct in their prediction of a growing caseload, they underestimated the capacity of the

Court to protect itself from falling behind in its work, for, as noted above, the 1925 Judiciary Act is still the law.

The Judiciary Act ended almost all obligatory review of U.S. Court of Appeals cases.[18] The legislation also ended the right of direct appeal to the Supreme Court for most types of U.S. District Court cases which had survived the 1891 revisions. Obligatory review of state court judgments was restricted to cases where the validity of a state statute was unsuccessfully challenged on federal constitutional grounds, or where a federal statute or treaty was declared invalid by a state court.[19] The Supreme Court was still technically obliged to take up legal questions certified by the lower courts and cases within its original jurisdiction, as specified in Article 3, Section 2, of the Constitution, but such cases have always been infrequent.[20]

Not until the 1970s did Congress again act to reduce the obligatory jurisdiction of the Supreme Court. Between 1970 and 1976 Congress eliminated a series of the remaining provisions allowing appeals to the Supreme Court directly from district courts. The justices have pressed Congress to go further and eliminate all mandatory appellate jurisdiction. The entire Court signed a letter in June 1978 suggesting that case selection should be entirely discretionary, and legislation eliminating almost all types of appeals has been introduced and will probably be adopted.[21]

The Court's interest in reducing its appeals jurisdiction is dictated by its concern over the proper handling of these cases, not by their relative numbers. Since 1925 the Court's certiorari jurisdiction has been the source of most cases reaching the Court. Usually about 90 percent of the caseload consists of certiorari cases. Most of the remainder are appeals. The Court receives only a dozen or so original-jurisdiction cases in a term. These usually concern state boundaries or resource rights. Certified questions are even rarer.[22]

The Limits of Obligatory Review

Over the years, the Court has developed its own methods for keeping its obligatory jurisdiction from taking too much decision time. Even before it published a rule on the subject, the Court refused to review appeals which were technically proper if, in the justices' view, they were without legal merit.[23] By 1928, the Court had adopted a rule outlining jurisdictional requirements, and soon the justices made this barrier to automatic review explicit. In 1936, the Court began to require appellants to file with other preliminary papers "a statement of the grounds upon which it is contended that the questions of law involved are substantial."[24] The Court thereby gave the opposing party the opportunity to move to dismiss on grounds of insubstantiality. Appellees routinely file such motions and the Court often grants them, summarily dismissing on jurisdictional grounds "for want of a substantial federal question." This has become the most frequent reason cited by the Court for dismissing the largest category of appeals, those from state courts.[25]

The substantiality requirement injects a discretionary element into the appeals process, making the obligatory appeals jurisdiction more like the wholly discretionary certiorari jurisdiction. This likeness is enhanced by similarities in the filing requirements for both types of review requests. The Court's rules prescribing the form and elements of jurisdictional statements and certiorari petitions have become very similar, the major sections paralleling each other.[26] Both types of requests are also considered at the same time by the justices and voted upon in the same way. Thus the number of votes required for noting jurisdiction in an appeal is the same as for granting certiorari. Nevertheless, the legal effects of the denial of petitions for certiorari and the dismissal of appeals are different.

The denial of certiorari is not a legal precedent. Lower courts may not rely upon a denial to indicate a Supreme Court position, and the Court feels under no obligation to defer to past denials or to explain them. Many of the justices have stated that the denial of a petition for certiorari implies no opinion by the Court on the merits of the dispute because denial can occur for any number of reasons unrelated to the merits of the case.[27] Justice Frankfurter, a frequent commentator on procedural issues, has suggested some of these reasons:

> Narrowly technical reasons may lead to denials. Review may be sought too late; the judgment of the lower court may not be final; it may not be the judgment of a State court of last resort; the decision may be supportable as a matter of State law, not subject to review by this Court, even though the State court also passed on issues of federal law. The decision may satisfy all these technical requirements and yet may commend itself to review to fewer than four members of the Court. Pertinent considerations of judicial policy here come into play. A case may raise an important question but the record may be cloudy. It may be desirable to have different aspects of an issue further illumined by the lower courts. Wise adjudication has its own time for ripening.[28]

Frankfurter concluded that a denial "simply means that fewer than four members of the Court deemed it desirable to review a decision of the lower court."[29] A few justices have indicated, however, that a series of denials can be construed to indicate in some cases the Court's disapproval of the legal grounds for complaint. This remains, however, a minority view.[30]

The dismissal of an appeal, on the other hand, is, at least in theory, always a disposition on the merits. The difference exists because litigants have a statutory right to a Supreme Court disposition in appeals cases. Dismissals are, therefore, Supreme Court precedents and bind the lower courts. The lower courts nevertheless have difficulty interpreting their meaning and importance, because these dismissals are almost always based solely on jurisdictional papers. Recently, for example, a lower court refused to give a Supreme court dismissal for insubstantiality any precedential weight. The Court made clear that this was a mistake in *Hicks v. Miranda:*

> The District Court was in error in holding that it could disregard the decision in *Miller II.* That case was an appeal from a decision by a state court upholding a state statute against federal constitutional attack. . . . We had no discretion to refuse adjudication of the case on its merits as would have been true had the case been brought here under our certiorari jurisdiction.[31]

This decision caused Court of Appeals Judge Tom Clark, a member of the Supreme Court from 1949 to 1967, to complain that the "adjudication" of appeals was too similar to the evaluation of certiorari petitions to merit separate treatment in the lower courts:

> The Supreme Court's statements in *Hicks v. Miranda* . . . to the effect that such dismissals are decisions "on the merits," seem to me to fly in the face of the long-established practice of the Court at least during the eighteen terms in which I sat. During that time, appeals from state court decisions received treatment similar to that accorded petitions for certiorari and were given about the same precedential weight.[32]

With the increased volume of cases reaching the Court, the justices have decided more and more appeals on jurisdictional papers alone, without full briefs or oral argument. The Court now receives about three hundred appeals each term, and most of them are decided summarily without opinion.[33] State court appeals are most often dismissed for insubstantiality, and federal court cases are generally affirmed summarily. The Supreme Court has thus created a procedure for controlling its obligatory appellate jurisdiction which to some extent frustrates the statutory differentiation established by the 1925 legislation.

Even the Court's handling of cases arising under the narrow original jurisdiction reflects an unwillingness to be trapped into full consideration of all petitions which fill technical requirements for review. Although these petitions comprise less than one percent of the docket, they are significant in the amount of time they require for resolution because they usually involve the evaluation of complex factual issues. In recent years, this portion of the Court's obligatory jurisdiction, like the appeals jurisdiction, has acquired a discretionary aspect. As Justice Harlan stated in a 1971 interstate pollution suit:

> Changes in the American legal system and the development of American society have rendered untenable, as a practical matter, the view that this Court must stand willing to adjudicate all or most legal disputes that may

> arise between one state and a citizen or citizens of another, even though the dispute may be one over which this Court does have original jurisdiction.[34]

Thus the Court has interpreted the constitutionally mandated original jurisdiction provision, like the congressionally created right to appeal, in a way that enables the justices to refuse review. This constriction of "mandatory" routes to review protects the Court's power over its agenda in the same way that certiorari jurisdiction does.

How the Court Evaluates Requests for Review

Although the Court's interpretation of its responsibility to give consideration to appeals and to original jurisdiction cases helps control the agenda, this device does not solve the problem of workload created by ever-increasing filings. As the caseload has increased, the Court has responded by changing its procedures for evaluating requests for review. All the justices once scanned all the requests and the accompanying papers themselves. Now law clerks, who are recent law school graduates, ordinarily summarize these materials for the justices. When preparing these summaries came to require too much of their clerks' time, some members of the Court began to divide up requests and exchange the memoranda prepared by their clerks. As the caseload has increased, the Court has also increased its permanent professional staff, although by congressional standards, the Court staff is still small. The Clerk of the Court, for example, has a staff of thirty to deal with the complex paperwork engendered by four thousand petitions per term.[35]

Another practical response to the demands of the docket involved the Court's handling of layman-drafted petitions, the most rapidly growing category of petitions before the Court (table 1.1). These requests, usually from inmates of federal or state prisons, began to constitute a significant proportion of incoming cases about 1940. Because they are submitted without legal assistance and without payment of filing fees or printing costs, the Court has had to devise

special procedures for their consideration. Beginning with
the 1947 term, the Court began to place them within its
recently established Miscellaneous Docket, the location for
petitions requesting special types of relief.[36]

Since that time the numbers of these cases have continued to increase disproportionately, and they now constitute over half the certiorari petitions filed every year. In
1970 the Court began listing these cases in a separate *in
forma pauperis* category. The different rates of growth for
the so-called paid cases and the *in forma pauperis* cases can
be traced in table 1.1.[37] Paid cases (mostly non-criminal) are
those that come to the Court with the proper number of
copies, so that no special procedures are required for their
consideration by the justices. As this table shows, the filing
of the (mostly criminal) *in forma pauperis* cases has increased
at a much faster rate than the filing of paid cases, despite the
consistently lower chances of review for *in forma pauperis*
cases.

Table 1.1   Grant rates for paid and *in forma pauperis* petitions

	Overall		Paid cases		I.f.p. cases	
Term	Acted upon	Percent granted	Acted upon	Percent granted	Acted upon	Percent granted
1941	951	17.5	773	19.4	178	9.0
1951	1,017	11.1	612	15.5	405	4.7
1956	1,425	12.4	664	20.9	622	6.1
1961	1,899	7.4	768	13.4	1,131	3.4
1966	2,470	7.2	1,043	11.6	1,427	3.9
1971	3,286	9.6	1,433	8.9	1,853	10.2[a]
1976	4,102	4.1	2,019	7.3	2,083	1.1

SOURCE: *Report of the Study Group*, table 3 (p. A3), with my addition of 1976
Term data from *U.S. Law Week*.

[a] The disproportionately high percentage of *i.f.p.* cases granted review in
1971 reflects an unusual proportion of capital cases held over from earlier terms
for joint consideration.

Preconference Case Processing

Upon arrival, all petitions, whether paid or *in forma
pauperis,* are assigned a docket number, and, unless the op-

posing party responds or waives his right to respond, case materials are held in the office of the Supreme Court clerk. Rule 24 of the Supreme Court Rules requires the clerk to allow thirty days for a response in all cases except those in which the United States is a party, where fifty days are allowed. The cases and their responses are then distributed directly to each justice's chambers a few weeks before he must vote on the case. Each packet consists of a copy of the certiorari petition or appeal, the response of the opposing party, and (sometimes) a reply brief from the petitioner. If one of the parties has filed a certified record of lower-court proceedings, it is available in the office of the clerk.[38]

The paid cases are filed according to Supreme Court rules that specify their content. Both Certiorari petitions and appeals must cite lower-court opinions, jurisdictional grounds, and relevant statutory material, as well as the questions presented to the Court. Lower-court opinions must be appended to these materials. Certiorari petitions must also include reasons why the Court should grant the writ, and appeals must show why the questions presented are substantial. Although the rules are specific about the topics to be addressed, they stress brevity. Twenty pages is usually enough for a certiorari petition, and ten pages is often sufficient for an appeal.[39]

Even though the paid cases are filed by lawyers and normally conform to specified forms, they vary greatly in quality. The federal government is the most active petitioner each term, and its petitions are of uniformly high quality because almost all of them are prepared by the highly trained staff in the solicitor general's office. Many of the other review requests, according to the justices themselves, are of poor quality or should never have been filed. A law student review of the 1958 filings revealed many cases alleging false conflicts between lower-court decisions and highly dubious federal law claims.[40] The student note cited verbosity and extended argument on the merits as other frequent defects in the petitions.

Various justices have complained about the quality of petitions in speeches before legal audiences. This irritation is not confined to speechmaking, as a 1951 memo for conference drafted by Justice Frankfurter makes clear:

> The memorandum is the precipitate of long concern over a serious evil in relation to the Court's work. The evil is the filing, week after week, of utterly baseless petitions for certiorari. My dam of patience with this disturbing imposition on the Court has been burst by some shameful instances of disregard of the grounds of certiorari jurisdiction on this week's conference lists. . . . I need not elaborate the reasons why this abuse offends every consideration relevant to the efficient and economical conduct of our business. I hope it is not too much to expect agreement that such abuse will not be stopped unless we bring drastically to the attention of the Bar that the abuse must stop.[41]

Frankfurter unsuccessfully urged the Court to assess 10 percent of the original judgment against both those who used the Court as "an easy instrument for their purposes of delay" and for those who displayed "inexcusable professional ignorance" by filing hopeless petitions. His experience on the Court had apparently caused Frankfurter to reverse his earlier, more charitable views about hopeless petitioning that he had held as a law professor.[42]

In forma pauperis petitions, because they are often drafted by laypersons, tend to be of lower technical quality than paid petitions. Frequently they are hard to read and evaluate. Sometimes a considerable investment in research time is necessary even to elucidate the legal arguments they contain. This problem was particularly serious in *in forma pauperis* cases before assigned counsel became usual in these cases.

The Court has experimented over the years with various procedures for alleviating the burden imposed upon the Court by lay-drafted petitions. Before 1930 the Court had established a separate route for lay-drafted petitions in order to decide in each case whether to undertake the printing and other costs necessary to enable all of the justices to review these cases. Not until Charles Evans Hughes became chief justice, however, did these petitions receive any great attention from the Court.[43] Despite their legal inadequacies, Hughes felt that they deserved careful consideration by the Court. As a result, he took on the job of researching their contentions and making the claims intelligible to the other justices. One of his clerks, Edwin McElwain, described the chief justice's practice in these cases:

> And so we find the master of complicated factual situations and masses of pieces of paper applying himself with his usual diligence to applications filed by madmen, thieves, bank robbers, and illiterate persons of every kind, and the results over a period of years have been quite astounding.[44]

The Court retained this means of reworking *in forma pauperis* petitions into usable legal format after Hughes left the Court, although later chief justices were less intimately involved in the process. Instead, law clerks in the chief justice's office undertook any necessary legal research, and they prepared short memos for the justices summarizing the relevant facts, decision below, and contentions. The memos usually contained a recommendation to grant or deny the petition. The chief justice distributed copies of the clerks' memos in each case to the individual justices. Before copying machines came into use, these memos were called "flimsies." Justice Harold Burton's papers indicate why: they were thin carbon copies of the original memos. Burton, who seemed always to receive one of the bottommost copies, must have had some difficulty reading them.

If it was a capital case or one which the chief justice's office deemed worthy of serious consideration, the petition itself, and sometimes the record below, was circulated among the justices before they made a decision on the petition. This economical method of making supporting materials available had one major drawback: the last justice to receive the materials sometimes had only a short time to review the contentions. Justice Clark remarked that when he was on the Supreme Court, he sometimes received a stack of materials nearly two feet high the night before the conference in which the current batch of *in forma pauperis*

petitions would be voted upon.[45] It was not until Warren
Burger became chief justice that *in forma pauperis* petitions
were copied by the Supreme Court clerk and distributed to
the justices along with paid cases for individual evaluation.

The Role of the Law Clerks in Case Selection

Despite the wide variation in the quality of review requests,
they all proceed through the Court along the same path.
Before the justices study the cases, the law clerks prepare
memos on each of them. Since 1972, at Justice Powell's
suggestion, five of the justices have opted to pool their
clerks for the memo writing.[46] These justices receive a
common memo drafted by a single clerk. This practice
helps the clerks to cope with the volume of their work,
which can be overwhelming, especially since the staffs of
the individual justices became responsible for researching
the *in forma pauperis* petitions. The influx of cases forces
each clerk to analyze thirty or more petitions a week. This
workload tends to affect the clerk's perception of the cases.
As a former Powell clerk has written:

> Sometimes, despite myself, I would forget they were
> people and think of them only as names on a legal page,
> parts of some abstract mental encounter. . . . People be-
> came simply items to type up quickly, because there
> were so many other cases, other claims, and the day had
> long since ended and one wanted to go home.[47]

The clerk memos are short summaries of relevant facts,
lower-court rulings, and the contentions of the parties.
These summaries may be formal or not, depending on the
clerk and his justice. A clerk memo prepared for Justice
Burton exemplifies the informal style adopted by some
clerks:

> Petitioner is a big Cadillac dealer who got caught buying
> the local Alderman; he has been fighting conviction for
> four years; his case has no merit and his brief is replete
> with overstatements, innuendo, speculation, and almost
> untruth. It would be a crime to touch this case.[48]

The memos always end with a recommendation for the disposition of the case: to grant or deny in certiorari cases; to affirm, dismiss, or note probable jurisdiction in appeals cases.

Although intended simply to summarize relevant legal issues for the justices' review decisions, the memos inevitably reflect the backgrounds of the law clerks who prepare them. For this reason it is important to understand how the clerks fit into the case-selection process in the Supreme Court, and to determine whether the role of the clerk in this process significantly influences the Court's review decisions.

Supreme Court clerkships have a venerable history. Justice Horace Gray began the practice in 1882, perhaps because he had previously used a law clerk when he was chief justice of the Massachusetts Supreme Court.[49] As the number of cases the Court handles annually has grown, so has the number of clerks. Among the current justices, Justice Stevens has two clerks, the chief justice has five, one of whom holds a long-term appointment, and the remaining justices employ three apiece.[50] The clerks assist the justices in legal research and opinion writing as well as in screening petitions.

The clerks are generally recently graduated young lawyers who did very well in law school. Although they usually have little professional experience, candidates have often clerked one or two years for a lower federal court judge before applying to the Supreme Court. The justices choose their clerks primarily on the basis of academic credentials, but individual justices take other factors into consideration, for example, the candidate's regional background, the law school attended, and the individual's apparent compatibility. Only rarely do friends of the justices suggest relatives or other young people who would not have been chosen on academic grounds.[51]

The background and experience of the clerks, of course, influence their perception of salient issues in the cases. A memo by one of Justice Burton's clerks in a 1947 case well known to feminists is illustrative. The case, *Goesaert v. Cleary,* involved a Michigan statute which expressly disallowed female barkeeps.[52] Burton's clerk, white and male as almost all clerks have been until recent years, did not believe that the case raised a significant issue:

> Next it is argued that the statute arbitrarily and un-reasonably discriminates between male and female bar-tenders. The statute in its terms does prohibit all women from being barkeeps. It does this despite the fact that women may lawfully get a license to own and operate a place selling liquor at retail. I don't see anything un-reasonable here.[53]

Burton must have agreed with his clerk. He voted against taking the case up on the merits, but four of his colleagues disagreed and granted review. On the merits, a majority of the Court, with somewhat more hesitation than Burton's clerk, found the Michigan statute constitutional.

Justice Burton's clerk memos, the only complete set yet available, indicates that clerk and justice agreed most of the time on whether review should be granted or denied. That they usually agreed on the proper disposition of cases, how-ever, does not mean that Burton simply relied on his clerk's recommendation in voting upon review requests. Available evidence indicates that Supreme Court justices have little difficulty in maintaining independence from their clerks.[54] A former clerk to Justice Black, for example, reports that the justice told him gleefully one day that in a particular case in which nearly all the clerks had suggested review, the justices voted unanimously not to hear the case.[55]

The extent to which the justices rely on the recom-mendations of their clerks seems to vary from issue to issue and from justice to justice. Thus Justice Clark recalled that he usually accepted without independent investigation his clerk's conclusion that a conflict of decision on an issue in the lower courts merited the granting of certiorari. His willingness to rely solely on law clerk evaluations, however, varied according to his estimate of the clerk's abilities on the subject at hand. He believed, for instance, that the clerks, because of their youthful idealism, could be trusted to give prisoner petitions generous readings, but they could not be assumed to have evaluated complex technical legal arguments carefully. He examined the materials in those cases himself.[56] Justice Brennan reported that he routinely looked over the Questions Presented section of certiorari petitions except in busy periods on the Court.[57] Justice Frankfurter claimed to have read through all certiorari petitions.[58]

Most of the justices have not commented on their handling of clerk memos, but it seems likely that all of them freely return to the petitions and accompanying material when they believe it might be helpful in deciding how to vote. At least none of the hundreds of former clerks who now teach and practice law have claimed that their memos were decisive in determining their justices' case-selection votes. On the contrary, those who have written on this subject have publicly disavowed influence on the Court's review decisions.[59]

Nevertheless, the press of cases does force each justice to find some balance between doing his own research on review requests and relying on his clerks. The papers that litigants file have long been far too numerous for the justices to read themselves. Even in the 1930s, when the caseload was less than one-fourth the size it is now, the volume of reading involved in going over all papers filed would have been beyond the abilities of the justices. In the context of arguing for a mandatory retirement rule, Attorney General Homer Cummings determined that each justice would have to read 344,232 pages each term to go over all materials filed with the Court. He likened this burden to reading *Gone with the Wind* before breakfast every morning.[60]

Although petitioners to the Court may accurately complain, as Philip Kurland has, that the use of law clerk memos reduces carefully drafted petitions to "pap" for quick judicial consumption, it does not seem accurate to assume that the justices have thereby delegated case selection to their law clerks.[61] Such an argument underestimates the justices' skepticism about clerk recommendations. It also ignores the clerks' strong desire to note in the memos the elements the justices consider important. Because a Supreme Court justice's recommendation can open the door to a successful law career, each clerk is understandably eager to satisfy his justice's expectations. The one- or two-year tenure of most clerks, and the vast difference between justice and clerk in age and experience, also makes clerks sensitive to the approbation of their employers. Notes former clerk J. Harvie Wilkinson:

> A Supreme Court clerkship is very much a baptism by fire. Doing 20 to 30 certiorari memos a week, a clerk is quickly compelled to develop a knack for stating the salient facts and issues in a case and a sixth sense for the particular kinds of questions his Justice will be looking for.[62]

Cramped quarters and the small size of the staff also help keep clerks and justices in touch. When Justice Powell joined the Court, he noted this aspect of his new position with some dismay:

> I have an office suite of only three rooms. I have one secretary, who serves as file clerk, receptionist, as well as a highly confidential personal secretary. . . . My three law clerks are crowded into a single small room, each doing his own typing in the absence of secretarial help.[63]

A Short-Cut to Decision: The Special List

During the term, only a few weeks pass between the justices' receipt of most review requests and their disposition by the Court. The Court convenes as a body to decide current review requests and other business on Fridays.[64] Usually the justices dispose of the week's intake of review requests by lunchtime during the Friday conference,[65] and they consider their final decisions in argued cases in the afternoon session of the conference.

Not all cases arrive during the October to June term, however. The Court receives hundreds of review requests over the summer. These are decided early each fall during a three- or four-day conference devoted solely to case selection. This conference traditionally occurs during the week before the new term begins. At this time the Court acts upon a huge number of cases. In the conference held during the week of September 25, 1978, for example, the Court considered 992 items, of which 865 were petitions for writs of certiorari and 59 were appeals. The Court denied 794 of these petitions for certiorari and disposed of 57 of the 59 appeals.[66]

Rapid preterm decision making has been routine for some time. During the chief justiceship of Charles Evans Hughes, McElwain reports, the justices decided two hundred to three hundred certiorari and appeals cases in the preterm conference. Since then, the numbers of petitions decided upon in the preterm conference has increased steadily (see table 1.2).[67]

Table 1.2   Cases considered in the preterm conference: A comparison

Case type	1951–53: Average number considered each term	1971–73: Average number considered each term
Paid cases	186	347
In forma pauperis	72	377
Other[a]	53	13
Total	311	737

SOURCES: 1951–53 statistics: Burton collection, Legal, 1953 Term, Box 263; 1971–73 statistics: October Term 1973, Statistical Sheet Number 1, Oct. 11, 1973.

[a] These are not parallel in the two sets of terms. In 1951–53 the category includes applications for rehearing and an approximately equal "miscellaneous" subcategory. In the 1971–73 statistical sheet there is no comparable category, and "other" here includes only original docket petitions.

The justices begin to prepare for the preterm conference well in advance. Justice Burton's diaries show that he prepared for the conferences throughout the month of September. Each day he religiously noted the number of petitions he went through, averaging about eight a day. Apparently the current justices, like Burton, also work during the summer recess to prevent the accumulation of certiorari filings from overwhelming them in the fall.[68]

The justices are able to dispose of these large numbers of cases in the preterm conference and in their regular conferences during the term in part because they have developed certain conventions for narrowing their agenda. Over the years, the means by which the Court has reduced the number of cases it must consider collectively have changed, but the object has remained the same: to keep case selection from taking too much time, while still permitting the Court to perform this function adequately.

Chief Justice Hughes was the first to adopt a technique for reducing decision time.[69] He introduced the concept of a "special" or "dead" list, an enumeration of cases the Court probably would not want to take up on the merits.[70] Those cases that remained on the list at the end of a conference were automatically denied review. Hughes and his clerks compiled the list themselves, circulating it a few days before the conference. The justices were free to delete cases from the special list at any time. The supporting materials for all the cases on the conference list, including those special-listed, were wheeled into the conference room, so a justice could change his mind about discussing a case even during the conference.

Disagreement with the chief justice's choice of cases, however, was apparently infrequent.[71] Requests for changes also occurred only rarely during Stone's, Vinson's, and Warren's chief justiceships. Justice Burton's records reveal only a dozen or so alterations in the special list each term, most of them occurring at the beginning of the term. Most deletions are correlated with an unsuccessful vote by the deleting justice in favor of review on the merits.[72]

The press of cases has altered this case elimination device somewhat over the years. Miscellaneous Docket cases soon became so numerous on the special list that it became more efficient to list only cases the Court might desire to vote for. The change from special-listing most Miscellaneous Docket petitions to listing only those the Court might discuss occurred in 1950, and it coincided with a decrease in the proportion of these cases granted review.[73] In recent terms, this practice has been expanded to cover all cases. The special list has now been replaced by a discussion list, compiled by the chief justice and his staff, which contains about 30 percent of the cases up for decision.[74] Associate justices sometimes add to this list before a conference by writing a note to the chief justice. The rest of the cases are denied review by unanimous consent without discussion or actual vote. As with the special list, each justice is free to add any cases he desires to the discussion list at any time. The justices can also request a delay in the disposition of any petition on the conference list, which includes all cases up for decision in the conference. Some of the justices prepare their own discussion lists to aid them in making these decisions.

The justices determine which cases they will discuss in conference on the basis of several criteria, if the Burton-period special lists are typical. The technical quality of a case, its procedural posture, the apparent rightness of the petitioner's claim, and the subject matter of the petition— all seem to be relevant criteria in this preliminary elimination process. The Court's tendency to special-list some subject matters oftener than others is clear when special-listed petitions are compared with incoming petitions. As table 1.3 shows, the subject-matter patterns are fairly stable. Subjects on which the Court received fewer than twenty petitions per term have been eliminated.

Although these data indicate how the justices tend to special-list certain subject matters more frequently than others, they provide no information on the actual composition of the special lists, because the subject-matter categories vary radically in size. When these special lists are analyzed to determine which subject matters are commonest, contract and common-law disputes predominate in all three terms. These cases comprise about one-fourth of the total special list each term. Federal taxation and federal criminal cases on the appellate docket are also consistently large categories of rejected cases, each normally accounting for 10 to 15 percent of the special list. U.S. regulatory and financial disputes, patent cases, and personal injuries vary more widely, but each tends to account for at least 5 percent of the special list.

Table 1.3   Subject matters special-listed in the 1947, 1952, and 1957 terms

	Percentage of total incoming petitions special-listed		
Subject matter of petition	1947 term	1952 term	1957 term
	(N = 266)	(N = 248)	(N = 419)
Contract and common law real-property disputes	61	67	70
Federal tax issues	62	39	62
Bankruptcy	58	32	63
Personal injuries	47	35	61
Patents	45	57	70
Federal regulation: property issues	40	19	26
Labor issues	36	27	31
Financial disputes between U.S. and corporations or individuals	35	30	57
Civil liberties issues[a]	13	12	22
State and municipal property regulation and taxation	24	29	43
All cases, Appellate Docket	39	36	49

[a] Criminal cases have been omitted from this tally because most of them were Miscellaneous Docket cases for which different selection practices applied.

The Weekly Conference

The weekly conference is a formal meeting. The justices arrange themselves around the conference table in a fixed order that changes only with changes in the membership of the Court.[75] After a traditional round of handshaking, conference discussion of review requests always opens with a statement by the chief justice summarizing the first case and giving his views on its proper disposition. Discussion begins in the order of seniority, each justice stating his views fully, and (reportedly) without interruption.[76] After general discussion the justices vote, some keeping a record of the votes cast in a personal docket book. A typical docket book entry for the 1955 term is shown in figure 1.1.

During the Burton period, the justices agreed more than half the time on the proper disposition of the petitions they

Court ____CA 9th_____   Voted on _____, 19 _____
Argued ____3/5____1956____   Assigned _3/4_, 1956 No. 201
Submitted _____, 19_____   Announced _3/26___, 1956___

DAVID HYUN, Petitioner
vs.
HERMAN R. LANDON, DISTRICT DIRECTOR, IMMIGRATION AND
NATURALIZATION SERVICE

7/ 1/55 - Cert. filed.
10/10/55 - Granted.
3/ 9/56 - Motion for leave to file br. of James C., Baker et al., as
    amici curiae.
3/14/56 - (Clark, J.) (Assgd. by Reed, J.)
3/12/56 - Motion of 3/9/56 denied.
3/26/56 - Per cur.: Judgment aff'd by an equally divided Court. Clark,
    J. took no part.
5/ 4/56 - Pet. for rehearing. Also suggestion and motion for vacation
    of disqualification of Clark, J.
5/ 7/56 - Denied. Clark, J. took no part.

	Cert.			Jurisdictional Statement				Merits	Question		Absent	Not Voting
	G	D	N	Post	Dis	Aff	Rev	Aff	No	Yes		
Harlan, J.	x								x			
Minton, J.		x							x			
Clark, J.												x
Burton, J.		x							x			
Douglas, J.	x							x				
Frankfurter, J.	x							x				
Reed, J.		x							x			
Black, J.	x							x				
Warren, Ch. J.		x						x				

Fig. 1.1   A typical entry in Justice Harold Burton's docket books

discussed in the weekly conferences. The voting breakdown
for 1947 to 1957 cases, is shown in table 1.4. Appellate
Docket (now Paid Cases) and Miscellaneous Docket (*in
forma pauperis*) cases are listed separately because the
Court's propensity to vote for on-the-merits, or plenary,
consideration varies dramatically between them. These
proportions remained relatively constant during Burton's
tenure. More recently, the pattern has changed somewhat.
Justice Brennan notes that the Court eliminates about 70
percent of the cases from any consideration in conference
without objection from anyone. The Court's unanimity on
which cases deserve review has apparently declined since
the Burton period, however. Brennan states that on the
average only 9 percent of the grants of review are unanimous,[77] whereas during the Burton period nearly one-third
of the cases granted review received the affirmative votes of
all the justices.[78]

Table 1.4   **Disposition of review requests by votes received:
1947–57 Term averages**

Voting category	Appellate Docket	Miscellaneous Docket	Overall
	(N = 7,617)	(N = 7, 422)	(N = 15,039)
Special-listed	42%	78%	60%
Review denied unanimously	21	17	19
Review denied non-unanimously	19	3	11
Review granted non-unanimously	13	2	7
Review granted unanimously	5	0	3
Total	100%	100%	100%

The Rule of Four

Four affirmative votes are required to grant petitions for
certiorari and to note jurisdiction in appeals cases. The origins of this rule are unclear.[79] Its existence first became

public knowledge when Justice Van Devanter described the rule and its rationale to the Senate Committee on the Judiciary in 1924:

> If there were five votes against granting the petition and four in favor of granting it, it would be granted, because we proceed upon the theory that when as many as four members of the Court, and even three in some instances, are impressed with the propriety of our taking the case, the petition should be granted.[80]

This four-vote requirement remains in effect for all cases, except in the rare situation where only six or seven members of the Court are voting.

Although the rule of four is almost always in effect, the justices may sometimes cooperate to satisfy its requirement. Justice Van Devanter reported that if two or three justices strongly desired to hear a case, the necessary remaining votes were sometimes volunteered by other members of the Court.[81] Whether or not the justices feel under an obligation to reciprocate when votes are volunteered we do not know, given the secrecy that surrounds the conference.

Whatever the implications of cooperative voting today, the practice must have occurred infrequently during the Burton period. The number of denials with two or three votes is too great to assume that the justices habitually offered their votes to satisfy the rule of four. Of those cases receiving one or more votes for review, 32 percent were denied despite two or three justices voting for review. The number of four-vote grants of review, on the other hand, is slightly larger than one might expect, suggesting that occasional cooperative voting may have occurred.[82] Chapter 5 explores the issue of cooperative voting in detail.

The extent to which the justices vote with an eye to the Court's probable disposition on the merits is also difficult to determine. One justice has admitted that he takes the probable outcome on the merits into account in case selection, voting to grant review for lower court decisions he agrees with and expects the Court to affirm, and voting to deny petitions whose probable outcome on the merits he considers undesirable:

A decision may seem outrageously wrong to me, but if I thought the Court would affirm it, then I'd vote to deny. I'd much prefer bad law to remain the law of the 8th Circuit or the State of Michigan than to have it become the law of the land.[83]

The relationship between the four-vote rule in case selection and one aspect of a justice's responsibility in voting on the merits became an issue in 1949 when Justice Frankfurter announced that he would no longer vote on the merits in Federal Employers' Liability Act evidentiary cases. These cases typically raised the issue of the jury's discretion in making personal injuries awards to railroad workers. Instead of voting with the rest of the Court in cases that four or more members of the Court had voted to hear, Frankfurter voted to dismiss certiorari as improvidently granted. Had four other justices taken up this practice on the merits, the rule of four would have been defeated. No one else adopted Frankfurter's stance, however, although some of the justices agreed that the Court should not be taking up FELA evidentiary cases.[84] Chapter 5 discusses the conflict among the justices in FELA cases in detail.

The Chief Justice's Leadership in Case Selection

The chief justice appears to be in an excellent position to influence the other justices in their selection of cases for plenary review. During the conference, the chief justice summarizes each case and gives his recommendations first. He also determines when to cut off discussion and call for a vote. As Charles Evans Hughes remarked in his 1927 lectures at Columbia University: "While the chief justice has only one vote, the way in which the Court does its work gives him a special opportunity for leadership."[85]

The extent to which various chief justices exploit this opportunity for leadership in case selection may vary according to the chief justice's basic personality structure. David Danelski has analyzed the relationship between leadership and personality in the chief justice. He argues that only occasionally does the chief justice have the temperament to be wholly effective in leading the conference.[86]

A successful chief justice is able to keep the other justices efficiently at work in the conference (task leadership), while keeping the atmosphere free from resentment and mis-understanding (social leadership).

Danelski analyzed the leadership abilities of Taft, Hughes, and Stone. He concluded that Taft and Stone were less successful than Hughes as task leaders. This conclusion is supported by evidence of the amount of time the Court required for petition screening during the tenure of each of these chief justices. For Taft, the preterm conference on accumulated review requests in at least one term consumed seven weeks of meeting time.[87] Stone also required long and frequent conferences for case selection.[88] Hughes, on the other hand, kept deliberation time to a minimum, allowing an average of three and a half minutes of discussion per review request.[89] Considering only case selection, it seems likely that Vinson, Warren, and Burger are all effec-tive task leaders because, since Stone, this phase of the Court's work has not consumed an inordinate amount of the Court's time.

Voting statistics from Burton's docket books also illumi-nate the social leadership element of the chief justice's position. This evidence shows that Chief Justices Stone, Vinson, and Warren voted alone for or against review less often than most of their colleagues (table 1.5). Assum-ing that the chief justices with whom Burton served held views as strong as their colleagues about the appropriate-ness of review, the most likely explanation for their non-individualistic voting behavior is that it reflects their sensitivity to the role of social leader on the Court. Accord-ing to this explanation, a chief justice's sensitivity to his special peacekeeping function on the Court causes him to suppress his individuality, voting with others as often as possible. As Danelski hypothesized:

> Chief justices have generally made the most of their po-sition to reconcile disagreement on the Court. . . . One would therefore expect a chief justice who actively em-braced this sector of his role to be more inclined to sup-press his own disagreements with colleagues, to keep them covert or at least nonpublic.[90]

Table 1.5   Lone votes of chief justices compared with associate justices, 1945–57 Terms

	Chief's rank in relation to associates	
Chief Justice	Lone votes for review	Lone votes against review
Stone (1945)	8–9 (tied)	5–9 (tied)
Vinson (1947–48)	Last	6–8 (tied)
(1949–52)	6–7 (tied)	5–6 (tied)
Warren (1953–54)	5	7–9 (tied)
(1955)	6	8–9 (tied)
(1956)	4	7–9 (tied)
(1957)	4	7–9 (tied)

The chief justice's tendency to suppress disagreement, if motivated by considerations of social leadership, should be especially strong in case selection, where lone votes for or against review can accomplish nothing. Case selection, unlike plenary decision making, affords the chief little time to persuade others to his view, and gives him no opportunity of attracting public support for a decisive individualistic stand unless he publishes a dissent from the denial of review. A chief justice's tendency to reduce conflict by suppressing his disagreement with his colleagues is thus encouraged by the absence of persuasive reasons for voting alone at this stage of the Court's work.

An alternative explanation for the results shown in table 1.5—but one rejected here—is that the chief justice seldom votes alone because he usually persuades other justices to join with him. This seems less plausible than the social-leadership explanation because it requires time for advocacy, and because it requires bargaining power. The chief justice has little of either in case selection. In addition, vigorous advocacy would tend to increase conflict, a tendency chief justices try to combat in other contexts.

Evidence that *any* member of the Court persuades his colleagues to change their opinions on reviewability is spotty. Justice Brennan, arguing against a proposal to divest the Court of case selection, claimed that many times a single justice persuades three or more colleagues to vote for review.[91] Others disagree, claiming that little discussion takes place during the conferences. Thus Justice Clark recalls that while he was on the Court, the justices had usually decided how they would vote before the conference. Even though various justices sometimes argued vigorously that the Court should or should not take a particular case, "We were usually not very impressed."[92] The difference of opinion between Brennan and Clark may be attributed partly to the presence of the argumentative and opinionated Justice Frankfurter on the Court during most of Clark's tenure, but not during nearly so much of Brennan's.[93] The secrecy of conferences and the reluctance of the justices to discuss them prevents more definitive answers to issues of persuasion and leadership on the Supreme Court.

Decision Criteria in Case Selection

Decision criteria, like the dynamics of the conference, remain largely unknown outside the Court. The evidence which is available suggests, however, that the justices share similar conceptions of reviewworthiness. Most petitions are rejected unanimously, and a significant proportion are granted review unanimously. This pattern suggests that the justices share many beliefs about reviewworthiness. The Court has attempted to communicate these shared criteria for case selection through one vehicle, Rule 19 of the Supreme Court's Revised Rules.

The Court's Published Decision Criterion: Rule 19

Rule 19 is the Court's only published guideline for its considerations in case selection. Formerly Rule 38(5) of the Supreme Court Rules, it has remained substantially the same in all but title since guidance on this subject was first published in 1932. It lists the following as "the character of reasons which will be considered" in granting or denying certiorari:

(a) Where a state court has decided a federal question of substance not theretofore determined by this court, or has decided it in a way probably not in accord with applicable decisions of this court.

(*b*) Where a court of appeals has rendered a decision in conflict with the decision of another court of appeals on the same matter; or has decided an important state or territorial question in a way in conflict with applicable state or territorial law; or has decided an important question of federal law which has not been, but should be, settled by this court; or has decided a federal question in a way in conflict with applicable decisions of this court; or has so far departed from the accepted and usual course of judicial proceedings, or so far sanctioned such a departure by a lower court, as to call for an exercise of this court's power of supervision.[94]

The conditions covered in this nonbinding "rule" are the same for all courts whose decisions are reviewable in the Supreme Court by writ of certiorari, but no analogue for appeals cases exists in the Supreme Court Rules.

Writers of manuals on Supreme Court jurisdiction have embellished Rule 19 with their own discussions of relevant issues in their attempts to advise lawyers on drafting successful Supreme Court petitions. In analyzing the rule, they have relied upon comments in accepted cases and elsewhere, and upon ad hoc reviews of the pattern of grants and denials. Critics of the rule have performed their own analyses of its applicability to actual decisions in order to show its inadequacy.

Legal commentators agree that Rule 19 properly stresses the existence of a conflict in the holdings of the Supreme Court and lower courts as a likely reason for review. As Stern and Gressman, authors of a popular manual on Supreme Court practice, state:

A well-established ground for granting certiorari is the existence of a conflict between the decision as to which review is sought and that rendered by the Supreme Court or some lower court whose judgment is final in the absence of Supreme Court review.[95]

The existence of a conflict between court decisions as a reason for review has been noted by the justices in their opinions for many years. Thus Frankfurter and Hart stated in their analysis of the Court's output during the 1933 term that conflict "remains by far the most frequent ground for granting the writ,"[96] and Tanenhaus et al. found that conflicts were cited 18.7 percent of the time as a reason for review during the 1956 through 1958 terms.[97] Unsurprisingly, the attention directed toward conflicts among courts as a reason for review has encouraged litigants to strain to show the presence of a conflict in their petitions.[98]

Disagreement among the lower courts or between a lower court and the Supreme Court on an important issue in a case does not always suffice for review, however. In a recent analysis of 2,122 rejected certiorari petitions and appeals 98 direct conflicts were identified.[99] The Court, at least in recent years, appears sometimes to require more than a conflict of lower court results before it will grant review. The appropriateness of the case for settling the conflict, the "ripeness" of the disagreement, and the importance of the conflict may be relevant to the Court's decision. The insignificance of the disputed issue, for example, may have been why the Court steadfastly refused all petitions on school regulations concerning student hair length, despite a 5-5 split among the circuits. As one litigator of these cases admitted:

> I think the Supreme Court is perfectly able to identify those issues involved in a split which ought to be resolved, and frankly, although we litigate a lot of long hair cases and made much of them constitutionally, I cannot honestly say that it is the world's most important issue.[100]

The importance of the conflicts the Court does not resolve has become a matter of dispute in recent years. Some observers and some sitting justices argue that the Court is failing to settle some conflicts in federal law which deserve review on the merits simply because of the increasing volume of petitions.[101] As Justice White warned in arguing for revision of the Court's appellate jurisdiction:

> There is no doubt that those concerned with the coherence of the federal law must carefully consider the various alternatives available to assure that the appellate

system has the capacity to function in the manner contemplated by the Constitution. As others have already
noted, there is grave doubt that this function is being
adequately performed.[102]

The Inadequacy of Rule 19

Although Rule 19 gives due emphasis to the importance of
conflicts in determining review, the rest of the rule does not
adequately describe the other considerations that influence
reviewability.[103] Some factors, like serious divergence from
"the accepted and usual course of judicial proceedings," are
hardly ever noted by the Court in cases it decides on the
merits. Other elements of the rule which draw distinctions
as to importance and substance are too broad to be helpful.
The justices' comments in opinions and elsewhere have
provided some (albeit limited) guidance in defining these
terms. Thus various justices have noted that they do not
consider "importance" in Rule 19 to refer to the eminence
of the parties or the amount of money involved, whereas
they do consider pertinent the number of people affected
by a judicial interpretation of a law or regulation and its
jurisdictional ramifications.[104]

Rule 19 also does not take a clear position on the relevance of the merits of the petitioner's argument for reversal, and the Court's pronouncements on this question are
inconclusive. Many justices have stated, as noted above,
that the denial of certiorari implies nothing about the
Court's view of the merits of the petitioner's argument for
relief. Moreover, the justices have taken pains to point out
that a lower court's erroneous result alone is not a sufficient
reason for review. Chief Justice Vinson stated the rationale
for this position:

> The Supreme Court is not, and never has been, primar-
> ily concerned with the correction of errors in lower
> court decisions. In almost all cases within the Court's
> appellate jurisdiction, the petitioner has already re-
> ceived one appellate review of his case.[105]

The Supreme Court practice of sometimes denying review, but later vacating and reversing when a similar case is

taken up, also shows that the Court does not always grant review for cases it believes were wrongly decided below. Yet observers have noted that the Court's perception of error in the lower court result is sometimes the only apparent reason for review.[106] It is difficult, however, to interpret the position of the Court on error below from case selection practices alone. It is possible, for example, that the Court's perception of an erroneous result below is relevant in many of the cases it does accept for review, even though the Court does not always review cases with which it disagrees.

Nevertheless, the Court's behavior on the merits does provide some indication of the relevance of error in case selection decisions. The Court's pattern has been to reverse about two-thirds of the cases it decides on the merits. It is possible that petitions tend to fall in either of two categories: cases the Court believes deserve extensive consideration regardless of the outcome below, and cases in which the decisions below simply seem so wrong that the Court feels compelled to undo the damage. The Court's practice of granting review and at the same time reversing in some cases each term, coupled with its lower reversal rate for fully considered cases, suggests that the Court makes such a differentiation. In addition to the Court's perception of the merits per se, it may be that the justices are more likely to consider an issue important when they confront it in the context of what seems to be a wrong resolution below.

The cases themselves provide only limited assistance in clarifying the meaning of Rule 19 because the Court does not cite reasons when it denies certiorari petitions. Some justices do publish dissents from the Court's denials, but these opinions represent only the views of the authors of the opinion. These occasional opinions, which have grown more frequent in recent years, have no precedential weight even when they purport to explain why the Court has denied review. As Justice Stevens has pointed out: "One characteristic of all opinions dissenting from the denial of certiorari is manifest. They are totally unnecessary. They are examples of the purest form of dicta."[107]

An additional problem is that the justices more often than not fail to discuss in their opinions on the merits why they have taken up cases. When the Court does mention why it takes a case, most frequently it is "the importance of the issue" or "to decide the issue presented."[108] The latter "reason" is not even an element of Rule 19. The infrequency of judicial comments in both accepted and rejected cases makes it impossible to use the cases to add meaning to Rule 19. Those interested in decision criteria can only guess at why the court chooses most of the cases it does for decision on the merits.

Were all petitions channeled through experienced Supreme Court lawyers, the inadequacies of Rule 19 would be less apparent. Assuming the Court is fairly consistent in its choices, much of what the rule lacks in specificity would be compensated for by the experience of the Supreme Court bar. The caseload would certainly be smaller and the rejection rate correspondingly lower. Except for members of the Solicitor General's staff, however, no sophisticated Supreme Court bar can be said to exist in the United States. Instead those who petition the Court are most often laymen or attorneys unacquainted with Supreme Court procedures. Many of the lawyers who bring cases to the Court do so only once or twice in their entire careers, and some appear to believe, with much of the public, that any case taken "all the way to the Supreme Court" will be reviewed if the justices feel the case was wrongly decided in the lower court. Because they petition the Court only a few times in their entire legal careers, these lawyers have no reason to show restraint in petitioning.

Whether the incomprehensibility of decision criteria or the ignorance and lack of restraint of those who file petitions is more to blame for the burden of the caseload has long been a matter of dispute among the justices and observers of the Court. The justices who have commented on the large number of rejected petitions blame the lawyers who bring cases to the Court for being inattentive to review criteria. Justice Harlan even claimed that the practicing bar shares "a fundamental misconception as to the role of the

Supreme Court in our Constitutional scheme."[109] Analysts of the Court's work, however, differ on whether the Court has done an adequate job of communicating its criteria to practitioners. For example, Frankfurter found baffling review decisions "relatively rare"[110] when he was a Harvard Law School professor, while the authors of a series of critical articles on the Court's certiorari practices found the Court's criteria inscrutable:

> If the Court wishes to do more than complain about the many petitions filed which probably are "unimportant," it will have to recognize that Rule 38 (currently Rule 19) as interpreted gives no standard whatsoever.[111]

Whatever the cause of the communications gap between Court and bar, the Court has not moved decisively to change the status quo. The Court seldom penalizes frivolous appeals, although it has the power to do so.[112] The Court has not redrafted Rule 19 to clarify and expand it, despite scholarly suggestions on how to improve it.[113] Nor has the Court announced review criteria by the route of occasional substantive opinions in rejected cases.[114] Regular notation of meaningful reasons for the grant in accepted cases would serve a similar purpose. The Court could also require lower courts to certify conflicts or other elements denoting reviewworthiness, but it has not.

Conclusion

Because the Court has long had the means available to reduce the influx of cases, the logical conclusion is that the Court intentionally subjects itself to the widest possible range of petitions. This interpretation is consistent with other choices the Court has made in establishing its procedures for case selection. At every turn, the Court has acted to maximize its institutional independence from Congress, litigants, and other courts. The earliest indication of the Court's interest in providing itself the widest possible scope for setting its own agenda was the energetic campaign of the Taft period justices for the 1925 Judiciary Act. Subsequently, the Court has whittled away at the small remaining portion of its jurisdiction that was intended to be obligatory. The Court has now worked itself into the position that it is no longer expected to decide any case as a matter of course.

The Court's tendency to preserve maximum discretion to decide or not in every case is also manifest in the veil of secrecy with which it has shrouded the case-selection process. The Court's only general statement of review criteria, Rule 19, gives little guidance about case-selection criteria. Its vagueness in effect releases the justices from any real obligation to follow it, and in addition to that, it is explicitly nonbinding. The Court's refusal to publish votes or to justify its decisions through even occasional *per curiam* opinions also contributes to the Court's power to exercise discretion unchecked. The Court thus prevents arguments that it should be consistent in applying its criteria for case selection.

The Court's unwillingness to commit itself publicly to meaningful standards in case selection also serves to enhance the Court's public image. The absence of published standards for review allows the Court to sustain the impression that even the most penurious and unsophisticated litigants can easily file appeals with the Supreme Court and get their cases reviewed on the merits if they were treated unjustly in the lower courts. No technical requirements appear to stand in the way of such appeals. The Court's practice of reversing more cases than it affirms contributes to this reassuring image of the Supreme Court as the corrective for unfair treatment elsewhere in the judicial system.

The image of a Supreme Court open equally to all does not reflect reality. The clearest example of variation in chances for review is between paid and *in forma pauperis* petitions. Lay-drafted petitions, as this chapter has shown, have always been reviewed much less frequently on the merits than paid petitions, and this continues to be true despite recent changes in the handling of *in forma pauperis* cases. In the 1978 preterm conference, for example, the Court granted review to only 1 of 437 *in forma pauperis* petitions, or .2 percent of the total. The comparable percentage of paid cases considered on the merits was 7.8 percent.[115]

Less obvious, but at least as important, is the advantage that accrues to the federal government and certain organizational litigants. The Solicitor General's office and the private lawyers who handle numerous petitions can anticipate many of the weaknesses in their cases that might otherwise prevent review. They have also learned how to marshal their arguments to touch upon the Court's concerns and interests. The absence of published standards of review-worthiness is not significant for these litigants. The lack of published standards, it might even be argued, works to the advantage of experienced litigants by diminishing the chances for the less experienced who must guess at review criteria without the benefit of petitioning expertise.

The Court's procedures for processing cases also tend to work to the advantage of experienced litigants. Traditionally, the justices have delegated as little authority as possible to others in case selection. The influx of cases, therefore, presses the justices and the clerks to their limits. In this situation, the litigants who project an image of competence and expertise cannot but benefit. Theirs will be the arguments read first and relied upon with least hesitation. In a calmer setting, on the other hand, the advantage would probably be less because the clerks and the justices would have more time to determine the credibility of litigants unfamiliar to them and more time to research poorly developed petitions. The institutional interests served by maximizing the Court's discretion to set its agenda, therefore, tend also to serve the interests of "repeat players" like the federal government and certain private litigants.

Two   Case Selection and Supreme Court Power

Scholarly assessments of the relevance of case selection to the Court's effectiveness vary radically. This question became an issue for debate in law journals when the Study Group on the Caseload of the Supreme Court, a high-level committee of eminent lawyers and law professors appointed by Chief Justice Burger, recommended in 1972 that the Court be relieved of case selection in order to gain more time for plenary decision making. In this group's estimation case selection is a burdensome chore of little significance to the primary mission of the Court.[1] This conclusion and the Study Group's proposal to assign case selection to a new court brought forth considerable negative response, one scholar even asserting that case selection and on-the-merits decision making were equivalent in public policy impact.[2]

Although the Study Group's proposal made Court-controlled case selection a policy issue for the first time, the underlying question of its importance had been raised before. Fowler Harper with various coauthors wrote a series of law review articles in the 1950s arguing that this aspect of the Court's work is crucial. Harper and Rosenthal stated their position in the first of these articles:

> It may be that the work which the Court doesn't do is as significant for the nation as the work which it does. When it decides a case involving important matters of public interest, it is making national policy. When it declines to review a case involving important issues, is it not also determining policy?[3]

In addition to its significance for litigants, case selection may be important to the Court as an institution in two respects. One is its value as a self-protective device. Because case selection requires no written justifications and proceeds in secret, it provides an easy way for the Court to decline involvement in politically volatile disputes. Such sidestepping can help the Court preserve its standing with the public. If relied upon too often, of course, avoidance of disputes hazards the credibility of the Court. Justice Rehnquist complained when the Court refused to decide a case concerning the rights of homosexuals:

> There is a natural tendency on the part of any conscientious court to avoid embroiling itself in a controversial area of social policy unless absolutely required to do so. . . . Unlike the District Court and the Court of Appeals, Congress has accorded to us . . . the discretion to decline to hear a case such as this on the merits without explaining our reasons for doing so. But the existence of such discretion does not imply that it should be used as a sort of judicial storm cellar to which we may flee to escape from controversial or sensitive cases.[4]

A closer look at the case-selection process in action will show that the nearly complete discretion exercised by the Court has both positive and negative aspects, and raises important questions concerning the proper role of the Court as an institution of government.

Case Selection and Institutional Power

Highly charged disputes that arouse the public's interest are a staple of the Supreme Court's yearly diet of certiorari petitions and appeals, but only infrequently do case outcomes threaten to cause widespread public criticism of the Court. A petitioner's case must tap a reservoir of public fear or resentment for the granting of relief to place the Court in a vulnerable position. The civil rights petitions of Communists and other dissidents in a period of cold-war tension, claims for abortion reform, and arguments for the wholesale abolition of the death penalty are examples of the type of case which can damage the Court's popularity and prestige.

The Importance of Supreme Court Review to Petitioners

While the Court's best interest may sometimes lie in limiting the occasions on which it feels compelled to issue unpopular on-the-merits decisions, the interests of the litigants bringing such cases are diametrically opposed. Litigants who request relief that would generate unfavorable public opinion are often seeking social change through judicial action. Supreme Court review is to the benefit of these litigants because it provides, at a minimum, exposure of the claims involved and, at best, victory on the merits. In 1932, for example, the Communist party was anxious to achieve Supreme Court review of the Scottsboro rape convictions regardless of the probable outcome on the merits. As Carter writes in his history of this famous case:

> Had the Supreme Court affirmed the death sentences, the Party could have pointed to this as evidence that the courts were instruments of the ruling class. A reversal of the decision [would have] confirmed the correctness of the "mass struggle" tactics. The Communists could not lose.[5]

Not only the Supreme Court, but the entire judicial hierarchy is attractive to change-minded interests and individuals. A judicial forum offers possibilities for the recognition of new claims that private institutions and other branches of government do not. Hart and Sacks suggest that courts are attractive to those with a sense of social maladjustment partly because courts cannot refuse to take up issues as easily as other governmental units:

> In the development of Anglo-American legal systems, courts have functioned characteristically as the place of initial resort for the settlement of problems which failed of private solution. All these systems include the immensely significant institution of courts of *general* jurisdiction. Courts are regularly open for the settlement of disputes as legislatures are not. They function ordinarily, as legislatures do not, under the obligation of deciding one way or the other the disputes which are submitted to them.[6]

In addition to providing an available forum for airing disputes, courts can perform a legitimizing function important to some litigants. A court can interpret existing law to validate new claims.[7] Another attractive feature for such litigants in our legal system is that a court may declare new claims constitutionally protected. This became an attraction for American litigants long before civil rights and civil liberties litigation became frequent. Frankfurter and Hart, in their 1933 article reviewing the Court's work, noted with dismay the tendency of attorneys to seek constitutional protection for their clients:

> A continuing phenomenon is in question. For upwards of half a century a large part of the bar has been steadily seeking to stretch constitutional provisions far beyond sensible limits.[8]

The Supreme Court, because it stands at the head of the legal system, and because of its prominence, is the logical focus for reform-minded litigants. These litigants often have organizational support to sustain the costs and delays of working through the appellate system to the Supreme Court. Much such litigation is, from the outset, directed there.[9] Expert litigation attorneys frame the issues and lead the lawsuit through the procedural hurdles that might otherwise prevent the granting of review. The Jehovah's Witnesses, for example, focused their campaign for religious freedoms on the Supreme Court, bringing the Court numerous cases between 1938 and 1958, and gaining review for fifty-five.[10]

The success of litigants like the Witnesses in gaining review encourages others to emphasize Supreme Court opinions as a prime vehicle for social change. Once aroused to the possibility of legal change through litigation, social-action groups tend to remain focused on this technique. As American Civil Liberties Union attorney Leon Friedman has noted:

> The Warren Court rulings helped inspire many dormant groups to take political action to improve their condition, and their spirit has not been dampened by the new climate of the Burger Court. Once awakened, these

groups are not going to turn back until substantial progress has been made toward achieving their political and legal rights.[11]

Litigation brought by unpopular groups and individuals seeking social change through Supreme Court adjudication is sometimes an offshoot of much more generalized movements for social change. Such litigation is energized, and sometimes financed, by the larger campaign.[12] Litigation pressure receives additional impetus when legislation favorable to the reform elements is enacted, because new legislation raises inevitable questions of scope and interpretation.[13] From figure 2.1 it can be seen how, as a social movement gains momentum, the Supreme Court's docket may be affected by the litigation the movement generates.

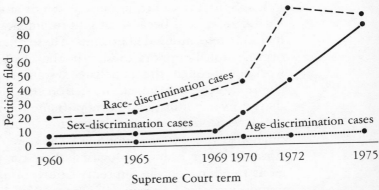

Fig. 2.1   A comparison of the numbers of race-, sex-, and age-discrimination petitions filed with the Supreme Court for the 1960–75 Terms. Adapted from *U.S. Law Week,* "Cases Docketed."

The pattern of race, age, and sex discrimination petitions received by the Court during the fifteen-year period covered in figure 2.1 parallels developments in these civil rights movements. Race cases, as the figure shows, have consistently been before the Court during this period, although their numbers increased substantially after the passage of federal antidiscrimination legislation. Sex-discrimination petitions show an even more dramatic increase. The growing number of these petitions probably reflects the rapid growth of the women's movement more than the impact of significant new antidiscrimination legislation. Age-discrimination allegations, on the other hand, had not yet come to the Court in large numbers by the end of the 1975 term, perhaps because the cause of the elderly had not at that point attracted sufficient leadership and resources to support new legislation or a litigation campaign.

The large numbers of filings in race- and sex-discrimination cases were encouraged to some extent by the Court's own rules in case selection. Its commitment in Rule 19 and elsewhere to resolve conflicts among lower courts encourages organizations to file simultaneous suits in a number of courts. With conflicting resolutions of the issues in the lower courts, Supreme Court review becomes more likely. The number of petitions also has the advantage of suggesting to the Court the importance of the issue.

This strategy of flooding the Court with conflicting lower-court decisions was employed successfully early in the 1970s by litigants favoring a liberalized abortion policy. Petitions based on varying outcomes in eight different lower courts were filed during the term in which the Court selected *Roe v. Wade* and *Doe v. Bolton,* the cases which resulted in the Court's ground-breaking proabortion decisions.[14] Many more cases were in the courts all over the United States. As Babcock and her coauthors describe the litigation campaign:

> There was a nationwide litigation campaign against abortion laws, which was inspired and directed by women who viewed this as a key issue for the current movement. Across the country, literally hundreds of cases of all kinds were brought to court, with cooperation among people differing in abilities and interests, but united in the idea that there must be access to abortion if women were ever to be truly equal.[15]

The proabortion litigation strategy suggests that Toqueville's often-quoted observation—"Scarcely any political question arises in the United States that is not resolved, sooner or later, into a judicial question"—remains true partly because activists manage their litigation to encourage

Supreme Court review.[16] The ability of organized and well-financed groups to encourage lower-court conflicts adds to the advantages that the federal government and other "repeat players" enjoy in gaining review. We shall see later the extent to which these advantages may actually affect the probability of review on the merits.

Institutional Pressures on the Court

When the public is aroused against an unpopular petitioner and the Court takes up the case and decides it in petitioner's favor, the Court becomes institutionally vulnerable. Such highly visible and controversial decisions threaten the Court's somewhat precarious position in our political system. As the history of relations between the Court and Congress shows, Congress has often reacted to unpopular Supreme Court decisions by proposing legislation to restrict the Court's powers.[17] The executive may respond to Supreme Court decisions by appointing new justices whose views differ from sitting members. Lower courts may defy a Supreme Court mandate, thereby damaging the Court's authority.

Internal restraints also operate to limit the Court. As Murphy summarizes the sources of restraint:

> First, there are the ideological restraints which the Justices impose upon themselves; next come the internal restrictions of the Court's being a collegial body and having to act largely through lower court judges. Third, the Supreme Court is also subject to restraints from the other branches of government. Congress can increase the number of Justices, enlarge or restrict the Court's appellate jurisdiction, impeach and remove its members, or propose constitutional amendments either to reverse specific decisions or drastically alter the traditional judicial role in American government.[18]

Reviewing a volatile issue may also cause the Court to establish a precedent that is difficult to rationalize later. When, for example, a controversy puts the Court in the position of validating an undesirable government action, the case might more prudently be avoided. The army exclusion order during World War II that required Japanese-Americans to report to detention camps may have been such a case. Justice Jackson, who conceded that the exclusion order might be reasonable as a military matter, objected to the Court's willingness to sustain its constitutionality:

> A military order, however unconstitutional, is not apt to last longer than the military emergency. Even during that period a succeeding commander may revoke it all. But once a judicial opinion rationalizes such an order to show that it conforms to the Constitution . . . the Court for all time has validated the principle of racial discrimination in criminal procedure and of transplanting American citizens. The principle then lies about like a loaded weapon ready for the hand of any authority that can bring forward a plausible claim of an urgent need.[19]

Such pressures to avoid decision have made the Court somewhat reticent in exercising its powers. This reticence is evident in the numerous procedural doctrines the Court has created for itself to limit plenary review. Standing, ripeness, the political question doctrine, and mootness are some of the self-imposed obstacles the Court has developed over time to limit the occasions of review on the merits.[20] Procedural obstacles to plenary review are, of course, not the only type of limitation the Court has imposed upon itself. The justices also restrict themselves, once they have decided to decide a case on the merits, in the extent to which they are willing to disregard precedent and lower court outcomes, and in the remedies they are willing to prescribe.

Using Case Selection Instrumentally

Although the law relating to standing, mootness, and other doctrinal obstacles to full consideration tends to be messy and exception-ridden, most of these self-limiting doctrines are sufficiently well defined that the justices are somewhat constrained in using them. Case selection is a more flexible route for preventing final review. Thus to the extent that the Court might actually desire to erect an obstacle to review, denial of the petition offers an easy opportunity for achieving this result.

Denial of review is an attractive means of avoiding consideration on the merits because the vote is secret and the Court never issues its reasons for denial. Even when one or more justices dissent from the denial, the views of the rest of the Court remain unknown. The criteria in Rule 19 are sufficiently vague and various to prevent even likely guesses about reasons for denial. In addition, the Court has repeatedly warned that the reasons for denial may be totally unrelated to the merits of the dispute.

Denials also seem to cause less public attention than dismissals after a grant of review. Thus *Mora v. McNamara,* a suit challenging the legality of the Viet Nam war, received little attention from the popular press, probably because it was denied review.[21] On the other hand, *DeFunis v. Odegaard,* which alleged reverse racial discrimination in law school admissions, received much more attention when it was granted review and then dropped for mootness after oral argument.[22]

The comparative attractiveness of using denial of review to avoid volatile disputes led Alexander Bickel, an advocate of "the passive virtues" of nondecision, to recommend that the Court use denials for this purpose.[23] In Bickel's analysis, such outcome-oriented denials could release the Court from the danger of overinvolvement in the political process without sacrificing the Court's capacity to resolve disputes when it did intervene:

> Some do and some do not care to recognize a need for keeping the Court's constitutional interventions within bounds that are imposed, though not clearly defined, by the theory and practice of political democracy. Those who do recognize this need have the choice of either limiting the occasions of the Court's interventions, so that the times will be relatively few when the Court injects itself decisively into the political process, or of restricting the category of principles that the Court may evolve and enforce.[24]

Bickel's recommendation that the Court limit the occasions of review rather than the principles of decision, carries with it certain difficulties of implementation, however. The first is the lack of enthusiasm the justices have for outcome-oriented decision making. The justices know they are expected to attempt to apply standardized rules of decision to cases, even in case selection. Calculation of probable adverse impact on the merits, a consideration not acknowledged in official pronouncements on review standards, would probably not constitute a legitimate criterion for decision in the minds of the justices.[25]

Another difficulty with using case selection to avoid decision in potentially prestige-damaging cases is that members of the Court might not all agree on the occasions for such denials or the wisdom of using the case-selection process in this way. If four justices disagreed, of course, the rest could be compelled to decide on the merits. Even if only one justice disagreed, he could prevent the rest from using the technical shroud of case selection to hide what was in fact a political decision. The lone dissenter need only publish a dissent from the denial of review to expose the motivation of his colleagues to the public.

Those who advocate an active role for the Court in our public life seem to be particularly hostile to Bickel's view that the Court should deny review to protect itself. A statement by former Justice Goldberg illustrates this attitude:

> It is no justification for the Court to avoid deciding a citizen's substantial claim of constitutional right on grounds that the Court may injure itself in such a case. In other words, I would reject that strain of "political self-protection" that underlies theories of judicial restraint.[26]

A second consideration tending to limit the Court's use of case selection to avoid resolving volatile disputes is external to the Court: the Court must take account of the public's interpretation of such denials. Regardless of the technical wording of Rule 19, commentators and litigants tend to interpret denials of review in practical and political terms. A *Civil Liberties Review* survey of one recent term's work, for example, considered unwanted denials of review and undesired on-the-merits results in tandem.[27] Newspaper reports are even more likely to consider the denial of review as a decision against the validity of the petitioner's claim. A long-range pattern of denials tends to be interpreted among observers as indicating negative Supreme Court policy making on the avoided issue.[28] For example, in a study of cases involving prisoner claims that double jeopardy guarantees should be applied equally in state and federal courts, Hanus described the large proportion of denials of certiorari as a "policy of status quo." In the same vein, he concluded: "Whatever the extra-constitutional reasons the Court may have for not applying this protection to the states, it is evident that certiorari has been the subtle tool for effecting that policy."[29] Thus while Rule 19, secret voting, and the frequent judicial expositions of the vague standards for denying review cloud the Court's reasons for denials, many observers remain unconvinced that the reasons are technical.

A more general problem with dispute avoidance as a means of preserving Supreme Court prestige is that denials in such circumstances can actually damage the standing of the Court. Denials can damage the Court's credibility because the Court is popularly perceived as a guardian of constitutional rights. Thus even if one accepts Bickel's warning against the Court's overextending itself, the costs of denial must also be recognized. As a critic of Bickel's position explains:

> The crucial point, however—the point that Bickel refuses to accept—is that resort to the "passive virtues" does not resolve this dilemma. It simply ignores one factor in the equation, for the fact is that every decision not to decide, just like decisions on the constitutional merits, may result either in adding to the reservoir of public acceptance (if only by remaining unnoticed, and thus adding to the inertial acceptability produced by the Court's continued functioning) or in depleting that accumulation.[30]

This objection and those just described seem weighty enough to prevent the Court from using case selection to avoid politically difficult cases very often. The infrequency of suggestions by Supreme Court observers that the Court is using case selection in this way also suggests that dispute avoidance is rare. Similarly, published dissents from denials of review, even those sharply critical of the rest of the Court, seldom contain any implication that the Court has used case selection in a political way to sidestep a volatile case.

The tradition of secrecy in Supreme Court decision making prevents a thoroughgoing evaluation of the dispute-avoidance issue, which ideally should be conducted with searching interviews supplemented by relevant records. Justice Burton's clerk memos and his records of case-selection votes do, however, provide some light on the issue. These materials are most illuminating when they concern the one type of case most likely to encourage dispute avoidance in the Burton period—race-discrimination litigation. Race cases, more than any others, touched a raw nerve during the period in which Burton sat on the Court.

Case Selection in Race-Discrimination Cases

With the end of World War II, racially discriminatory legislation came under broad attack in the courts. The NAACP Legal Defense Fund and other activist groups and individuals pursued suits on a variety of issues, from housing restrictions and miscegenation statutes, to segregated education and recreation.[31] The Supreme Court was the focus of this litigation campaign because it promised to be the most likely forum for overturning state-mandated discrimination. Consequently, achieving review for the most promising cases became a key element in the litigation planning of the civil-rights lawyers.[32]

An indication of the intentions of strategists in the civil rights movement is the argument of James Nabrit, a law professor, at one of the periodic Howard University brainstorming sessions on civil rights litigation. In contrast to some of the more cautious speakers present at this 1952 meeting, Nabrit contended that the Court did not need any help in avoiding a showdown on *Plessy v. Ferguson.* Nabrit argued instead that the Court needed to have its hand forced:

Wherever the Negro is laboring under constitutional
disabilities in the South, there is the best place to attack.
The attack should be waged with the most devastating
forces at hand. . . . The Supreme Court will have to
worry over community attitudes. Let us worry over the
problem of pressing for our civil rights. . . . Let the
Supreme Court take the blame if it dares say to the
entire world, "Yes, democracy rests on a legalized caste
system. Segregation of races is legal." Make the Court
choose.[33]

Nabrit's argument persuaded the group. As Kluger reports:

The net effect of all this speculation and brainstorming
was a far stronger and more determined effort by
Thurgood Marshall to convince the Supreme Court to
strike down segregation.[34]

Justice Burton's papers provide the opportunity to view
this campaign from the Court's perspective. His term on the
Court, 1945–57, covered the period in which the onslaught
of suits was steady and public resistance to integration was
strong. The papers contain clerk memos evaluating the
arguments of the civil rights lawyers and suggesting how the
Court should respond. Burton's docket books indicate how
the Court actually did respond to these petitioners.

Burton's clerks sometimes recommended denial of
review when, in their assessment, public reaction to a
pro–civil rights decision would be adverse. Early in the civil
rights campaign, clerks worried that an antisegregation
result would upset deeply rooted community standards.
The clerk memo in *Shelley v. Kraemer,* which challenged
judicial enforcement of racially restrictive housing
covenants, voiced this kind of consideration:

Considered entirely apart from the constitutional
problem, an abrupt and sweeping judicial invalidation of
all restrictive covenants might well create about as many
problems as it would solve.[35]

The clerk suggested that this was more properly a legislative
problem and recommended denial.[36]

In later years, after early civil rights victories, clerks

sometimes reasoned that antidiscrimination decisions needed time in order to be peacefully accepted. More civil rights decisions, by this reasoning, might tip the balance toward public violence or open defiance of the Supreme Court by lower courts. Thus in *Holmes v. City of Atlanta,* a suit challenging segregation at the city's public golf course, the clerk wrote:

> On the merits, I think that *Plessy v. Ferguson,* 163 U.S. 537, cannot withstand attack in the public recreation area. The effect of the segregation cases is far reaching. I would recommend a denial here solely for the purpose of maintaining the ground already gained in that decision. In time people will adjust to the concept of non-segregated public education. When they do, the way will be easier for intelligent disposition of the problem raised in this petition. In fact, if we are willing to hold off for a time, the answer may come from within certain communities presently opposed to what, after all, must be regarded as the inevitable in a democratic community.[37]

The justices, in contrast to some of Burton's young clerks, proved less chary of Supreme Court involvement in the civil rights struggle. The Court sometimes granted review unanimously when the clerk recommended a denial. In most cases the vote was unanimous to grant or deny. When the vote was nonunanimous, the petition was usually denied with Black and Douglas voting to grant (see table 2.1).

Although the Court was unwilling to duck civil rights petitions because of anticipated adverse public reaction alone, the justices might be persuaded to vote to deny review when a technical weakness could be construed to justify a denial.[38] *Naim v. Naim,* a 1955 challenge to Virginia's miscegenation law, provides the clearest illustration of the use of a minor deficiency in a case to avoid review. In that case Burton's clerk wrote:

> In view of the difficulties engendered by the segregation cases it would be wise judicial policy to duck this question for a time. If cert. was involved our course would be clear. But what to do here? In the instant case a state

Table 2.1   Case-selection votes in major race-discrimination cases,
                1946–57 Terms

Term	Case name	Vote
1946	*Shelley v. Kraemer* (restrictive covenants)	Cert. granted unan. except Jackson
1948	*Sweatt v. Painter* (segregated legal education)	Rutledge, Murphy, Douglas, Black
1949	*McLaurin v. Oklahoma State Regents* (segregated graduate education)	Juris. noted unan.
1949	*Sweatt v. Painter*—voted on again, apparently	Cert. granted unan.
1950	*Rice v. Arnold* (segregated golf course)	Cert. granted unan.
1951	*Rice v. Arnold*—new petition, lower court refused mandate	Cert. denied, Douglas and Black dissenting
1951	*Brown v. Board of Education* (segregated education)	Juris. noted unan.
1952	*Bolling v. Sharpe* (segregated D.C. education)	Cert. granted unan.
1954	*Illinois Commerce Comm. v. Illinois Central RR* (segregated transportation)	Cert. denied, Black and Douglas dissenting
1955	*Naim v. Naim* (miscegenation)	[Discussed in text: various votes]
1955	*Holmes v. City of Atlanta* (segregated golf course)	Cert. granted unan.
1956	*Hood v. Board of Trustees* (segregated education)	Cert. denied, Douglas and Warren dissenting
1956	*NAACP v. Alabama* (restrictions on organization for rights)	Cert. granted unan.
1957	*Speed v. City of Tallahasssee* (bus segregation)	Cert. denied, Douglas and Black dissenting
1957	*Florida ex rel. Hawkins* (law school segregation, lower-court defiance)	Cert. denied, Frankfurter, Brennan, Harlan dissenting

NOTE: This list omits cases alleging racially restrictive juror selection. These petitions were too numerous for inclusion here and involved the weighing of nonracial elements in many cases.

> statue has been upheld against a claim of invalidity on federal constitutional grounds. I don't think we can be honest and say that the claim is unsubstantial. Consequently appellant has tapped our obligatory jurisdiction. I don't think we should enter a judgment on the merits without oral argument since the problem is of real importance. And, moreover, it is very doubtful that the issue is rendered less substantial by the absence of a record on the reasonableness of the legislation. It is with some hesitation, however, that I recommend that we NPJ ["note probable jurisdiction," the equivalent of granting review]. This hesitation springs from the feeling that we ought to give the present fire a chance to burn down.[39]

The first vote in conference was Douglas, Reed, Black, and Warren to note jurisdiction, the remainder of the Court for dismissal. Despite the necessary four votes for review, for some reason the case was held over for discussion in a subsequent conference. The next vote was Douglas, Reed, and Black to note jurisdiction. Later, a third vote was unanimous to vacate and remand for lack of an adequately presented record on appeal, the very grounds on which the clerk saw no basis for a refusal to decide the case.[40] Justice Clark, who wrote the *per curiam* opinion in *Naim v. Naim*, recalled that the probable impact of the Court's decision had been an important consideration in the decision.[41] The Court eventually took up a virtually identical case and, in 1967, it declared miscegenation prohibitions unconstitutional in *Loving v. Virginia*.[42]

The record of clerk memos and Supreme Court voting in the Burton period civil rights cases suggests that the Court may differentiate between prestige-threatening cases which contain a procedural peg upon which to hang a denial and those for which the only justification for denial is adverse impact. Where there are technical grounds for denial, the Court may be willing to include the impact factor in its decision. A 1956 Frankfurter memo for conference in a Civil Rights Act damage suit illustrates this position. After suggesting procedural obstacles to taking up the case, Frankfurter stated:

Insofar as it is relevant to take into account the currents
of opinion affecting our segregation cases, I do not think
it would help things to seize jurisdiction in this case,
with a view to affirming the Court of Appeals.[43]

Without some technical basis to justify a denial, however,
the Court may be reluctant to exerciese its discretion to
deny. In making this differentiation, the justices reveal
their sensitivity to what Kalven calls the hybrid role of the
Supreme Court:

The Court thus has a hybrid role: and the arresting
thing is that were its role to be purified in either
direction—by having it become more simply a court and
nothing more, or by having it become, bluntly, a political agency and nothing more—it would lose its power
and purpose. The special burden of the Court then, is to
exercise great political powers while still acting like a
court, or, if we prefer, to exercise judicial powers over a
wide domain while remaining concrete, realistic, and
alert as to the political significance of what it is doing.[44]

The Court's perception of its dual legal-political role, if
Kalven is correct, should encourage the Court to consider
the political impact of its case-selection decisions but limit
the willingness of the Court to use its power to duck politically dangerous cases. While the evidence is necessarily
scanty, the behavior of the Court in race cases arising between 1945 and 1957 supports Kalven's interpretation.
Judicial perceptions of the Court's hybrid role thus may
explain the failure of the justices to make case selection an
instrument for preserving the power of the Court.

Case Selection and Social Change

The importance of case selection to the institutional
strength of the Court can be evaluated apart from its value
in preserving the Court from hearing difficult cases. Case
selection also sensitizes the Court to social change. As a device for making the Court more aware of social change, case
selection performs two functions: it helps to keep the Court
abreast of new trends in litigation, and it helps to maintain

the Court's flexibility in responding to change. This suggests a shift in presuppositions about the responsibilities of the Court. Whereas the primary consideration of those who emphasize the self-preserving value of case selection is the reputation of the Court as a dispassionate and apolitical dispute-resolving body, the primary consideration for those who emphasize the sensitizing function of case selection is the Court's responsibility to those treated unfairly by our legal system. These concerns seem diametrically opposed, those most concerned with preserving the institutional authority of the Court tending to be least concerned about the Court's image as an available forum, and vice versa.

Case Selection as a Supreme Court Resource

The cases filed in the Supreme Court reflect shifting currents of opinion in our society. "Each age," Justice Douglas has noted, "brings the Court its own special worries, anxieties and concerns. The main outlines of the life of the nation are mirrored in the cases filed with us."[45] The docket thus helps alert the Court to impulses for legal and social change. The broad spectrum of cases reaching the Court also gives the justices the opportunity to respond to these new legal issues. According to Justice Brennan:

> The Court's calendar mirrors the ever-changing concerns of this society with ever more powerful and smothering government. The calendar is therefore the indispensable source for keeping the Court abreast of these concerns. Our Constitution is a living document, and the Court often becomes aware of the necessity for reconsideration of its interpretation only because cases filed reveal the need for new and previously unanticipated applications of constitutional principles.[46]

Frankfurter, even before he joined the Court, made a similar observation about the importance of the caseload in helping the Court modernize its views:

> An issue for which certiorari once seemed inopportune may, through the accumulation of similar instances, or in the clearer perspective of the ramifications of the particular problem, later emerge as obviously important.[47]

The Court's recent willingness to adjudicate petitions alleging sexual discrimination illustrates the relationship Frankfurter described between the volume of claims and change in the Court's perception of the importance of issues. As figure 2.1 showed, sex-discrimination petitions increased dramatically in the early 1970s, just before the Court became deeply involved in this issue for the first time in its history.

In earlier years, when sex-discrimination petitions were few, the Court showed little sensitivity to the issue. This is evident from the disposal of the few petitions which did reach the Court during the Burton period. Although the petitions of the Burton period raised claims that would win overwhelming judicial approval today, those cases were always special-listed.[48] The only exception to the rule of special-listing sex-discrimination allegations was *Goesaert v. Cleary*, a particularly egregious case of state-mandated discrimination.[49] Even this case won review with only the minimum four votes necessary for review.

The four-vote grant of review in *Goesaert* illustrates a second means by which case selection operates to make the Court more responsive to social change. The Court's rule that only four positive votes are necessary to grant review permits a minority of the Court to lead more reluctant colleagues into responding in full to cases the majority would prefer not to decide. Four-vote grants can thus plunge the Court into controversial new issues. The Court's far-reaching involvement in segregated education, for example, began with a four-vote grant of review for *Sweatt v. Painter*.[50] Justices Murphy, Rutledge, Douglas, and Black, the most liberal members of the Court in the 1940s, voted alone for review in the first year the case was considered.[51] Such grants are not necessarily rare. During the Burton period, four-vote grants of review comprised an average 23 percent of the favorable review decisions. Case selection, relying as it does on the rule of four, can thus operate as a liberalizing influence on the Court.

Case selection can also help the Court as a whole to plan for important changes in the law. When it has resolved to decide a difficult problem frequently arising before it, case selection permits the justices to choose the most appropriate dispute for the announcement of new doctrine. This was how the Court selected *Gideon v. Wainwright* to establish the right to free counsel in noncapital felony cases.[52] A former clerk described the process of selection:

> The Court determined, even before the 1961 term began, that it would find the best case it could and would use it to overrule *Betts v. Brady,* the 1942 decision which had rejected the absolute right to counsel claim. And a sifting process began. Justice Harlan—for whom I worked—would ask, as to each case that might be resolved on the ground ultimately taken in *Gideon,* whether there were peculiar facts that would prevent the Court from reaching the broad question, or whether there were other unsatisfactory elements in the case that would cause greater popular resentment to the decision than it deserved. One case which seemed perfect in all other respects was rejected because it involved a charge of molesting little girls.[53]

Court-managed case selection thus can permit the justices to give certain on-the-merits decisions maximum force and palatability.

Court-managed case selection also permits the justices to allow lower-court results to "percolate" until the various sides of a problem have been exposed by lower-court decisions. The Court can then more confidently resolve the issue. Especially when a case arises under a new statute, the justices try to avoid taking the case too early. Instead they seem to prefer that the question first be resolved in as many circuits as possible.[54]

Finally, the opportunity for sidestepping volatile cases discussed earlier also has a more positive side. This avenue of escape permits the Court to venture into issue areas where the ramifications of wholesale involvement might otherwise discourage intervention. Its discretion to limit its involvement in race-discrimination problems, for example, enabled the Court to delay review for some claims of segregated recreation while accepting conceptually similar cases on segregated education. Were the Court limited in its capacity to escape, at least temporarily, from the logical implications of an initial unpopular on-the-merits decision, such initial decisions might be less frequent.

The Study Group Proposal and Its Demise

None of the functions discussed above received attention from the Burger-appointed Study Group on the Caseload of the Supreme Court. Instead, their report presented case selection as a time-consuming, nonjudgmental activity, which could easily be divorced from other Court functions. An indication of the approach is the report's repeated use of the word "screening" to describe the case-selection process.[55] Plenary decision making, on the other hand, was assessed very differently. The report stressed the value of time spent in on-the-merits decision making and opinion writing:

> To maintain the constitutional order the Court must decide controversies that have sharply divided legislators, lawyers, and the public. And in deciding, the Court must strive to understand and elucidate the complexities of the issues, to give direction to the law, and to be as precise, persuasive, and invulnerable as possible in its exposition.[56]

The Study Group's argument for changing current case-selection practices rested on the alleged necessity of relieving the Court from a growing burden of work in order to give it ample time for decision making:

> The indispensable condition for the discharge of the Court's responsibility is adequate time and ease of mind for research, reflection, and consultation in reaching a judgment, for critical review by colleagues when a draft opinion is prepared, and for clarification and revision in light of all that has gone before.[57]

In stating that more time was necessary for the reflection and consultation incident to intelligent opinion writing, the Study Group based its conclusion on statistics showing a dramatic increase in the number of petitions before the Court:

The statistics of the Court's current workload, both in absolute terms and in the mounting trend, are impressive evidence that the conditions essential for the performance of the Court's mission do not exist.[58]

Having evaluated case selection as no more essential to the Court than swearing in each new member of the Supreme Court bar, the recommendation for relieving the Court of case selection followed logically. The Study Group recommended the creation of a national court of appeals that would evaluate all petitions for review now filed in the Supreme Court.[59] The new court would have discretion to deny review, to certify cases to the Supreme Court, and to resolve certain conflicts between circuits on its own initiative. Denial of review by the national court of appeals would be final, as would decisions on the merits in cases involving conflicting lower-court decisions. Certification to the Supreme Court for either denial or final decision there would be reserved for those petitions deemed most worthy of Supreme Court attention, presumably several hundred petitions per term.

This proposal for a drastic restructuring of the case-selection function seemed to take the legal profession by surprise. Chief Justice Burger's choice of the Harvard Law School professor Paul Freund, however, should have provided some warning of the possible outcome of the study. Freund had long been convinced that the work of deciding which cases to determine on the merits is a time-consuming, but otherwise unimportant part of the Court's work. In 1959 he wrote of the then current two thousand petitions per year: "This mounting docket of cases looms as a serious barrier to the true mission of the Supreme Court: to clarify, expound, and develop the law in its most significant national aspects."[60]

When Freund's earlier opinion became the basis of the prestigious Study Group's major recommendation, the reaction was largely unfavorable. Former Chief Justice Warren and several other retired and sitting members of the Court vigorously attacked the case-selection proposal.[61] This negative response from Supreme Court justices, especially from retired Chief Justice Warren, had a devastating impact on the proposal. Favorable response at this level, in contrast was muted. Chief Justice Burger and Justice Rehnquist published articles supporting workload relief through court reform, but did not really respond to the sharp attacks directed at the national court of appeals proposal.[62] Burger refused to endorse the Study Group recommendation, although he mentioned it favorably in his many discussions of court reform. The American Bar Association, committed to some version of a national court of appeals as a means of relieving the Court's mounting workload, also failed to defend the screening proposal vigorously.[63] Members of the Study Group wrote in its defense, but strong outside support was not forthcoming.[64]

The Study Group's case-selection recommendation appears to have died under the weight of adverse comment, and concern over the Court's caseload has taken a different direction.[65] The next major proposal for reform, that of the congressionally created Commission on the Revision of the Federal Court Appellate System (CRFCAS), left case selection in the Supreme Court's hands.[66] That proposal also suggests a national court of appeals, but one empowered to accept cases referred to it by the Supreme Court and transferred from certain lower courts. The CRFCAS proposal, released in mid-1975, has been better received than the Study Group's report. It has not, however, resulted in the creation of a national court of appeals. Nevertheless, if Congress does revise the federal appellate structure, it will probably rely on a proposal like the CRFCAS model as the basis for change.

Case Selection and the Supreme Court's Role

Although the Study Group's case-selection proposal is no longer a viable policy option, the debate it engendered suggests a connection between attitudes toward the proposal and underlying views on the proper role of the Court. I think it can be assumed that those who believe the current method of case selection to be an expendable function that simply takes judicial time away from important responsibilities have a narrower view of the Court's function than those who support the continued existence of Court-controlled case selection. This division of opinion on the importance of case selection, and consequently on the Study Group's proposal, is analogous to the well-known cleavage between judicial activism and restraint familiar to students of constitutional law. Evidence connecting views about case selection and conceptions of the Court's proper role is indirect, however. The Study Group proposal did not address the issue of the Court's proper role, and critics of the proposal tended to slight the issue in favor of constitutional arguments against the Study Group proposal, such as whether it is inconsistent with the Constitution's requirement of "one Supreme Court."

Earlier proposals for reducing the burden of case selection, on the other hand, touched on the question of the role and performance of the Court more directly. Thus even though President Roosevelt's 1937 proposal for increasing the Court's membership was couched in terms of the "almost unendurable burden" of considering certiorari petitions, his actual position on the appropriate role of the Court was well known to everyone.[67] Two decades later, when Henry Hart started a second debate on the Court's workload, he made clear his critical attitude toward the Court's on-the-merits performance: "Few of the Court's opinions, far too few, genuinely illumine the area of law with which they deal."[68] Several years before the current national court of appeals debate, Philip Kurland also connected workload with the quality of the Court's on-the-merits decisions: "A reduction in the Court's burdens might even give the Court the time to read and perhaps, to master the extralegal authorities that the Justices are now prone to quote."[69]

The Study Group proposal differs from these workload-oriented criticisms of the Court in its restrained, neutral language regarding the Court's on-the-merits performance; yet retired Justice Douglas saw in it an essential similarity to earlier critical commentary. Alluding to the conservatism of the lower state and federal courts, Douglas concluded: "The mini-court is therefore a far more effective court-packing plan than the one FDR dreamed up."[70] Retired Chief Justice Warren also regarded the proposal as an attack on the Court:

> We are witnessing a different and more elusive assault on the functions of the Supreme Court. The assault is both cynical and formidable, for it is being mounted for seemingly laudable purposes by some respected judges, scholars, and practitioners.[71]

Absent from such condemnations of the Study Group's motivations, however, are attempts to explain why its report ignored the value to the Court of Court-controlled case selection. Even the legal director of the American Civil Liberties Union, who called the Study Group's failure to discuss the importance of case selection "breathtaking," failed to come to grips with this issue.[72]

One explanation for the Study Group's failure to address the issue, it might be suggested, is that members were ignorant of the dynamics of the case-selection process. The composition of the Study Group, however, makes this hypothesis untenable. Members were selected with regard to their familiarity with Supreme Court procedure and practices, and the committee even included three former Supreme Court clerks, who could scarcely have failed to appreciate the importance of case selection to the Court.[73]

It seems more likely that three related factors underlie the failure of the Study Group to address the importance to the Court of maintaining the current method of case selection. First, the Study Group may have rejected the argument that the Court has an obligation to respond quickly to newly perceived injustices and to use the full range of its resources in fashioning solutions to these problems. Retired Chief Justice Warren's description of the importance of denials is illustrative. It reveals his sense of urgency about Supreme Court responsiveness to legal change:

> Denials can and do have a significant impact on the ordering of constitutional and legal priorities. Many potential and important developments in the law have been frustrated, at least temporarily, by a denial of certiorari.[74]

If one believes, contrary to Chief Justice Warren, that the Court has no special obligation toward legal development, one might well conclude that Court-controlled case selection serves no important function.

A second factor which may well underlie much of the disagreement between the Study Group's supporters and its critics concerns the Court's image as a ready guardian of individual rights. As we have seen, the current method of case selection gives the erroneous impression that the Supreme Court is equally open to all petitioners with legitimate grounds for legal relief. The Study Group proposal would have detracted from this positive public image of the Court. As one observer noted:

> It struck me that the various criticisms of the Freund Committee report related not just to its reducing access to the Supreme Court and limiting the control of the Supreme Court over its own docket but also concerned isolating the Supreme Court from the petitions and problems of the little man, the individual, the person with an appealing case which involves a principle of national importance. . . . It strikes me that the public would lose something which is almost intangible but nevertheless precious, the right to petition the Highest Court and explain in the petition why a case should be heard by it.[75]

While such a statement does little to illuminate how case selection actually works, it does suggest the importance of case selection to the public's view of the Court. If it is conceded that the image the Court projects influences its institutional effectiveness, the connection between case selection and the Court's authority is apparent. Proposals to limit the Court's control over its agenda thus raise significant issues of judicial power and its exercise.

Finally, the Study Group and at least some of its critics differ in the extent to which they acknowledge personal judgment as an important ingredient in case selection. The Study Group, it will be recalled, consistently characterized case selection as "screening" and differentiated it sharply from plenary decision making. In this view the identity of the screening personnel is irrelevant, as long as screeners are competent. If, on the other hand, it is acknowledged that case selection requires individual judgment, which is necessarily idiosyncratic, then changing the decision making body can be expected to have a significant impact on case-selection decisions.[76]

Conclusion

The Supreme Court's nearly unfettered discretion to set its own agenda, we have seen, is part of the foundation of its institutional strength. Court-controlled case selection permits the Court to sidestep or postpone politically damaging disputes. It helps the Court respond to changing litigation patterns, and it enhances the Court's image as an available forum. It follows that locating case selection in another court, or otherwise limiting the range of incoming cases, would have a negative effect on the Court's power as an institution.

Until recently, the Court appeared united in its determination to extend and protect its power over its agenda. As chapter 1 noted, the Court's actions concerning case selection have consistently served to maximize its discretion. Even those like Justice Frankfurter who were most reluctant to rely on the full range of the Court's power in their decisions, sought to preserve the Court's right to un-fettered case selection.

The national court of appeals debate precipitated by the Study Group report ended this traditional unanimity. In the debate Justices Burger and Rehnquist emerged as supporters of a national court of appeals. They have been joined by Justices White, Powell, and Blackmun. Although couched in the language of workload, their support for a change in case selection seems to reflect, at least in part, the position that the Court has become too powerful in our system of government. If this interpretation is correct, the long-standing debate between justices who prefer judicial restraint in social problem solving, and justices who favor a more interventionist judiciary, has finally come to involve, as it should, Court-controlled case selection.

In the context of this debate, the current method of case selection appears to be viewed primarily as a tool for the activist position. Of course, advocates of judicial restraint could adopt Bickel's view that the discretion of the Court to choose cases is a good opportunity for exercising the "passive virtue" of nondecision. Bickel himself, however, seems to have abandoned this position.[77] A member of the Study Group, he supported the national court of appeals proposal and wrote in its defense.

One aspect of Court-controlled case selection not addressed by proponents and opponents of change is the advantage it gives to repeat litigants, principally the federal government. The advantage to these litigants appears to be the inevitable by-product of unfettered discretion in case selection.

Three   The Uneven Impact of Case Selection upon Litigants

Just what sort of litigants and types of litigation does the Supreme Court tend to favor in its selection of cases to be heard? Close study of large numbers of routine dispositions may make it possible to suggest some answers to this question. Focusing the discussion on the docket as a whole, moreover, has its own value. As Frankfurter and Fisher observed in connection with on-the-merits decision making on the Supreme Court:

> Cases in their aggregate profoundly affect the angles of intersection of government and enterprise, of national authority and the localities. Moreover, the disposition of voluminous undramatic cases—their procedural determination and the atmosphere which they generate within the Court—inevitably has its reflex bearing upon the disposition of the dramatic cases.[1]

The major problem in analyzing the disposition of the "voluminous undramatic cases" that come to the Court, of course, is that the criteria the Court uses to select cases for decision on the merits have always been shrouded in mystery. Rule 19 and the statements of the justices have, however, clearly articulated at least one standard for reviewworthiness: the importance of the legal issues a petition raises. An often-quoted statement by Chief Justice Hughes, for example, suggests that legal importance is the only consideration the justices take into account in their decisions:

> The question before the Supreme Court is, manifestly, the importance of the question of law involved, the importance of an authoritative determination by the tri-

bunal invested with that important function. We consider these various applications with respect to that, not as to to the parties, not as to the amount of money involved, not as to counsel, but as to the law.[2]

This statement by Chief Justice Hughes contains two assertions that are relevant to the discussion here: that the Court chooses cases with regard to its position as final arbiter in our legal system, and that the party petitioning the Court is irrelevant to this determination. I have earlier suggested, contrary to Chief Justice Hughes's assertion, that the identity of the petitioning party does indeed influence the granting of review—frequent litigators with financial resources have a distinct advantage in gaining review.

Considerations Influencing the Grant of Review: The Existing Scholarship

In the absence of practical judicial statements about review criteria, scholars have examined the pattern of grants and denials and postulated a number of considerations that appear to influence review. These fall into five groups. One is the potential impact of the litigation. In this connection, observers have suggested that the number of people affected, the amount of related litigation pending or anticipated, and the seriousness of the penalty involved influence review chances.

A second is conflict in interpretation of a statute or rule among two or more lower courts or between a lower-court decision and a previous Supreme Court decision. This ground for review is mentioned prominently in Rule 19 of the Supreme Court Rules, as noted earlier. The existence of conflicts is always discussed by legal scholars commenting upon case selection, in part because of Rule 19, but also because the presence of conflicts among courts does correspond frequently with grants of review.[3]

A third is the Court's perception of the importance of the subject matter. This consideration was noted first by Frankfurter and Landis, who commented specifically on the

Court's declining interest in resolving common-law disputes.[4] Others have remarked on this and other trends in the Court's preferences, for the most part without critical discussion or statistical evidence.[5] Harper and Leibowitz, however, went further in presenting statistics on the ratio of grants to denials in a wide variety of subject matters over a twenty-five year span.[6]

A fourth kind of consideration is the care with which the petition is drafted. Those who write manuals outlining proper petitioning procedures attach much importance to the technical aspects of the process.[7] Closely related to this feature of the petition is its presentation of issues in lower courts. One of the few studies that actually tested this variable showed that the adequacy of the record in a habeas corpus case significantly improved its chances of gaining review.[8]

The final type of consideration is the merit of petitioner's argument that the case was wrongly decided in the lower court. The hypothesis, in other words, is that the justices tend to make essentially the same determination in case selection as they do on the merits: granting review to cases they want to reverse. Several writers have suggested that the Court's practice of granting review and reversing summarily in some cases each term indicates that merit factors influence case selection.[9] Some also have noted the petition-enhancing value of a respected judge's dissent, and disagreement between the trial and appellate courts, both of which may indicate that petitioner's claim has merit.[10]

Political scientists interested in case selection have commonly assumed that policy preferences influencing plenary decision making also determine what cases the Court selects.[11] One political scientist has even suggested that a subgroup on the Court sometimes manipulates case selection to achieve the policy results it desires in decision on the merits.[12] Such research (discussed in chapter 4) usually focuses on ideological differences among members of the Court rather than on shared values.

An article by Tanenhaus and three associates may be the best-known attempt to determine review criteria from the pattern of grants and denials.[13] It is cited in the literature on American politics more than any other research on case selection. The Tanenhaus research also differs from other efforts to outline review-influencing characteristics in what it undertakes to explain. This article describes factors associated with review in terms of a hypothesis about how the Court actually processes its caseload. Because it is well known, and because it attempts to go beyond the description of correlations to an explanation of how review occurs, the Tanenhaus research merits detailed discussion.

Cue Theory: A Critique

The Tanenhaus research tested the correlation between review on the merits and the following four variables: the United States as petitioner, disagreement between trial and appellate courts on the proper outcome of a dispute, civil liberties petitions, and petitions raising economic issues.[14] Economic issues proved to have no special association with review, but the other three factors correlated positively with review on the merits, suggesting that their presence increased the chance of plenary review.[15]

The authors hypothesized that these three factors, which they termed cues, correlated positively with the grant of review because they play an important role in the petition-screening process. The Court, they theorized, is burdened with a large number of petitions and desires to work through them as rapidly as possible, and so it has devised a shortcut for eliminating cases—a search for cues. The justices rely on the presence of one or more cues to signal that a petition is worthy of careful scrutiny:

> The presence of any one of these cues would warn a justice that a petition deserved scrutiny. If no cue were present, on the other hand, a justice could safely discard a petition without further expenditure of time and energy. Careful study by a justice of the petitions containing cues could then be made to determine which should be denied because of jurisdictional defects, inadequacies in the record, lack of ripeness, tactical inadvisability, and so on, and which should be allotted

some of the limited time available for oral argument, research, and the preparation of full opinions.[16]

The list of cues, which these scholars did not presume to know in detail, may have grown out of the justices' understanding of what factors are usually associated with cases they want to hear on the merits. The authors did not, however, discuss the origins of the cues.[17]

In suggesting that the justices made use of cues, the authors hypothesized that the screening of petitions consisted of two different operations: a quick perusal in which cues alone were noted, followed by a thoroughgoing examination of petitions containing one or more cues. In hypothesizing this two-step review process, the authors followed the lead of Gibbs, who suggested—but made no attempt to test—a similar two-step decision-making model.[18] Neither Gibbs nor the Tanenhaus group had any information on the validity of the two-step model because the details of petition examination, which probably vary considerably from justice to justice, are unknown outside the Supreme Court. Nor were the authors able to test their reconstruction of the petition-screening process by analyzing actual case-selection votes. Burton's records, still the only data on case-selection voting that we have, had not yet been made public.

Had Tanenhaus and his coworkers had Burton's voting records available when they wrote, they could have tested the cues against the special list. As we have seen, the special list was at that time the repository for petitions deemed unworthy of conference time. Cases containing cues should not, therefore, be special-listed if the Tanenhaus theory is correct. The absence of data on which cases were special-listed, however, forced the Tanenhaus group to devise an ingenious method for testing the cue hypothesis. Relying on the statements of Chief Justice Hughes and others that between 40 and 60 percent of the petitions filed were clearly without merit, the authors hypothesized that these petitions contain no cues and are not examined beyond the initial perusal. The rest of the petitions, containing one or more cues, constitute the pool from which cases are selected.

Because only 15 to 17 percent of the entire docket was reviewed on the merits during the period studied, the authors concluded that the grant rate for the pool of cases containing cues must be between 25 and 43 percent.[19]

They showed that when the United States was petitioner, when there was disagreement between lower courts, or when a civil liberties issue was involved, the Court granted review significantly oftener than when none of these cues was present. The percent of cue-containing cases granted review ranged from the high of 47.1 percent of U.S. petitions, to the low of 12.8 percent of petitions where the lower courts in the case disagreed on outcome. Overall, 27.5 percent of the petitions containing at least one cue were granted, whereas the Court agreed to decide only 7.1 percent of the petitions containing no cues. The authors explained the 7.1 percent grant of review in cueless cases as the effect of untested cues. Because their analysis showed that the data conformed to the proposition that 25 to 43 percent of the cue-containing cases would be granted review, the authors concluded that cue theory is a valid description of case-selection practice.

The Burton data permit a more direct test of cue theory than was possible when these researchers wrote. The actual special lists of this period can be examined for the presence of cue-containing petitions. Such an examination provides a clear-cut test of the validity of cue theory because the absence of cues among the summarily rejected cases is a logical corollary of cue theory. The presence of cue-containing cases on the special list indicates that either the Court is relying on a different set of cues to establish the special list, or that the Court gives all petitions fuller consideration than the authors hypothesized.

The available special lists cover almost the same period as the Tanenhaus research. Those authors sampled cases between the 1947 and 1958 terms, using every fifth petition in all but two terms, 1952 and 1956, where they used all cases. My analysis, which follows, covers all petitions from the 1947 through the 1957 terms.

The only other differences between the two sets of data

concern two fairly minor differences in inclusion and exclusion. One is the presence in my analysis of appeals as well as certiorari petitions. It is unclear whether the Tanenhaus research included appeals cases. Although the title and introduction of the article seem to indicate that appeals were excluded, the list of excluded case types in the methodology section does not mention appeals.[20] The second minor difference is that my analysis excludes all Miscellaneous Docket cases, whereas the Tanenhaus research included these when they contained lower-court citations. The difference should have little effect on my analysis because the Tanenhaus group excluded all criminal civil liberties issues from their civil liberties cue category. Their decision to exclude these criminal cases had the practical effect of placing them in the cueless pool, thereby inflating the rejection rate in cueless cases because of the very high rejection rate for Miscellaneous Docket petitions.

When we examine the actual voting in cue-containing cases, we see that cases involving dissension in the lower courts and civil liberties issues are well represented on the special list, even though they are special-listed considerably less often than cueless cases (see table 3.1). Civil liberties cases, as Tanenhaus defined them, were special-listed 16 percent of the time, and cases in which the lower courts disagreed with each other (a variable tested only for the 1947 term here) were special-listed 27 percent of the time during that term. Only the petitions brought by the federal government seem to fulfill the prediction that cue-containing cases will not be special-listed.

Overall, however, the pattern of voting in U.S. cases does not support cue theory. As table 3.1 shows, the difference in the percentage of cases special-listed and those rejected unanimously after conference discussion is small. If the mere presence of the federal government as petitioner were the crucial factor in preventing special listing, one would expect more unanimous denials after the Court had considered cases with care in conference. The same problem with the cue-theory explanation is also evident in the other two categories where special listing was more frequent: in each

Table 3.1   Case selection in cases containing "cues," 1947–57 Terms
                 (Percentages)

| | Tanenhaus cues | | | |
Disposition	U.S. petitioner	Dissension below[a]	Civil liberties issue[b]	All other appel. docket
Special-listed	1	27	16	45
Cert. denied unan.	8	23	22	21
Cert. denied nonunan.	25	25	26	18
Cert granted nonunan.	41	16	21	12
Cert granted unan.	25	9	15	5

[a] Data for 1947 Term only included here.

[b] The definition used here is, of course, Tanenhaus's. The analagous category used in subsequent analysis in this book differs from this one in litigant specificity. It also differs in these minor respects: Tanenhaus includes only alien deportation cases, while I include all alienage cases; Tanenhaus includes military justice cases, but I place them in my "federalism" category; Tanenhaus includes disbarment, regulation of occupations and professions, and right-to-work cases, while I exclude them.

instance, the Court was almost as likely to special-list as to reject a case unanimously after conference discussion. This pattern suggests that the factors which control special listing and those which control voting after discussion may be similar.

Of course something differentiates special-listed cases from those discussed in conference, but the available evidence indicates that these considerations may be the very ones that Tanenhaus saw as controlling review decisions after the initial search for cues had been completed: "jurisdictional defects, inadequacies of the record, lack of ripeness, tactical inadvisability, and so on."[21] Burton's clerk memos and the voting patterns show that cases with serious defects in the record from below, factual disputes, moot disputes, and cases the Court knew it did not want to hear, such as disputes over state regulation of property rights, tended to be special-listed.

No easily identifiable case characteristics are invariably associated with special listing in the Burton period, however. This suggests that the justices do not rely on a set of cues to separate cases into those worthy of scrutiny and those to be discarded summarily. With the assistance law clerks provide in digesting cases and writing memos, there is little reason to suppose Supreme Court justices in need of such an abbreviated preliminary screening procedure. It seems more likely that the justices consider the salient aspects of all petitions, using the clerk memos to cut down decision time. The justices may reach a decision by engaging in a weighing process. The pattern of case-selection voting in the Burton period suggests that a few case characteristics—including probably the Tanenhaus cues—may encourage the justices to vote for review, whereas others act like demerits, preventing review in the absence of strong reasons favoring review. The special-listed cases are those that contain one or more demerits and no countervailing considerations in favor of review.

The pattern of voting in federally brought cases supports this interpretation. These cases, because of the Solicitor General's careful screening, seldom contain review-discouraging characteristics, so that the Court seldom special-lists them. In fact, as table 3.1 shows, U.S. cases are sufficiently impressive that in the Burton period they usually received at least one justice's vote for review. The findings of Ulmer and two associates are parallel. These researchers used the Burton data to show that among cases discussed in conference only government-brought cases had disproportionately good chances of review on the merits.[22] Voting evidence thus indicates that the Court is impressed with the reviewablility of U.S. cases. Because of their quality, the clerks and justices probably read the petitions with special care. They may well believe that the issues raised in U.S. cases are generally more worthy of review than others. There is no evidence, however, that the justices initially separate them from the rest in an attempt to save reading time.

Even if cue theory had validity as a description of the

reviewing process, however, it would still be an unsatisfying explanation of the special-listing phase of case selection. The question would remain: Why did the Court adopt these cues? The Court's choice of cues could hardly be accidental or unimportant, because the cues were hypothesized as a means of eliminating large numbers of cases from consideration. Any set of real-life cues would have to be a creature of Supreme Court policy. Yet the Tanenhaus article, like much process-oriented literature, pays little attention to this issue of policy choice.[23]

Characteristics of Cases Granted Review

Although the actual voting records do not support cue theory as a valid description of the Court's procedures in case selection, they do support that part of the Tanenhaus research associating certain case characteristics with the grant of review. Other factors, we have seen, are also associated with review. The problem is to determine how these characteristics relate to each other, how adequately they account for the cases granted review, and what considerations in the minds of the justices might underlie the correlations indicated.

A survey of the Burton-period cases shows that five categories account for all but a handful of the cases granted review:

1. Cases in which the United States was either a petitioner or respondent
2. Civil rights and civil liberties cases
3. Labor disputes, including those concerning injuries to workers
4. Cases raising issues of federalism—disputes between states, between state and nation, between military and civil government, etc.
5. Criminal cases

The Court did not grant review with equal enthusiasm in all five types of cases. Sheer numbers of petitions help account for the volume of criminal cases decided—the Court received more of these petitons than any other kind but granted only about 3 percent of them. Federalism cases, on the other hand, though fewer in number, were more frequently decided on the merits because the Court often granted review.

Revising these categories to reflect the identity of the petitioner rather than simply the issue involved produces a striking pattern. Except in the federalism cases, certain claimants were much more likely to gain review than their adversaries. Table 3.2 shows the percentages of these revised categories granted review during the Burton years. "Residual" cases here include all cases excluded from the litigant-specific categories above, that is, cases in which the U.S. government was respondent, cases in which corporations or individuals petitioned against labor unions or injured workers, and, in the civil rights and civil liberties area, cases in which states or individuals petitioned the Court to reverse a pro–civil rights/liberties result. To prevent double counting, I excluded cases from the labor and criminal categories in which a labor or ciminal petitioner raised a First Amendment, racial discrimination, or federalism claim. Cases brought by the United States on behalf of labor and those U.S.-brought cases involving federalism were counted as U.S. petitions. Also, the two U.S.-brought civil rights/liberties claims in this period were counted as U.S. cases to make the categories mutually exclusive.

The right-hand column of table 3.2 shows the proportions of the Court's on-the-merits attention each of these case types received. It is clear that, except in federalism cases, a few petitioners dominated the Court's agenda during the Burton period. The success of these petitioners in gaining review is especially noteworthy when compared with the lack of success of some of their counterparts in litigation. As the slim probability of review for "residual" cases indicates, the Supreme Court had little inclination to hear suits in which the United States was respondent or corporations were petitioning against labor union victories below, or states were attempting to reverse pro–civil liberties results. Like "criminal petitioner" cases, "residual" cases took up considerable plenary decision time through the weight of their numbers alone.

Table 3.2   Chances of review by category of case, 1947–57 Terms

Category	Petitions submitted	Petitions granted review		
		Number	Percentage this category	Percentage of total
U.S. petitioner	554	366	66	26
Civil rights/ liberties petitioners	630	235	37	17
Criminal petitioners				
Paid cases	977	93	10 ⎫	
Miscellaneous			⎬	13
Docket cases	7,422	111	1 ⎭	
Federalism issues	578	225	39	16
Labor petitioners	593	152	26	11
Residual cases	4,273	262	6	18
Total cases	15,027[a]	1,444		

[a] This figure has been reduced by the number of multiple filings over the Burton period.

When unfavored litigants did succeed in having their cases decided on the merits, they prevailed less frequently than petitioners who were favored in case selection. Thus "criminal petitioner" and "residual" cases won reversal 50 percent and 45 percent of the time, respectively, during the Burton period, whereas U.S., labor, and civil rights/liberties petitioners all had more than a 60 percent chance of winning reversal of lower-court judgments in the Supreme Court. This correlation between case-selection preferences and reversal on the merits suggests the importance of judicial perceptions of error in the review decision, a consideration I shall discuss in connection with individual voting patterns.

These rough statistical breakdowns of differential petitioning success and relative plenary decision time draw into question the assertion of Chief Justice Hughes quoted earlier: that the identity of the petitioning party is irrelevant to review. Except in federalism cases, the party petitioning, especially if it is the United States, is highly correlated with the granting of review.

Access to Review: Why It Varies

The current pattern of case selection suggests that differences in the success rate of litigants in gaining review may be attributable primarily to two factors: the conception the justices hold of the proper work of the Court, and the differences that exist in the petitioning expertise of litigants. Beliefs of the justices concerning the role of the Court are obviously relevant to how they set their agenda in a system with few fixed boundaries to the exercise of discretion. Less obvious in such a system is the factor of the litigant's expertise, but it is nonetheless present, as we have seen.

These two factors are not necessarily compatible. The justices have the unquestioned power to implement their conceptions of reviewworthiness, but they have no control over the expertise factor. It could even be argued that the two considerations tend to work against each other—differences in litigant abilities and preparation tending to interfere with the object of selecting cases most worthy of the Court's attention.

The interplay of these two review-inducing considerations is most obvious in cases brought by the federal government. No litigant has more petitioning expertise than the Solicitor General's office, and few bring the Court as wide a range of issues. In addition, the U.S. cases are the largest category decided on the merits, and the category granted review most frequently. An analysis of how U.S. cases come before the Supreme Court is therefore a logical starting point for examining the relationship of case selection, litigant expertise, and judicial conceptions of the appropriate role of the Court.

The Federal Government, Successful Petitioner

The Supreme Court's tendency to review federally brought petitions is long-standing and well known. The ability of the government to gain review, for example, encouraged Tanenhaus to deem the "U.S. as petitioner" a cue. The success of the federal government in gaining review is particularly notable when compared with the lack of success of those who oppose it. This pattern developed early in the history of discretionary jurisdiction. Frankfurter and Landis noted a disparity in the chances of review of cases brought by and against the United States as early as the 1929 term, just four years after the Judiciary Act.[24] Table 3.3 shows this relationship during the Burton period. The comparison makes it clear that some characteristics peculiar to the United States as a petitioner are crucial in determining the reviewworthiness of litigation involving the federal government. The slightly higher than average grant rate in cases brought against the United States (15 as against 10 percent) indicates, in addition, that subject matter may also be a significant factor encouraging review.

Table 3.3   Access to review for U.S. as petitioner and as respondent, 1947–57 Terms

	Number of cases	Denied review	Granted review
U.S. petitioner	554	34%	66%[a]
U.S. respondent	2,670	85%	15%

NOTE: Here $\chi^2 = 5740.0$, indicating a nonrandom distribution, and $p < .001$.

[a] Tanenhaus found that 47.1 percent of U.S. cases were granted review. The lower percentage is probably due to his including cases in which the government officially stated that review would not be opposed.

Most observers attribute the willingness of the Court to take up U.S. petitions to the special relationship of the government's lawyer to the Supreme Court.[25] The federal government is represented by the Solicitor General in most litigation before the Court. He is typically a distinguished attorney of wide experience.[26] Although the Solicitor General is formally an employee of the Justice Department subordinate to the Attorney General, a well-established tradition allows him considerable independence.[27]

When the United States loses a case that could be appealed to the Supreme Court, the Solicitor General usually decides whether or not the case will actually be appealed. He permits only 10 to 15 percent of government cases lost below to proceed. Even when an agency or the lawyers in the Justice Department who may have handled a case below recommend an appeal, the Solicitor General often refuses to give permission. According to Brigman, the Solicitor General approves staff recommendations to petition the Supreme Court only about 60 percent of the time, whereas he nearly always follows staff recommendations against seeking review.[28]

If the Solicitor General assents to an appeal, his small expert staff prepares the case for the Supreme Court. The quality of the staff work is indicated by the comments of Burton's clerks, who occasionally noted the excellence of the government briefs in their memos to the justices. Tanenhaus reported that the clerks, and even the justices, turn first to the government brief when they are confused by a difficult point.[29]

In case selection and preparation, the Solicitor General cultivates the image of an officer of the court, rather than an ordinary litigant eager to win, no matter what. Thus the Solicitor General will "confess error" when he comes to believe that the position urged by the government is untenable. This solicitude for the well-being of the Court took a new turn in the early 1960s when the Solicitor General began appearing as *amicus curiae* for nongovernmental litigants. In this role the Solicitor General sometimes even aids those opposing federal agencies, especially those few agencies which have independent power to take cases to the Supreme Court.[30]

The balancing of the pressures from below to take as many cases to the Court as possible with the Court's unwillingness to be inundated is a delicate matter for the Solicitor General. Scigliano suggests that the Solicitor General enters into a kind of reciprocal arrangement with the Court:

> If he presses too many cases upon it, the Court reacts by increasing its rejection rate and he cuts back; when he

does so, the rejection rate goes down and, spurred by the feeling that he is not pressing enough (and probably by agency remonstrations as well), he increases his activity. The range of movement in certiorari petitions appears to be between 60 and 80 percent, with the point of equilibrium about 70 percent.[31]

This review rate, combined with the large number of U.S.-brought cases, even after the Solicitor General's culling, means that U.S. petitions comprise a high proportion of the cases the Court decides annually. As we have seen, these cases made up 26 percent of all cases decided on the merits between 1947 and 1957. Since the Burton period, the Solicitor General has taken on much more *amicus* work, so the amount of the docket in which the United States is either petitioning or supporting another petitioner has grown even larger. Now, as in earlier years, no other litigant receives nearly as much attention as the United States.[32]

The federal government is also more successful than most litigants on the merits. It won about 70 percent of the cases in which it petitioned during the Burton period. The United States also won about half of the cases in which it was respondent, a higher percentage than most respondents enjoy. In recent years, the government's success in gaining favorable decisions on the merits has declined somewhat, although its success in gaining review has not.[33]

The Solicitor General's considerable success both in gaining review and in winning on the merits should not be interpreted simply as the effect of a broad, underlying pro-government bias of the justices. The tendency of the Court to grant government petitions does not extend to state-brought cases. On the contrary, unless they raise issues of federalism, these cases are no more likely to be reviewed than ordinary cases. Baum's research on certiorari practices in the California Supreme Court indicates that state petitions enjoy no special likelihood of being reviewed even in state appellate courts.[34]

Another indication that the Supreme Court's apparent preference for the Solicitor General as a petitioner is not attributable merely to a bias in favor of the government is the unevenness of the Solicitor General's access to final review. Although the United States succeeds oftener than its adversaries in getting all types of litigation before the Court, it was much less likely during the Burton period to win review in some subject areas than in others (table 3.4). The review chances for these subjects stayed in approximately the same rank order throughout the Burton period.

Table 3.4   U.S. cases: Likelihood of review, 1947–57 Terms

Type of case	Percentage granted review
Antitrust	86
Other federal regulation (FDA, FCC, etc.)	82
Labor	74
Criminal	73
Aliens	65
Taxation	60
Subversion	57
Money disputes (contracts & condemnations	49

These figures and those presented in table 3.3 present a mixed picture of the influence of the Solicitor General in case selection. The success rate of the government obviously depends on the type of dispute, indicating the relevance of subject matter to the review decision. Nevertheless, even in the most insignificant disputes, those over contract compliance and condemnation awards, the government won review in about half the cases it appealed, whereas those who opposed the government enjoyed no such ability to have their cases heard. This pattern suggests that the participation of the Solicitor General in a case is important to its chances for review, but that the subject-matter preferences of the Court are also relevant.

The Solicitor General's Two Advantages. That part of the government's success in gaining review which is attributable to the Solicitor General's management of the case can be described more generally as the value of being a "repeat player" in the litigation system. Galanter uses this terminology to describe litigators like the Solicitor General's office, and he contrasts their opportunities with those of "one shotters."[35] Galanter describes various advantages enjoyed by the repeat player who by definition: "has had and anticipates repeated litigation, . . . has low stakes in the outcome of any one case, and . . . . . . has the resources to pursue . . . long-run interests."[36] The advantages Galanter describes which are relevant to case selection are: expertise, ready access to specialists, enjoyment of economies of scale, low start-up costs for any particular case, credibility, the ability to play the odds, the ability to play for beneficial structural changes as well as immediate gains, and the ability to discern which outcomes will make the most tangible differences.

Rothstein described a similar set of advantages held by frequent litigators in his discussion of the problems of delivering legal services to the poor. What Rothstein says of the large-volume litigators, like credit companies and landlords, who typically bring and win civil suits against poor people, clearly applies to the Solicitor General's office:

> The large volume litigant is able to achieve the most favorable forum; emphasize different issues in different courts; take advantage of differences in procedure among courts at the state and federal level; drop or compromise unpromising cases without fear of heavy financial loss; stall some cases and push others; and create rule conflicts in lower courts to encourage assumption of jurisdiction in higher courts.[37]

The advantages flowing from the Solicitor General's sponsorship of Supreme Court litigation thus appear to be the manifestation of a more general phenomenon: the advantage of the frequent over the occasional litigator.

To conclude that much of the government's success in gaining review is attributable to the expertise of the Solicitor General in sponsoring government litigation is not, however, to dismiss the importance of the views the justices hold about the proper work of the Court. Indeed, a major ingredient in the expertise of the Solicitor General is his ability to anticipate and articulate the Court's fundamental concerns. The Solicitor General puts before the Court many cases that involve national law-making jurisdiction and enforcement of Congressional mandates—matters essential to the efficiency of national government. The fairly high grant rate for cases in which the United States was respondent suggests the position of the Court on the significance of these issues. When the United States is petitioner, the Court may feel a special responsibility to resolve these disputes because they are often cases that probe the limits of a regulatory agency's statutory authorization.

Of course, a profederal government bias probably plays some role in the Court's perception of important issues, especially during periods like the Burton years, when respect for the national government was at a high level on the Court. The Court may also be sensitive to the government's side in some measure because the justices work in the seat of the national government, and because many of them have a long-standing familiarity with government enforcement problems gained from their experiences before joining the Court. The grant rate in U.S.-brought suits, however, appears more consistent than the popularity of the national government among Supreme Court justices. This consistency suggests that progovernment bias is a secondary influence in federal access to the Supreme Court, and that the expertise of the Solicitor General and his ability to anticipate Supreme Court concerns are primary variables.

Other Successful Litigants

Although no other litigant approached the 66 percent review rate enjoyed by the federal government during the Burton period, labor and civil rights/liberties claimants gained review oftener than many other categories of litigants. As in the U.S. cases, the success of labor and civil rights/liberties claimants in achieving review is particularly striking when compared to their adversaries' lack of success. This difference between opponents in the same subject areas appears to be primarily attributable to the variables just discussed: a combination of petitioning expertise and the Supreme Court's view of its decision-making responsibilities.

Labor Claims. Except for Federal Employers' Liability Act litigation, scholars have generally overlooked the Court's preference for labor-brought cases during the Burton period. Nevertheless, differences in access to the Court are significant (see table 3.5). Labor cases are defined here as all cases brought by unions, and those brought by individuals in their employment capacity to recover for injuries or contested wages. Cases involving federalism and free speech claims, categories discussed later in this chapter, are listed separately in this table.

Table 3.5   Access to review in labor cases, 1947–57 Terms

	Number of cases	Percentage denied review	Percentage granted review
Labor petitioner			
No other factor involved	593	74	26
Civil liberties claim	8	63	38
Federalism issue	65	42	58
Corporate petitioner			
No other factor involved	418	91	9
Civil liberties claim	6	100	0
Federalism issue	15	60	40

NOTE: For overall labor-corporate dichotomy, $\chi^2 = 45.52$ and $p < .001$.

It might be argued that in many of these cases the union is merely a stand-in for the National Labor Relations Board, making the greater likelihood of review simply another instance of preference for the federal petitioner described above. But when union suits against the National Labor Relations Board are compared with analogous corporate suits, it is clear that a separate variable is present. When unions sued the NLRB, they won review 36 percent of the time. Corporations, which sued four times as often, were successful on only 7 percent of their appeals.[38]

Union and employee petitioners enjoyed two advantages in petitioning during the Burton period. One advantage involved the tendency of a few major unions, like the AFL-

CIO, to bring many of labor's cases to the Court. In these suits labor gained the "repeat player" advantage enjoyed by the Solicitor General in disputes involving the federal government.

The other advantage of labor over its adversaries concerned the Court's decision-making priorities. The National Labor Relations Act, collective bargaining, and other labor prerogatives were comparatively new in the Burton period, and lower courts were often conservative in interpreting labor's rights. This situation meant that labor, not corporations, most frequently raised fundamental issues of statutory interpretation to which the Court felt compelled to respond. Labor petitions thus touched upon the Supreme Court's perception of its basic decision-making responsibilities, one of which is to secure fair interpretation of significant congressional legislation in the lower courts.

In no field was the Court's tendency to grant review so as to correct lower-court interpretations of federal legislation more obvious than in Federal Employers' Liability Act evidentiary cases. These disputes between employers and employees concerned the application of federal legislation to the compensation of certain workers for injuries. Like labor cases generally, they raised issues concerning the scope of congressionally mandated rights. The Court's reasoning in granting review was particularly obvious in FELA cases, however, because there was open disagreement on the Court over the advisability of taking them up on the merits. Some members took the position that the Court had an obligation to prevent narrow interpretations of the role of the jury by lower courts. Others, especially Justice Frankfurter, opposed review as a waste of Supreme Court resources. As Justice Douglas, a proponent of review, described the clash:

> The difference between the majority and minority of the Court in our treatment of FELA cases concerns the degree of vigilance we should exercise in safeguarding the jury trial—guaranteed by the Seventh Amendment and part and parcel of the remedy under this Federal Act when suit is brought in state courts.[39]

Civil Rights and Civil Liberties Claims. The interest of the Court during the Burton period and since then in disputes over civil rights and civil liberties has been noted more frequently than its interest in labor's claims. the Tanenhaus research discussed earlier focused on the propensity of the Court to review this type of case, and even those who have not investigated case selection assume preferential selection in speaking of the post–1937 Supreme Court as a civil liberties–oriented court.[40]

Civil rights and civil liberties claims are defined here to include petitions alleging race discrimination, restrictions on freedom of speech, voting rights, and religious freedom, and deprivations of due process concerning personal (but not property) rights. All petitions by aliens or others concerned with their citizenship status are included. Criminal cases, although conceptually within this category, are not listed here because the considerations influencing petitioning are special in these cases.[41]

Individuals claiming infringements of civil rights and liberties were much more likely to get review than their adversaries, often state or local governments (see table 3.6). The only exception was when the federal government was petitioner, when, for reasons the next chapter discusses, the Court was likely to grant review.

Table 3.6   Civil rights–civil liberties cases, 1947–57 Terms

	Number of cases	Percentage denied review	Percentage granted review
Civil rights–civil liberties petitioner	630	63	37
State or private petitioner opposing civil liberties result below	61	93	7

NOTE: $\chi^2 = 23.21$ and $p < .001$

The civil rights–civil liberties category outlined here differs from the analogous Tanenhaus category in one major respect: mine is litigant-specific. All race-discrimination cases, for example, are not lumped together here as they are in the Tanenhaus study.[42] The muddying effect of aggregating cases by issue rather than by appellant can be seen by comparing cases in which race discrimination is either attacked or defended. Of the seventy-six petitioners claiming actionable race discrimination during the Burton period, forty-two, or 55 percent, gained review on the merits. Their adversaries, mostly southern states and local authorities, were much less successful when they petitioned to reverse a pro–civil rights result in the lower court. Thirty-eight of these thirty-nine petitions were denied review.

The tendency of the Court to favor civil rights and civil liberties claimants during the Burton period reflected its attitude of responsibility toward constitutional adjudication. Unlike labor claimants, civil rights–civil liberties claimants had to rely primarily on the interpretation of constitutional guarantees to justify their arguments for relief, because this period predated the comprehensive civil rights legislation that now exists. It also seems clear that when the Court granted review in these cases, it acted not simply because there was a Constitutional basis for the claim, but because the claim rested on personal rights. Constitutional claims of equal protection and due process brought by commercial interests over their rights of property were almost invariably denied during this period unless they raised federalism issues. The Court usually special-listed such property-rights claims, a phenomenon indicating their unanimity on the undesirability of deciding these issues on the merits.[43]

The contrast between the Court's attitude toward property rights and personal rights suggests that the well-known double standard for on-the-merits adjudication—by which personal rights claims receive more careful scrutiny than property rights claims—has its analogue in case selection. Available evidence indicates that the Court reoriented its case-selection criteria to exclude property rights cases from review at about the same time it shifted its standards in decisions on the merits. (1937). The only long-range case selection statistics that are at all helpful in addressing this issue are published annually by the *Harvard Law Review*. The few subject-matter categories that have remained consistent over a long period suggest the Court's declining interest in property rights issues (table 3.7).

Table 3.7   Three types of property cases reviewed: Annual averages, 1929–38 and 1955–63 Terms

	1929–38		1955–63	
Type of case	Number	Percentage	Number	Percentage
Bankruptcy[a]	594	18	170	6
Patent, trademark, copyright[b]	416	18	294	4
Taxation: federal[c]	1,554	26	629	16

SOURCE: *Harvard Law Review*. Data for some years between 1939 and 1954 are missing.
[a] $p < .001$, $\chi^2 = 14.33$.
[b] $p < .001$, $\chi^2 = 29.37$.
[c] $p < .001$, $\chi^2 = 26.03$.

Both in case selection and on the merits, the reason for the shift appears to be the same: a change in the Court's perception of its decision-making responsibilities.[44] As Abraham said of the Court's growing interest in scrutinizing civil rights and civil liberties claims:

> Gradually the Court embarked upon a policy of paying close attention to any legislative and executive attempt to curb basic rights and liberties in the "non-economic" sphere. During the remaining years of the Hughes Court and continuing through the Stone Court (1941–46), the Vinson Court (1946–53), and particularly the Warren Court (1953–69), the chief concern was to find a balance between the basic civil rights and liberties of the individual and those of the community of which he is a part.[45]

The argument that the post–1937 preference of the Court for civil rights–civil liberties claiments reflects a changed perception of its role does not, however, exclude the expertise factor described earlier. Even though this period predated widespread rights-oriented litigation campaigns, those organizations which were centralized and which used litigation regularly were highly successful in gaining review. Although there are not enough cases on the same subject matter to compare civil rights litigant experts with novices in gaining review, the success of the experts is apparent. The NAACP, as we have seen, had considerable access to the Court during the Burton period, with Thurgood Marshall involved in much of the petitioning. In over half the cases in which Marshall was the attorney of record the Court granted review.[46] None of his cases was special-listed. The Jehovah's Witnesses, under the direction of Hayden Covington, had similar success in gaining review in religious freedom cases. At least one justice voted for review in more than two-thirds of the cases in which he was attorney of record, and he was successful in gaining review over one-third of the time.[47] Civil rights–civil liberties claims appear to have been favored in case selection for the same reasons that federally brought claims and labor claims were preferred: a combination of litigant expertise and judicial perceptions of the Court's decision-making responsibilities.

The pattern of grants and denials in church-state conflicts taken to the Supreme Court between 1951 and 1971 suggests that the expertise variable remains important. Sorauf compared the success of three expert litigating organizations to others raising the same First Amendment issues and concluded:

> Since the United States Supreme Court is the "ultima Thule" of constitutional litigation, success in it must at least be partly measured by success in reaching it. By this standard, the record of the three groups is especially impressive. They sponsored 20 of the 56 cases with separationist plaintiffs, and 8 of the 20 (40 percent) reached the Supreme Court for review; only 2 of the other 36 (5.5 percent) reached the Court. Alternatively, one can look at the "appeal achievement" rate. The three groups succeeded in 47.1 percent (8 of 17) of the cases in which they as sponsors sought U.S. Supreme

Court jurisdiction, either by appeal or certiorari. In the remainder of the cases in only 13.3 percent (2 of 15) did the Supreme Court take jurisdiction by appeal or certiorari.[48]

Federalism Cases and the Court's Role

The Court tended to prefer one other type of case during the Burton period: federalism disputes. This category of cases, unlike the three just discussed, involves no specific type of litigant. The vast majority of petitioners in this category are the business and local government interests that fared so poorly in the U.S., labor, and civil rights–civil liberties cases just discussed. The tendency of the Court to review federalism cases, in other words, indicates that the issues in dispute can be more important than the identity of the petitioning party.

Federalism cases are distinguished by the common issue they raise: that of jurisdictional boundaries between quasi-independent units of authority. Some federalism cases are brought by business interests which complain that state taxation and regulatory legislation violate the commerce clause; some are brought by escaped prisoners seeking to avoid extradition to another state. Litigants with a divorce or money judgment in hand also fit this category. They cite comity and conflicts of law in their attempts to gain enforcement of out-of-state judgments. These claims all concern the lawmaking power of one governmental unit in opposition to other units. For this reason, petitions concerning the boundaries of state jurisdictions vis à vis the quasi-separate bodies of admiralty, military, and Indian law are also analyzed in this category.

Of course, many civil rights–civil liberties claims could logically be classified as contests over the constitutional limits of state lawmaking power and, hence, federalism cases. These were not included in the federalism category, however, because they appear to be independently associated with the decision to review.[49] Another reason for separate analysis is that federalism cases, unlike civil rights–civil liberties claims, involve personal rights either not at all, or only indirectly. Federalism cases are usually disputes over the regulation and control of property interests. Although various types of petitioners raising federalism claims differ somewhat in their chances of gaining review, overall the federalism issue, like the three litigant categories just discussed, correlates significantly with success in gaining review (see table 3.8). The exceptionally high rate of success achieved by labor petitioners in this category also suggests that review-inducing factors may be cumulative.[50]

Table 3.8   Cases in federalism, 1947–57 Terms

Petitioner	Number filed	Proportion granted review
Labor	65	58%
States	77	48
Criminal	24	46
Business	283	39
Military	38	37
Judgment seekers	58	21
Indians	33	9%
Total	578	

NOTE: On the average 39 percent of the petitions involving questions of federalism were granted review.

Because the federalism category includes a wide range of petitioners and specific issues, the Court's behavior in these cases cannot be explained in terms of litigant expertise, federal legislation, lower-court attitudes, or judicial favoritism toward any class of litigants. Rather, the common thread tying these cases together, the problem of defining jurisdictional boundaries, appears to be primarily responsible for the petitioners' success in gaining review. The most plausible explanation for the tendency of the Court to decide these cases on the merits, in other words, is that the justices feel that the Court, as forum of last resort, must play a crucial role in preserving amicable and efficient relations among quasi-sovereign governmental units.

The Court's Role from Another Perspective

One means of verifying that the types of cases the justices select for review are causally related to their shared beliefs about the proper role of the Court is to define what types of decision the highest appellate court in any federal constitutional system must decide if it is to be effective. These duties can then be compared with the major categories of cases the U.S. Supreme Court decides. If actual case preferences match those required by a federal system like ours, the argument for judicial sensitivity to the Court's role is supported.

The top appellate court in any complex legal system must perform at least three functions if the system is to operate effectively: it must maintain proper jurisdictional boundaries between the decision-making units; it must ensure its hegemony as the final interpreter of the general laws and constitution; and it must supervise the nonjurisdictional conflicts of general significance which are bound to develop in the interpretation and application of legal rules by the lower courts.

Scholars and judges have often commented upon all three functions as they manifest themselves in our Constitutional system. Throughout our history, as these observers have noted, jurisdictional conflicts have been frequent and severe. These conflicts are reflected in the output of the Supreme Court as they are in the work of other parts of government. Not surprisingly, Frankfurter and Landis, in their examination of the Supreme Court, labeled the maintenance of a proper balance between state and federal powers "our central political problem."[51] Case selection in federalism cases reflects the sensitivity of the Supreme Court to this responsibility.

The other two functions that the highest appellate court must perform if the system is to remain healthy—ensuring hegemony in interpreting general laws and the constitution, and supervising nonjurisdictional conflicts of general significance—have also received much comment from scholars and members of the Supreme Court. Such writers interpret much of the work of the Supreme Court in light of these two functions. As Chief Justice Vinson, for example, has stated:

> The function of the Supreme Court is, therefore, to resolve conflicts of opinion on federal questions that have arisen among lower courts, to pass upon questions of wide import under the Constitution, laws, and treaties of the United States, and to exercise supervisory power over lower federal courts.[52]

Rule 19, which notes the importance of these functions more obliquely, reflects the consensus of the justices that these are important responsibilities of the Supreme Court. The willingness of the justices to review labor claims, civil rights and civil liberties claims, and petitions of the federal government reflects the agreement of the Court about these duties.

It might be objected that these patterns reflect only a partial consensus, since only four votes are necessary for the grant of review. It should be noted, however, that the justices during the Burton period were unanimous to review in these preferred categories a significant percentage of the time and that the level of agreement is much higher in these categories than in nonpreferred categories (table 3.9).

Table 3.9   Unanimity in various categories of cases, 1947–57 Terms

Case type	Percentage of total incoming cases granted review unanimously
Preferred case categories	
U.S. petitioner	25
Civil rights–civil liberties claims	14
Labor claims (all)	15
Labor claims, excluding civil rights–civil liberties and federalism issues	11
Federalism issues	11
All other cases	
All criminal	0
Residual cases	2

The pattern of grants and denials in broad categories of cases which emerged from my analysis of the Burton materials does, I believe, illuminate basic judicial attitudes. The justices do indeed seem to act upon certain shared ideas about the proper work of the Supreme Court, ideas that correspond with the responsibilities of the court of last resort in any complex legal system. This conclusion raises the question of how Court members differ in their perceptions of the Court's responsibilities.

Four   Differences among the Justices in Case Selection

The nonunanimous certiorari and appeals votes cast during the Burton period provide us with data for drawing a few very interesting, albeit tentative, conclusions about how the justices differ in their views of the proper role of the Supreme Court. Some 18 percent of all case-selection decisions were nonunanimous in those years.[1] Although this is a small and not necessarily representative fraction of all decisions, the lack of unanimity offers us a basis for answering certain kinds of questions. As Pritchett observed in his books about decision making in the Roosevelt and Vinson Courts:

> The fact of disagreement demonstrates that the members of the Court are operating on different assumptions, that their inarticulate major premises are dissimilar, that their value systems are differently constructed and weighted, that their political, economic, and social views contrast in important respects.[2]

Disagreement among Supreme Court justices in case selection can be traced to two sources: differences in assessments of the merits of cases, and differences in presuppositions about the amount and type of work the Court should take up on the merits. A justice can hardly avoid coming to a tentative conclusion about the merits of a case during the case-selection process because, in preparing to vote, he must become acquainted with the circumstances of the dispute and the arguments of the opposing parties. The Burton papers indicate that even the law clerks may feel competent to pass on the merits at this stage in the proceeding: Burton's clerks frequently suggested resolutions of cases in their memos. Case selection thus forces a justice to decide the extent to which his views of the correctness of the lower court outcome should be relevant to review.

The extent to which a justice will allow his assessment of the correct outcome in the lower court to influence his vote for review depends on what he considers the most appropriate role of the Court to be. A justice who stresses the obligation of the Supreme Court to correct lower-court mistakes, for example, will vote for review when a justice with the same interpretation of the merits, but a different view of the responsibility of the Court, will not. Similarly, two justices with identical views of the merits might differ in case selection if they disagreed about the number of cases the Court can responsibly resolve in a term. Even the shared goals for Supreme Court adjudication discussed earlier can occasion disagreement in case selection because the justices can be expected to differ in how they evaluate specific cases in light of these goals.

Such differences in judicial conceptions of the proper work and workload of the Court may well be related to the ideological differences that split the justices on the merits. Nevertheless, it seems worthwhile to consider them separately first, with judicial perceptions of the role of the Court analyzed as an intervening variable between judicial views of the merits of disputes and case-selection votes.

The Significance of the Merits in Case Selection

According to Rule 19 and the published statements by various justices on review criteria, perception of error in a lower-court result is not the primary consideration in the review decision. Justice Vinson, for example, stressed the independence of case selection from judicial views of correct outcomes in litigation:

> If we took every case in which . . . our prima facie impression is that the decision below is erroneous, we could not fulfill the Constitutional and statutory responsibilities placed upon the Court. To remain effective, the Supreme Court must continue to decide only

those cases which present questions whose resolution will have immediate importance beyond the particular facts and parties involved.[3]

The preponderance of reversals among on-the-merits decisions, however, suggests that assessment of the correct outcome of a case frequently does influence case selection. Other evidence supports this interpretation.

Votes to Review and Votes to Reverse: Earlier Studies

Two social scientists, Lawrence Baum and S. Sidney Ulmer, investigating the relation between case selection and plenary decision making by means of actual voting data, have concluded that a single variable influences both stages of decision.[4] Ulmer's work, based on samples of nonunanimous votes during the Burton period, is the most directly relevant here. In one study he compared the voting behavior of the justices in case selection and on the merits, using state and federal criminal cases.[5] He showed that the propensity to hear prisoner claims corresponded closely to the propensity to support petitioning prisoners on the merits, that is, to reverse the lower-court decisions of which they complained. The same relation existed in government cases generally, and Ulmer concluded that a favorable or unfavorable attitude toward institutional authority explained the patterns he found.

In a more comprehensive study, Ulmer used chi-square tests and lambda coefficients to show the relationship between case selection and voting on the merits.[6] He hypothesized that the relationship is psychologically determined by the same underlying factor(s), and that the vote for or against review predisposes the corresponding vote on the merits:

Theories of cognitive dissonance and attitudinal stability would lead one to expect some consistency in decisional direction if the factors underlying both decisions are identical or similar. Moreover, if the judge is conditioned to respond in a particular way to the stimulus (S) presented by a case on the first trial (t_1), the conditioned relationship may be reinforced by the mere act of response.[7]

Ulmer sampled the granted cases without regard to subject matter and found that support for a petitioner at the case-selection stage, that is, voting to review, correlated positively with support for the petitioner on the merits (voting to reverse). For eight of the eleven justices Ulmer examined, he was able to show that knowledge of a justice's case-selection vote enhanced somewhat the ability to predict the vote of that justice on the merits.[8] Ulmer did not attempt in this article to specify what variable caused the voting patterns he found.

Baum, apparently building on Ulmer's findings, examined decision making on the California Supreme Court and found the same kind of relation between case selection and on-the-merits voting that Ulmer discovered on the U.S. Supreme Court.[9] In one study Baum used proximity scaling to order the members of the California court, concluding, as Ulmer had, that judges make the same type of assessment in case selection that they make on the merits.[10] This assessment, Baum hypothesized, consists of each judge's application of his policy goals to lower-court results. Each decision maker, in Baum's view, acts as a monitor in case selection, voting to take up cases in order to "correct" them in light of his own policy views.[11]

Another View

The association between voting to review and to reverse which Ulmer and Baum found is evident when we compare the percentage of each justice's votes to reverse in cases he voted to decide with his votes to reverse in those cases he voted against deciding (table 4.1). My analysis includes all of the nonunanimous cases in which the Court granted review, and, unlike Ulmer's, all of the Burton-period justices. I have ordered the justices by the difference between the two categories of votes. This difference provides an estimate of the relationship between voting to review and to reverse for each justice and permits a ranking of the justices' merits consciousness.[12]

The justices differ significantly in the extent to which the considerations favoring review and reversal parallel each other. All justices, however, were more likely to vote to reverse a case they voted to review than one they did not vote to review. This analysis suggests, as does the research of Baum and Ulmer, the fundamental incompleteness of any model of case selection that downplays the similarity between case selection and voting on the merits.

Table 4.1   **Votes to review and votes to reverse in nonunanimous cases, 1947–57 Terms**

Justice	Percentage of votes to reverse in cases he voted to review[a]	Percentage of votes to reverse in cases he voted against reviewing[b]	Difference
Whittaker	93.1	42.9	50.2
Rutledge	85.2	36.7	48.5
Black	80.4	35.8	44.6
Minton	64.0	25.4	38.6
Warren	75.7	41.8	33.9
Vinson	60.6	31.0	29.6
Douglas	75.3	46.0	29.3
Jackson	62.1	34.4	27.7
Frankfurter	66.8	39.3	27.5
Brennan	79.0	51.6	27.4
Reed	58.1	31.0	27.1
Clark	62.3	35.4	26.9
Harlan	62.3	41.3	21.0
Murphy	74.4	57.1	17.3
Burton	56.4	39.4	17.0

[a] For each justice except Whittaker, both the number of votes for review and the number for reversal was near or over 100. Whittaker's percentage was based on 27 votes to reverse in the 29 cases he voted to review.

[b] The numbers on which these percentages are based are lower than in column 1, especially for review-prone justices who sat on the Court only a short time. The number of instances was near or above 100 for everyone listed here except Murphy, Rutledge, Brennan, and Whittaker. Percentages for these four are based on over 20 but fewer than 50 instances.

The association between voting to review and voting to reverse is also evident in a comparison of four- and five-vote grants of review (table 4.2). The percentage of reversals was consistently higher throughout the Burton period when five justices initially voted for review. This pattern indicates that the proportion of reversals would rise if five votes were necessary to gain review. The rule of four thus tends to camouflage the actual similarity between votes to review and votes to reverse.

Table 4.2   Relation of four-and five-vote grants of review to outcome on the merits, 1947–57 Terms

	Percentage Reversed on the merits	
	Four votes cast for review	Five votes cast for review
1947–48	39.1	66.7
1949–52	40.3	44.8
1953–54	41.3	59.1
1955	46.4	63.2
1956	50.0	56.0
1957	44.0	63.6

NOTE: As in earlier tables, the time segments represent "natural courts."

A note from Justice Frankfurter to Justice Burton praising Burton's vote to reverse in the well-known Willie Francis case suggests that the justices themselves connected voting to review with voting to reverse:

> For me it is one of the most cheering experiences since I have been on this Court to have you, who felt so strongly against taking the case at all, come out in favor of reversal as a result of your own conscientious reflections.[13]

(Despite his praise, Frankfurter voted with the majority to allow Louisiana to make a second attempt at electrocuting the petitioner.)

A former clerk's description of his justice indicates that others closely involved with the Court have also connected a justice's perception of the merits to case selection. Edwin McElwain, law clerk to Chief Justice Hughes, claimed that Hughes routinely considered the merits of the controversy in deciding whether to vote for review:

> Although at that stage the question before him was ordinarily whether certiorari should be granted or juris-

diction noted, he usually went into the merits of each case and often, it is believed, decided them then and there in his own mind.[14]

Hughes decided the merits, McElwain asserts, at least in part to prevent grave miscarriages of justice. If the Burton-period justices perceived their decision-making responsibilities as McElwain says Hughes did, it is not surprising that votes to review are correlated with votes to reverse.

Were the justices in case selection merely deciding the dispute as they would on the merits, however, it seems likely that the differences between the two categories of votes in table 4.1 would be closer to 100 percent. A justice who was voting to review simply to gain the opportunity to reverse on the merits should never, except when mistaken about the policy issue involved, vote to affirm a case he votes to review. Nor should he vote to reverse when, despite his negative vote, the Court hears a case on the merits.

Yet one or both types of behavior occurred regularly for every justice, suggesting that a justice's perception of the merits of a case was not the only significant variable influencing case selection. The inadequacy of the single-variable explanation is particularly evident where the relationship beteen case-selection votes and votes for reversal is weakest, that is, for the justices at the bottom of the ranking given in table 4.1. The problem is the same whether the variable assumed to control both decisions is deemed "merits consciousness" or Baum's "policy goals" or Ulmer's "attitude toward institutional authority."

Merits Consciousness and the Court's Role

Judicial beliefs concerning the essential work of the Supreme Court help explain the imperfect correlations between votes to review and votes to reverse evident in table 4.1. A justice's failure to vote for reversal in every case he voted to review can be interpreted to mean that he believed the subject to be too important to pass over, or that he found a conflict among lower-court interpretations, or that he encountered some other issue of court administration unrelated to the merits of the particular dispute. Likewise, a justice's votes to reverse in cases he voted against reviewing can be attributed to his view that the case was wrongly decided below, but not important enough to rate a vote for review. Viewed in this light, the departures from pure merits consciousness seen in table 4.1 are consistent with the analysis in the previous chapter which linked the views the justices shared about their appellate-court responsibilities with voting patterns. The relevance of this variable in nonunanimous cases simply indicates that the justices were not always in agreement in their perceptions of case significance.

The considerable differences in merits consciousness among the Burton-period justices show that the justices also varied significantly in how they balanced their views of the merits against other reasons for favoring or opposing review. In no area of case selection are these differences more obvious than in U.S. petitions. Black and Douglas stand out from the rest of the Court in their case-selection behavior in these cases. While most of the Court voted as the concepts of importance and of the Solicitor General's expertise would lead one to expect, Black and Douglas voted in the opposite way. The differences between their voting patterns and those of the other justices are worth special analysis (see table 4.3).

Most of the justices voted more often for government cases involving civil rights and civil liberties than for any other type of government cases. Douglas and (especially) Black, on the other hand, seldom voted to decide government-brought cases involving personal liberties. Instead, their voting pattern fits their well-known stance favoring civil rights and civil liberties petitioners on the merits. In voting as they did, Black and Douglas were refusing to disturb the victories of civil rights and civil liberties litigants won in the lower courts.

The tendency of Black and Douglas to vote in keeping with their pro–civil liberties views on the merits is even more evident when votes in civil rights–civil liberties cases brought by the federal government are compared with votes in cases brought against the government (see table 4.4).

Table 4.3   **Differences among justices in their support for three types of U.S. petitions: Nonunanimous cases, 1947–57 Terms**

Justice[a]	Percentage of votes for review		
	Regulation	Civil rights and civil liberties	Financial Matters
Reed	68.3	67.3	69.9
Brennan	61.3	62.5	58.3
Warren	58.1	65.4	50.0
Harlan	57.8	76.9	60.9
Clark	56.6	61.5	41.9
Vinson	54.5	60.6	44.7
Burton	54.5	60.0	50.9
Jackson	34.0	42.0	27.7
Minton	33.0	46.0	29.5
Frankfurter	24.4	38.3	22.8
Black	52.4	22.0	53.0
Douglas	50.3	34.5	33.0

[a] Murphy, Rutledge, and Whittaker are omitted here because of inadequate participation. The only other justices whose percentages should be viewed with caution are Brennan and Harlan. Brennan participated in only 51 U.S.-brought cases in this period, and Harlan voted in 81. Most of these cases involved regulatory issues. The remaining justices all participated in over 100 U.S.-brought cases apiece.

Black's consciousness of the merits in personal liberties cases involving the United States corresponds with his high degree of merits consciousness in case selection generally. Douglas, however, appears to have been less merits-conscious overall than he was in these U.S. cases. The difference in Douglas's voting behavior may be partly attributable to his view of the Supreme Court's responsibility for protecting personal liberties. According to this hypothesis, his belief that protecting civil liberties was a primary mission of the Court caused him to vote to examine these claims on the merits much oftener than most of his colleagues. Cases which the civil rights–civil liberties claimants had already won, on the other hand, held no such importance for him, and so he felt no particular inclination to take them up on the merits. A justice's conclusion that a certain issue is particularly worthy of resolution by the Supreme Court

Table 4.4   Differences among justices in civil rights–civil liberties cases brought by and against the U.S., 1947–57 Terms

Justice[a]	Percentage of votes in favor of review	
	U.S. Respondant	U.S. Petitioner
Reed	19.9	67.3
Brennan	61.0	62.5
Warren	42.0	65.4
Harlan	42.9	76.9
Clark	13.0	61.5
Vinson	12.5	60.5
Burton	22.8	60.0
Jackson	25.2	42.0
Minton	7.1	46.0
Frankfurter	44.4	38.3
Black	80.3	22.0
Douglas	73.8	34.5

[a] As in table 4.3, the percentages for Brennan and Harlan should be viewed with caution. Brennan voted in only 12 of these U.S.-brought cases and Harlan voted in 13. All other members of the Court voted in at least 25 civil rights–civil liberties cases involving the U.S. as either petitioner or respondent.

might thus increase his tendency to take the merits into account in that subject area.

The voting on case selection in U.S. cases shows that another member of the Court was also particularly merits-conscious, but probably for quite different reasons. As table 4.4 shows, Justice Reed seldom voted to review civil rights and civil liberties cases brought against the United States. Yet Reed voted for the government over two-thirds of the time when it was petitioner, even in those cases concerning purely financial matters (table 4.3). To Reed, almost any U.S.-brought case was worthy of the Court's attention, perhaps because he had been Solicitor General before he joined the Court. (It should be noted, however, that Jackson also had been Solicitor General and Justice Clark had been Attorney General. Neither man showed the willingness Reed did to vote for review in U.S. cases regardless of the subject matter involved.)

Voting to Review: Differences among the Justices

Federal cases were not the only ones in which the Burton-period justices varied significantly in voting for review. As in U.S. cases, part of this variation in the frequency of votes to review is probably attributable to merits consciousness. Lower courts in this period tended to be more conservative than some members of the Supreme Court, and it was the politically liberal justices who tended to vote for review most frequently. But simple merits consciousness can not completely account for the tendency of some justices to vote for review oftener than others.

The summary given in table 4.5 shows that certain justices during the Burton period were much more likely to vote for review than others were. The justices often divided into two groups on this issue, with twenty percentage points or more separating them in some terms. Black and Douglas were the long-standing members of the review-prone group, whereas Frankfurter and Burton were mainstays of the review-conservative group. The remaining justices voting in more than one of these segments of time also tended

Table 4.5 Differences in the propensity to vote for review: Nonunanimo⟩

Justice	1947–48	1949–52	1953–54
Murphy	59.1	—	—
Douglas	53.4	60.6	60.5
Black	42.8	55.7	54.4
Rutledge	48.5	—	—
Brennan	—	—	—
Warren	—	—	31.2
Reed	28.2	37.7	30.6
Harlan	—	—	—
Jackson	22.2	29.8	31.1
Burton	21.6	33.2	22.7
Frankfurter	23.2	29.4	25.7
Clark	—	25.1	26.2
Vinson	—	21.0	26.9
Whittaker	—	—	—
Minton	—	13.1	10.4

to be consistent in the strength of their propensity to vote for review. Generally, when a justice's propensity to vote for review dropped or rose from one period to the next, other "carryover" justices changed in the same direction. The rank order of the justices thus remained fairly constant over the entire period.

The justices were also moderately consistent in voting for review regardless of the political liberalism or conservatism of the petitioning party. In federalism cases, for example, where the petitioner was often a corporation or an individual seeking to protect property rights, Murphy and Douglas led the voting for review, and Minton remained in last place.[15] The review-prone justices may thus have been less conscious of the merits in their overall tendency to vote for review than the previous analysis of U.S. cases standing alone might suggest. It should be noted in this connection that among political liberals during the Burton period, only Black and Douglas voted in U.S. cases in a way consistent with consciousness of the merits. Brennan and Warren, the other liberals on the Court whose votes in U.S. cases were

ises, 1947–57 Terms

1955	1956	1957	Percentage Overall	Rank Overall
—	—	—	59.1	1
55.0	58.9	54.1	58.0	2
56.6	57.6	53.9	53.3	3
—	—	—	48.5	4
—	42.3	44.1	43.2	5
43.2	53.7	37.7	39.8	6
30.4	—	—	33.2	7
30.9	35.5	30.6	32.3	8
—	—	—	27.8	9
29.1	29.6	23.0	27.4	10
24.0	33.3	27.9	27.4	11
27.8	31.5	25.4	26.2	12
—	—	—	25.0	13
—	—	21.1	21.1	14
18.4	—	—	13.2	15

numerous enough to analyze, voted frequently for review regardless of who was petitioning.

Changes in the membership of the Court did not disrupt voting propensities, even when they affected how a majority could be expected to vote on the merits. This suggests that those who voted often for review did so with little regard to probable outcome on the merits, and even without regard to marshaling enough votes to gain review. The review-prone justices, in other words, appear to have been unconcerned with the impact of their case-selection votes in specific cases.

Review-prone justices may well have been concerned, however, about the competence of the lower courts to reach fair results. The evidence available suggests that review-prone and review-conservative justices differed in the degree of trust they accorded the lower courts. Justice Black's view, according to his son Hugo, was that lower-court judges could not be trusted to exercise good judgment without close supervision by the Supreme Court:

> They got awesome power, Son. If we don't watch them, nobody will. The Congress watches us, but they can't watch them. Some of them puff up like kings, and we're the only thing standing between them and their victims.[16]

The attitude of review-conservative justices seems to have been much different. Justice Harlan, who was similar to Frankfurter in his reluctance to vote for review, described this difference to Justice Black's son:

| Table 4.6 | Voting propensities of selected justices: Nonunanimous cas |

| | Number of justices | |
	0	1
Burton	47	78
Frankfurter	27	92
Douglas	243	353
Black	221	326

The biggest difference between your father, on the one hand, and me and Justice Frankfurter on the other hand, is the basic assumption we make about judges. Your father believes that you have to keep judges tethered— you can't trust their consciences loose without some kind of bridle.[17]

Available materials also suggest that review-prone and review-shy justices differed in their conceptions of how plenary decision making should proceed. This is most obvious when differences in voting frequencies are examined in detail. With the data presented in table 4.6 I have done this for the four justices who sat togeteher throughout the Burton period. Douglas and Black, as we have seen, were consistently review-prone, whereas Burton and Frankfurter were not.

It is clear that if two other justices had consistently voted with them, Black and Douglas would have engaged the Court in several times as many cases as either Frankfurter or Burton. The willingness of Black and Douglas to involve the Court in this number of on-the-merits decisions indicates that they placed little value on time-consuming methods of decision making. These men thus exhibited in their case-selection behavior their own willingness to reach decisions quickly and to justify them without ado.

The data in table 4.6 also shows that Black and Douglas participated in many more four-, five- and six-vote grants of review than either Burton or Frankfurter. Only when seven or eight votes were cast were Burton or Frankfurter slightly

47–57 Terms

:ing with justice named

2	3	4	5	6 or 7
88	95	94	95	220
109	103	83	81	219
237	186	139	117	216
198	187	128	107	195

more likely to have voted for review than Black or Douglas. This pattern indicates that Black and Douglas must have voted for review in many cases without paying much attention to the ideological similarities and differences with their colleagues that were always in evidence on the merits. Black and Douglas thus appear to differ from Burton and Frankfurter less in the types of cases they voted to hear than in the numbers they felt competent to decide on the merits.[18]

In the weekly conferences, the contrast between the two approaches to case selection must have been continually apparent and frequently irritating. Conflict could be expected because the Burton-period justices tended to be fixed in their voting propensities. Frankfurter, for example, described his own approach in unambiguous terms:

> I am, in the main, alert against taking cases except those that obviously call for determination by this Court. By "obviously" I mean cases about which there can hardly be a difference of opinion around the table.[19]

To review-conservative justices like Frankfurter, the more review-prone justices must have seemed insensitive about the workload that would be imposed on the whole Court if more cases were granted review. To the review-prone justices, those colleagues who seldom voted for review must have seemed somewhat insensitive to the plights of petitioners.

The Merits and Votes for Review

In attempting to determine more precisely why review-prone and review-conservative justices disagree about the number of cases the Court should decide on the merits, it is important to distinguish opposition to review based on satisfaction with lower-court results from opposition attributable to other causes. Likewise, it is important to learn the extent to which those justices who frequently vote for review do so because they are dissatisfied with lower-court outcomes. The measure of merits consciousness developed earlier provides a means of making this differentiation.

The interrelationship between review proneness and merits consciousness can be examined for Burton-period justices by cross-tabulating the data of table 4.1, which scales the justices according to their merits consciousness, with those of table 4.5, which rank them according to their tendency to vote for review. The resulting chart (fig. 4.1) permits a rough differentiation of review-prone and review-conservative justices according to their degree of satisfaction with lower-court results.

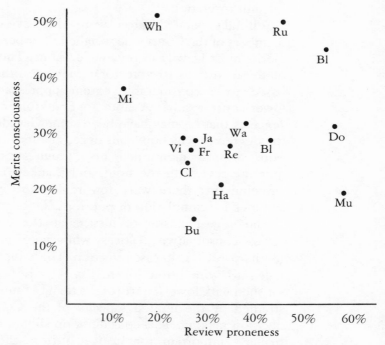

Fig. 4.1   Merits consciousness against review-proneness among Burton-period justices. Graph based on data presented in tables 4.1 and 4.5.

This tabulation sharply differentiates the most review-prone members of the Court. For Rutledge and Black, the merits were an important ingredient in their tendency to vote frequently for review. Black's suspicion of lower-court incompetence was apparently founded partly on his disagreement with the decisions they reached. Rutledge's position may have been a function of his attitude toward decision making generally: his biographer has noted that he always voted his convictions.[20] Douglas and Murphy, on the other hand, took considerably less account of lower-court results in their voting. Their propensity to vote for review may instead be attributable to a view that no important obstacles prevented the Court from deciding more cases than others believed it should. Douglas's often-noted position that the Supreme Court is not overworked supports this interpretation.[21]

Whittaker and Minton were the review-conservative members of the Court who weighed their perceptions of the merits most heavily in review decisions. The disinclination of these justices to vote for review, in other words, was based to a considerable extent upon satisfaction with lower-court results. A note to Frankfurter from Minton suggests that he may have been somewhat defensive about the degree to which he considered the merits in case selection. Minton mentioned his "tough attitude" towards granting review in the note, and thanked Frankfurter for agreeing that there were few reviewworthy cases in the summer's accumulation of petitions.[22]

The largest cluster of justices in this analysis are the review-conservative justices who were not particularly merits-conscious in case selection. These justices, I suggest, failed to vote often for review less because they were satisfied with lower-court results than because they felt constrained by the limited capacity of the Court for judicial decision making. This consideration should have been particularly important for Justice Burton, the least merits-conscious of all the justices examined here.

Reasons for Opposing Review: The Case of Justice Burton

Burton's court papers provide a good indication of his concern for careful decision making. His papers contain numerous drafts of his opinions, each with marginal notes and corrections in his own handwriting. Burton was equally careful in case selection. Every summer, we have seen, Burton allotted plenty of time for reviewing the accumulation of petitions. He worked through them meticulously, recording the number of petitions he reviewed each day in his diary. Burton also expected well-considered work from his clerks. Judging from the unvarying format his clerks used in their certiorari memos, Burton's expectations were quite fixed. It also seems reasonable to conclude that the certiorari memos provide a fairly accurate impression of Burton's own case-selection criteria.

In their memos, Burton's clerks raised a variety of obstacles to review: the unreviewability of factual error ("I would not have convicted, had I been on the jury. But the issue was one of fact"),[23] mootness ("Since this case arose, the loyalty program has been revamped, a new standard set, and specific power given for readjudication. Thus I can see no reason to review the question presented here"),[24] the scope of legitimate agency discretion ("I can see no reason for taking cert unless someone wants to rewrite the immigration laws"),[25] lack of importance of the question presented to future litigation ("The Solicitor General claims that the question has arisen only once in 40 years"),[26] the responsibility of the state courts for state court error ("This Court cannot correct errors of the State Courts in matters of state law in the guise of affording due process of law to the parties"),[27] lack of a federal question ("A reading of the record convinces me that petitioner probably was not guilty, but there is no federal question here"),[28] and proper respect for state level discretion ("I seriously doubt that this Court can or should interfere with what a State declares to be its 'public policy,' even if in so doing the State has misconstrued federal statutes").[29]

Burton's clerks were capable of recommending denial even in the face of pitiable facts. Thus in a case in which the petitioner was sentenced to be executed, a clerk wrote: "It appears that Petitioner's lawyer has been guilty of almost criminal negligence, but the federal claim quite clearly was not raised in time. . . . I don't see how we can do other than deny."[30]

Burton's clerks had obviously been instructed that error alone was not a sufficient reason for review. When a Burton clerk did recommend review, it was never simply to correct error unless leaving the erroneous result unchanged might have misled other courts. In a case in which the question was whether or not death was accidental, for example, Burton's clerk wrote:

> The decision is clearly wrong. However, the case arises on diversity jurisdiction, presents only a question of state law, and such a problem has been thought of late not to present a sufficiently substantial issue meriting attention of the Court.[31]

A typical recommendation in favor of review, on the other hand, cited the importance of the question presented or a conflict among the circuits. In *Ullmann v. U.S.*, the clerk wrote:

> This is the first case involving the new immunity statute. That fact, and the fact that the opinion below is such an indecisive one, points to a grant here despite the fact that the decision may be correct and there is no conflict.[32]

To gain Burton's vote for review, it seems, a petition had to appeal to Burton's sense of legal importance and it had to be without serious procedural or other obstacles to review. It seems likely that Burton maintained this high standard for review in part because it suited his deliberate and careful approach to the decision-making process. His sensitivity to procedural and other barriers thus helped Burton keep his tendency to vote for review in line with what he believed to be the proper number of cases for on-the-merits decision. A highly sensitive standard for review also justified frequent inaction, which suited Burton's restrained view of the Supreme Court's function. On the merits, Burton was a frequent companion of that paragon of judicial restraint, Justice Frankfurter.

The connection between Burton's view of the judicial function and his tendency to vote only infrequently for review is more apparent when it is considered alongside the other justices' behavior. On the Court as a whole, the parallel between restraint in voting for review and restraint on the merits is striking. Pritchett's analysis of ideological differences among judges is particularly useful in showing this connection because the subjects of his analysis included most of the justices who sat during Burton's tenure.[33] Those men Pritchett labeled "libertarian activists" in *Civil Liberties and the Vinson Court* were the most review-prone justices to sit during the entire Burton period. Pritchett's "less libertarians" are among the least review-prone justices. Frankfurter, Pritchett's lone example of libertarian restraint, is somewhere near the middle in case selection, as he is in Pritchett's typology.

Pritchett describes the libertarian activist as the judge whose sympathies are aroused by the underdogs in our society and for whom "the *result* is the test of a decision."[34] A believer in libertarian restraint, on the other hand, emphasizes the process of judicial decision making and the non-democratic basis of judicial power. For Pritchett, a justice's activism or restraint is a function of the interaction of two variables: his sympathies toward underdogs and "the conception which the justice holds of his judicial role and the obligations imposed on him by his judicial function."[35]

What we know about the frequency with which Supreme Court justices vote for review is consistent with this two-dimensional interpretation of judicial motivation. Judicial conceptions of the Court's proper role, specifically, views about the proper workload of the Court, appear to be important in determining the frequency with which Supreme Court justices vote for review. Differences in responsiveness toward underdogs also seem relevant to case-selection voting. Review-prone justices were willing to go further than their colleagues in voting to hear petitioners who raised new claims for rights not yet established in precedent or legislation. These were also the types of cases about which the Court disagreed most in case selection: civil rights and civil liberties claims, and criminal cases. In more established areas of litigation, like federalism, the review-prone justices were relatively less likely to favor review, although they still tended to be more likely to vote for review than their colleagues. It is not surprising, for example, that Justice Murphy, one of the most review-prone justices in this period, viewed the Court's plenary role much more expansively than many of his colleagues. As he described his philosophy to his brother George:

> You will see that I go further than the rest of the Court. As a rule the Court is ticklish about invoking the Constitution if the case can be decided on any other grounds. For my part, I want to utilize the great charter whenever it is necessary to sustain the rights of man.[36]

If this analysis is correct, the relationships suggested here should hold good in any period of the modern Court's history. Proponents of restraint on the merits will always tend to be restrained in their propensity to vote for review, and those who see fewer obstacles to relief on the merits will always be more inclined to vote for review more frequently. Merits consciousness may diminish the tendency to vote for review somewhat in a period when the lower courts are liberal in recognizing new rights, but the relationship between judicial views of the function of the Court and the overall tendency to vote for review should remain roughly the same.

The conclusion that a justice's view of the degree of restraint appropriate to the Supreme Court is primarily responsible for the frequency with which he votes for review raises a long-debated question: Do judges disagree in voting because of the political attitudes they bring to their jobs or because their perceptions of the behavior appropriate to a judge and the work appropriate to a court differ? The Burton-period data are not susceptible to any analysis that can provide a definite answer to this question, although the voting patterns analyzed thus far are suggestive.

Were the political attitudes of the justices the only relevant variable in their decision-making, achieving the desired results on the merits would be the only consideration in case selection. The voting patterns in both unanimous and nonunanimous cases during the Burton period indicate, however, that the justices selected cases with something more than the result they desired on the merits in mind. More particularly, these voting patterns seem to reflect judicial sensitivity to the role of the Supreme Court on the merits. Without the independent verification that can only be provided by systematic interviews, unfortunately, a more direct analysis of the relationship between political attitudes and judicial perceptions of the proper role of the Court and of the judge is impossible.

The question of role versus attitude may not be clear-cut enough to yield a satisfying answer, even when optimum data are available. Howard came to the conclusion that the question was essentially unanswerable after interviewing thirty-five circuit court judges on three federal courts of appeal about their political beliefs and their conceptions of the judicial role:

> A classic question in the theory of judicial decision-making is whether judging is "political behavior" or "judicial role behavior." The short answer from this study is a qualified neither. . . . While past political orientations and role perceptions may be useful conceptual prisms to order complex values and experience, these ideological constructs are too generalized to control or to explain individual decisions in doubtful cases on the three tribunals.[37]

A second major problem, Howard concluded, was that "political orientations and role conceptions are not mutually exclusive."[38]

Result Orientation in Case Selection

One aspect of the relationship between role perceptions, political attitudes, and case-selection votes is susceptible to analysis, however: the question of whether the justices cast their case-selection votes with an eye to probable results on the merits. The result-oriented justice would vote against review when he believed a majority of the Court would disagree with him on the merits. He would favor review only when he was reasonably certain that his view of the correct outcome would prevail on the merits or when he wanted to write an influential dissent. Such behavior in case selection would enhance a justice's chances of seeing his policy preferences become law.

A justice who decided how to vote in case selection by estimating probable results on the merits would be in conflict with the familiar ideal of judicial conduct which stresses that judges consider only the case before them without trying to promote their policy preferences and without attempting to second-guess their colleagues. A finding that one or more of the justices during the Burton period was result-oriented in case selection would thus indicate that, for some justices, following one's political predispositions was more important than attempting to be dispassionate in decision making.

Although it conflicts with the ideal that a judge should try to ignore his own policy preferences in reaching decisions, the hypothesis that at least some members of the Court anticipate the reactions of their colleagues and vote accordingly in case selection has intuitive appeal. The justices work together daily, often for years, so a colleague's reaction could often be anticipated. A justice of fixed views who desired to see them implemented in decisions could hardly be ignorant of this route to success. Furthermore, firm opinions on the policy issues raised by the cases could be anticipated, given the age and pre-Court experience of many of the justices. Supreme Court justices have often been political people accustomed to acting upon their policy views in the period before appointment to the Court.

This conception of result-oriented decision making also has support in the literature on the Supreme Court. Walter Murphy's *Elements of Judicial Strategy,* for example, illustrates how a result-oriented justice can minimize the constraints of the traditional role.[39] More specifically, Justice Frank Murphy's biographer describes how he learned "one of the less obvious tools of the trade:" voting against certiorari when the Court would probably reverse a lower-court result of which he approved.[40] A certiorari memo prepared for Murphy exemplifies such result-oriented reasoning:

> This is another case like the *Steele* case of last term in many respects. There is only one result as far as you are concerned—the one reached by the CCA [Circuit Court of Appeals]. There is no reason for taking the case ex-

cept to affirm it—and that would create the usual furore and perhaps result in another mess like *Screws.* I can imagine several of the Brethren waxing eloquent over the state action point. The CCA was plainly right here and nothing more need be said on the issue by us. The possibility of a reversal in this case would be enough to make you fight to deny cert. Fortunately, there are no conflicts.[41]

Similarly, an anonymous justice on the current Court admitted to a *Time* reporter that he routinely calculated the probable outcome of a case when he made his review decision.[42] He stated that he would not vote to grant review in a case he believed wrongly decided below if he believed the majority was likely to affirm the lower court's wrong conclusion.

Review votes in cases the Court later decided on the merits can provide an empirical test of result orientation in case selection. If a justice characteristically estimated the Court's probable decision on the merits, he would, except when he erred, be with the majority on the merits in the cases he voted to review. If, on the other hand, the outcome and the justice's on-the-merits votes in these cases were dissimilar, the pattern would suggest an absence of result orientation in case selection. Similarity between individual votes and outcome does not necessarily show that a justice is result-oriented, however. A justice's on-the-merits voting and the Court's decisions might be similar because the views of that justice happened to coincide with those of the majority in most cases. Such a person would "win" on the merits by default rather than by design. A comparison of individual votes and outcomes, in other words, can prove that result orientation did *not* exist for particular justices, but it cannot prove that it *did* exist for others.

Such a comparison is made in table 4.7. To facilitate analysis, I have shown the differences between individual on-the-merits votes and majority outcomes in each justice's subset of cases. It is clear that every justice voted to reverse the cases he voted to hear oftener than the Court as a whole did, but for some justices the difference was much greater than for others.

Table 4.7   **Result orientation in case selection, 1947–57 Terms: Non-unanimous cases—justices voted to review—certiorari granted**

Justice[a]	Percentage justice voted to reverse	Percentage court voted to reverse	Difference	Propensity to to vote for review[b]
Rutledge	85.2	57.0	28.2	4
Black	80.4	56.3	24.1	3
Douglas	75.3	53.2	22.1	2
Murphy	74.4	52.3	22.1	1
Brennan	79.0	61.8	17.2	5
Frankfurter	66.8	53.0	13.8	11
Warren	75.7	62.6	13.1	6
Jackson	62.1	50.5	11.6	9
Minton	64.0	57.1	6.9	14
Reed	58.1	51.6	6.5	7
Clark	62.3	58.5	3.8	12
Vinson	60.6	57.0	3.6	13
Harlan	62.3	59.9	2.4	8
Burton	56.4	55.0	1.4	10

[a] Whittaker omitted for lack of participation.
[b] Justices ranked by their tendency to vote for review generally.

Contrary to what one would expect if result orientation were characteristic in case selection, the justices who voted oftenest for review were least successful in getting the majority to vote with them on the merits. The divergence between individual and majority votes for the review-prone members of the Court seems too great to be attributable to mistaken views of the probable final outcome. The pattern for the remaining justices can be explained more plausibly as the effect of their tendency to be in agreement with a majority of their fellows on the substantive issues that came before the Court, rather than the effect of result orientation in case selection. Result orientation in case selection implies an attitude toward the judicial function that justices like Burton and Vinson and Harlan, the members of the Court whose final votes conform most closely to the majority's, strongly disavowed.

Baum came to a similar conclusion about the absence of result orientation in case selection in his research on the

California Supreme Court.[43] Baum based his analysis on the California Court's reputation for sensitivity to defendants' rights in criminal procedure cases. According to his hypothesis, if outcome orientation were operating, conservative justices in these cases should vote less often for review than their liberal colleagues. The reverse, however, was true. Even when the more conservative members of the Court would almost certainly be in the minority on the merits, they voted for review. As Baum concluded, "This response pattern suggested strongly that justices responded to the lower-court decision alone and did not take into account their own court's possible decision."[44]

Although both Baum's research and the analysis I have undertaken here suggest that result orientation is not characteristic of case selection on a collegial court, neither analytic technique is precise enough to show more than general tendencies. It is possible, for example, that some justices calculate outcomes in cases that are particularly important to them, but not in others. The crude measure here would not reflect such a strategy. The measure here is also too broadly based to reflect the type of Court-wide policy orientation on particularly sensitive issues discussed in chapter 2.

Conclusion

Voting patterns in nonunanimous case-selection decisions during the Burton period suggest two ways in which Supreme Court justices disagree. One stems from differences in judicial responsiveness to the merits of the petitioners' claims: the justices are familiar with the arguments of the contending parties when they make their review decisions, and it seems clear that they take their evaluations of the merits into account in voting. The other source of nonunanimity originates in differences among the justices in their beliefs about the proper work and workload of the Supreme Court. These differences of opinion affect the extent to which the justices are willing to take their views of the merits of cases into account in voting for review.

Evidence from the Burton period suggests that these two sources of nonunanimous votes are not completely independent of each other. Instead, a justice's resolution of the merits of cases coming before him appears to be related to his presuppositions about the number of cases the Court should resolve in a term. Interpretations of the merits and views on the proper workload of the Court appear to be related because both depend upon one's attitude toward the exercise of judicial power. The justices most likely to cite considerations of judicial restraint on the merits, according to this hypothesis, will be those least likely to vote for review and vice versa.

Whether judicial restraint is basically a rationalization for withholding relief from petitioners for whom a justice has little sympathy, "a means rather than an end,"[45] cannot be determined with certainty from case-selection voting patterns in nonunanimous cases. The Burton data indicate, however, that most justices who tend to vote frequently for review do so in a wide variety of cases, and similarly, that the less review-prone are restrictive with their votes across the board. A comparison of votes to review with votes on the merits in the same cases also suggests that members of the Supreme Court do not simply vote their policy preferences in case selection. Nor do justices appear routinely to calculate probable outcomes on the merits in deciding whether or not to vote for review. Instead, the norm appears to be that a judge should attempt to be dispassionate and apolitical. The conception the justices share of their role thus seems to limit the range of behavior which would otherwise be possible in case selection.

To argue that judicial views of the proper role of the judge and judicial conceptions of the appropriate work of the Court on the merits are important in case selection is not to argue that judicial attitudes toward litigants are irrelevant. The differing views of judges about the amount and type of work appropriate to courts and the relief due litigants are probably shaped by some of the same predispositions that produce different degrees of sympathy toward litigants. The influence of such attitudes on case-selection votes, however, appears to be indirect.

Five   Alignments among the Justices in Case Selection

Patterns of association among justices in selecting cases to review—if such patterns exist—will tend either to support or to discredit the explanation of voting differences suggested in the last chapter, because any explanation of how decisions are reached involves certain expectations about patterns of association when there is disagreement. An examination of voting alignments can thus lead to important insights about the politics of decision making in a collegial body.

Such an analysis of alignments among justices in case selection can be useful in a variety of ways. First, it can show whether there are cohesive subgroups within the Court. The presence of cohesive voting groups, in the face of the diverse legal and factual issues confronting the justices in the cases, would suggest the importance of one or a few underlying variables in case selection. Focusing on patterns of association can also facilitate comparisons between the case selection process and consideration on the merits. Strong similarities in voting patterns at both stages of decision would suggest that the justices make case selection decisions primarily on the basis of their analysis of the merits. Finally, analysis of voting alignments can show whether a minority of the Court sometimes agrees to vote together in case selection to achieve policy results it desires on the merits. This possibility is worth exploring because the rule of four provides an easily exploited opportunity for a minority to force the majority into resolving cases it does not want to consider on the merits. If a faction could anticipate getting the results on the merits it desired, it could use case selection to accomplish its policy ends.

Such a view of case selection has support in the literature. In two well-known articles, Glendon Schubert has argued that a bloc of justices forced the majority to decide certain worker petitions in Federal Employers' Liability Act (FELA) cases.[1] The voting bloc did this, Schubert contended, to achieve the policy results it desired on the merits. The Burton-period votes, which Schubert did not have when he wrote, provide an opportunity to test his hypothesis.

Alignments among Justices: An Overview

I have suggested that differences among the justices can be analyzed in terms of their disagreement about the merits of cases, the balance of competing considerations in favor of plenary review, and the desirable workload of the Court. Agreement between pairs of justices, often called bloc analysis, offers a way to examine the interplay of these and other variables in case selection. The following analysis is based on all nonunanimous cases, regardless of subject matter, which were voted upon during the Burton period.

Making Voting Alignments Yield Maximum Information

The precise effect of any single variable on case-selection votes is difficult to assess when votes are analyzed in terms of alignments between pairs of justices. Multiple variables tend to make it difficult to pinpoint causal relationships. Bloc analysis of case selection votes yields clearer results, however, if the basis for analysis is interagreement in favor of review rather than overall interagreement. Statistics on overall interagreement, that is, vote totals that include both votes for and votes against review, tend to be swamped by the tendency of most justices to vote against review most of the time. When we tabulate nonunanimous cases during the Burton period by the number of votes they received, the disproportionate number of negative votes is obvious (table 5.1). Limiting consideration to the relatively infrequent votes in favor of review thus avoids the methodological problems raised by large numbers of nearly unanimous votes against review. It also isolates the affirmative act of

Table 5.1   Voting for and against review, 1945–57 Terms

Votes on review		Number of cases
For	Against	
1	8	762
2	7	635
3	6	381
4	5	317
5	4	190
6	3	159
7	2	159
8	1	127
		2,730

NOTE: Total positive votes = 8,476; total negative votes = 15,094 (excluding cases in which there was less than full participation).

voting together for review from the more passive alternative of voting with others, usually many others, against review.

Those who analyze alignments on the merits face a similar difficulty in choosing the statistical material from which to generalize. Such analysis must decide whether or not to restrict themselves to dissent on the merits, or whether to measure overall interagreement. Joel Grossman was able to show the value of restricting analysis to dissenting votes in a study of voting behavior during the chief justiceship of Earl Warren. He demonstrated that analysts who use overall interagreement on the merits to describe like-minded subgroups of justices cannot determine whether the alignments they find are closely associated dissenters, or merely frequent companions in majorities.[2] Supposedly nonaligned justices, in fact, voted with each other almost as often as the "blocs" that emerged from overall interagreement scores.

In an analysis of alignments at the case-selection stage, using only votes in favor of review has additional advantages. Restricting analysis to positive votes shows more precisely whether or not the justices who seldom vote for review tend to vote as a group when they do vote for review, or whether they associate freely and randomly with their review-prone colleagues. Affirmative-vote statistics are also useful in determining whether outcome-oriented voting blocs are operating in case selection. Analysis of overall interagreement data, on the other hand, cannot with precision reveal coalitions to gain review, because it places most of the justices together most of the time.

The insight that can be gained from bloc analysis based on positive case-selection votes can be enhanced by including certain additional information. One valuable additional statistic about each pair of justices is the frequency the pair were the only justices to vote for review. This information helps indicate the closeness of the ideological fit between two individuals. In the analyses to follow, these figures, stated as percentages of all two-vote cases in the period, are included for each pair of justices. In the tables they are enclosed in parentheses to facilitate identification.

Another means of improving analysis is to include information about plenary voting with case-selection information. In what follows I have included dissenting blocs on the merits. I chose agreement in dissent, rather than overall interagreement on the merits, because dissent from the majority of the Court seems more analogous to voting in favor of review, usually against the majority of the Court. Alliances in both stages of decision stand out sharply.

Finally, each justice's lone votes in favor of review are included. In the following tables they are bracketed and placed along the diagonal in both case-selection and dissent matrices. These lone votes are expressed as percentages in the case-selection tables, and as numbers in the dissent tables.

For this analysis I have divided the Burton period into "natural" courts—periods marked by deaths or retirements of justices. This increases the number of votes for analysis without adding complicating personnel changes. Analysis based on natural courts does not, however, entirely eliminate the effect on voting of absences due to accidents or injury. Such interruptions are noted whenever they occur. Their effect is minimized within the case-selection matrices themselves because alignments are expressed as percentages of votes in favor of review over total opportunities for voting together.

The First Natural Court: 1947 and 1948 Terms

The most striking feature of alignments in the 1947–48 natural court[3] is the association between Rutledge and Murphy and Black and Douglas both in case selection and in dissent (tables 5.2, 5.3). Among the four, Murphy and Rutledge were the most closely associated, but just barely. Douglas was almost as likely to vote with Murphy as Rutledge, and Douglas voted more frequently with Murphy than Rutledge did in two-vote cases. Together, Murphy, Rutledge, Douglas, and Black—the four members of the Court most likely to vote for review—were associated strongly enough in case selection to constitute a voting bloc, if in defining the term we use a modification of Sprague's criterion as a cut-off point.

The term "bloc" in this context refers only to the degree of association among justices, not to their motivations in voting together.[4] Analysis here indicates that despite the association of these four justices they do not seem to have been trying to vote as a bloc. The two-vote percentages indicate that every pair, but especially Murphy-Douglas and Black-Douglas, often voted alone for review, against fellow bloc members. The high percentages of lone dissents for each of these justices also indicate the absence of an intention to vote as a bloc.

Clearly the remainder of the Court did not regard Murphy, Rutledge, Douglas, and Black, the most review-prone members of the Court, as a bloc in opposition to themselves. The less review-prone members of the Court were more likely to vote for review with bloc members than with each other. This was true overall, even in the two-vote cases. The pattern indicates the absence of a counterbloc, and it also shows the willingness of bloc members to vote with or against anyone for review, even when that meant voting alone against the rest of the Court.

Table 5.2   Interagreement in favor of review and two-vote pairs, 1947–48 Terms

	Ru.	Mu.	Do.
Rutledge	[2]	37	32
		(9)	(9)
Murphy		[6]	36
			(13)
Douglas			[7]
Black			
Reed			
Burton			
Vinson			
Jackson			
Frankfurter			

KEY TO TABLE

All numbers are percentages.

Numbers in ( ) are percentages of cases receiving only two votes in whic
this pair of justices voted together.

Numbers in [ ] are percentages of the justice's total votes for revie
which he cast alone.

Numbers in neither parentheses nor brackets are the percentage o
agreement between the pair of justices, derived from the number of cases i
which both favored review divided by the total number of opportunitie
they had to vote together.

STATISTICS: Total of 455 cases, 95 two-vote pairs; no prolonged ab
sences; court cohesion = .15; criterion = .30; largest bloc satisfying cr
terion = Rutledge, Murphy, Douglas, Black.

Bl.	Re.	Bu.	Vi.	Ja.	Fr.
28	15	11	13	13	13
(6)	(1)	(1)	(3)	(1)	(2)
29	20	13	15	16	17
(5)	(2)	(1)	(3)	(0)	(4)
27	14	11	11	12	12
(13)	(5)	(2)	(2)	(2)	(0)
[5]	14	10	12	9	8
	(1)	(0)	(3)	(1)	(0)
	[2]	12	12	12	11
		(1)	(0)	(1)	(2)
		[1]	10	10	9
			(2)	(2)	(2)
			[1]	8	7
				(0)	(0)
				[1]	7
					(2)
					[1]

Table 5.3   Interagreement in dissent, 1946–48 Terms

	Ru.	Mu.	Do.
Rutledge	[5]	72	56
Murphy		[4]	55
Douglas			[10]
Black			
Reed			
Burton			
Vinson			
Jackson			
Frankfurter			
Total dissents this period	103	92	103

KEY TO TABLE

All numbers are cases, not percentages.
Numbers in [ ] are the number of the justice's lone dissents.
Numbers not in brackets are the number of cases in which the pair of justices voted together in dissent.

SOURCE: Pritchett, *Civil Liberties,* table 4 (p. 181).

The on-the-merits patterns show the ideological similarity of bloc members—their average interagreement in dissent was higher than that of any other group. The Murphy-Douglas-Black-Rutledge bloc also opposed the majority of the Court frequently, as their higher than average number of dissents indicates. Jackson and Frankfurter constituted a strong two-man opposition bloc on the merits, an association not apparent in case selection. A larger counterbloc, consisting of Vinson, Jackson, and Frankfurter, was also present on the merits but absent in case selection. Both of these blocs were probably absent in case selection because of their general disinclination to vote for review.

The Second Natural Court: 1949–52 Terms

During the longest natural court of the Burton period, 1949–52, only Douglas and Black were strongly aligned (tables 5.4, 5.5). They agreed 36 percent of the time, and their votes accounted for 44 percent of all two-vote cases throughout the four-year period. Rutledge and Murphy,

Bl.	Re.	Bu.	Vi.	Ja.	Fr.
61	8	10	3	12	15
58	2	3	5	13	18
55	8	8	7	12	13
[2]	6	6	6	5	6
	[3]	27	21	25	16
		[6]	27	33	29
			[0]	26	22
				[7]	58
					[8]
85	52	69	50	95	96

formerly the most review-prone and most highly associated members of the Court, both died in the summer of 1949.[5] President Truman replaced them with Clark and Minton, men who showed no particular tendency to vote for review with each other and little inclination to vote for review at all.

As in earlier years, no pairs of justices tended to vote in opposition to Black and Douglas for review. The votes of Black and Douglas with others account for most of the two-vote cases not accounted for by Black and Douglas as a pair. The pattern is similar in dissent on the merits. Black and Douglas filed dissents together much oftener than anyone else, and the remaining justices tended to dissent oftener with Black and Douglas than with most other members of the Court. The only notable exception to this pattern was the interagreement in dissent between Jackson and Frankfurter.

As in the 1947–48 natural court, there was some relation between the tendency to vote for review and the tendency to dissent on the merits. Black and Douglas led the Court in both respects during the 1949–52 period. Their high level of dissent in comparison to most of their colleagues and their much greater propensity to vote for review reveals their ideological isolation. In the previous natural court the relationship between dissent and the propensity to grant review was weaker. The 1949–52 period also suggests that

Table 5.4   Interagreement in favor of review and two-vote pairs, 1949–52 Terms

	Bl.	Do.	Re.
Black	[9]	36 (44)	16 (5)
Douglas		[10]	20 (5)
Reed			[3]
Frankfurter			
Jackson			
Burton			
Vinson			
Clark			
Minton			

NOTE: For key to table see table 5.2.

STATISTICS: Total of 991 cases, 81 two-vote pairs; no prolonged absences; court cohesion = .15; criterion = .30; largest bloc satisfying criterion = Black, Douglas.

Table 5.5   Interagreement in dissent, 1949–52 Terms

	Bl.	Do.	Re.
Black	[27]	79	11
Douglas		[18]	21
Reed			[6]
Frankfurter			
Jackson			
Burton			
Vinson			
Clark			
Minton			
Total dissents this period	148	130	59

NOTE: for key to table see table 5.3.

SOURCE: Pritchett, *Civil Liberties*, table 4 (p. 181).

Fr.	Ja.	Bu.	Vi.	Cl.	Mi.
18	14	16	13	14	6
(5)	(2)	(4)	(2)	(2)	(0)
20	17	19	17	17	9
(4)	(3)	(4)	(0)	(2)	(0)
14	19	20	18	17	10
(1)	(3)	(6)	(2)	(0)	(0)
[1]	16	14	13	13	8
	(1)	(0)	(1)	(0)	(0)
	[1]	18	17	15	9
		(2)	(1)	(0)	(0)
		[2]	17	17	10
			(1)	(0)	(0)
			[1]	15	10
				(0)	(0)
				17	10
				(0)	(0)
				[2]	14
					(0)
					[0]

Fr.	Ja.	Bu.	Vi.	Cl.	Mi.
49	27	16	13	6	16
33	18	16	14	7	14
13	16	11	15	2	17
[8]	46	13	2	1	10
	[13]	9	5	3	11
		[2]	7	4	10
			[1]	8	16
				[0]	4
					[3]

Fr.	Ja.	Bu.	Vi.	Cl.	Mi.
101	80	44	40	15	47

the tendency to vote alone for review might be connected with the tendency to dissent alone.

The Third Natural Court: 1953 and 1954 Terms

I have treated the 1953 and 1954 terms as one natural court, despite the replacement of Jackson by Harlan during the 1954 term (tables 5.6, 5.7).[6] Harlan's case-selection votes were few in number because he joined the Court late in the term, and they are omitted here.[7]

Case selection in the 1953–54 natural court resembles the 1949–52 period. Black and Douglas remained the most closely aligned pair by a considerable margin, accounting for over half of the two-vote cases, and these men were again the most review-prone justices, by about the same margin as in 1949–52. Black and Douglas also had by far the highest percentages of lone votes for review, a pattern consistent with their earlier lone-vote behavior. Finally, as in earlier terms, the rest of the Court tended to vote at least as often with this pair as with their less review-prone colleagues, the

Table 5.6	Interagreement in favor of review and two-vote pairs, 1953–54 Term		
	Bl.	Do.	Wa.
Black	[9]	38	19
		(51)	(1)
Douglas		[12]	20
			(3)
Warren			[2]
Clark			
Burton			
Reed			
Jackson			
Frankfurter			
Minton			

NOTE: for key to table see table 5.2.

only exceptions being Reed and Jackson in two-vote cases.

Warren, who subsequently aligned closely with Black and Douglas in case selection as well as in on-the-merits voting, had not yet differentiated himself from the more review-conservative members of the Court. Warren's pattern is similar in dissent where he also showed no special affinity for Black or Douglas.

In this natural court, the relationship between case selection and plenary voting is somewhat different from that of previous terms. Lone votes for review were no less common than they had been previously, but lone dissents on the merits became less frequent with Warren's chief justiceship, and the overall rate of dissent also dropped. The most review-prone justices, Black and Douglas, again led the Court in dissenting, in keeping with earlier patterns. Yet the third-ranking dissenter was Minton, consistently the least likely member of the Court to vote for review. Half of Minton's dissents were with Douglas, a justice with whom Minton never showed any particular propensity to vote for review.

Cl.	Bu.	Re.	Ja.	Fr.	Mi.
16	12	11	14	8	7
(0)	(2)	(3)	(0)	(3)	(0)
16	12	13	15	18	7
(1)	(2)	(3)	(3)	(9)	(0)
19	15	14	12	14	9
(1)	(0)	(2)	(0)	(2)	(0)
[1]	13	14	14	12	9
	(1)	(2)	(2)	(0)	(0)
	[2]	13	10	9	7
		(2)	(0)	(0)	(0)
		[6]	15	8	7
			(13)	(3)	(0)
			[3]	14	8
				(3)	(1)
				[1]	7
					(0)
					[0]

STATISTICS: Total of 454 cases, 46 two-vote pairs; Jackson's votes absent for the 1954 Term; cohesion = .13; criterion = .26; largest bloc satisfying criterion = Black, Douglas, Warren.

Table 5.7   Interagreement in dissent, 1953 Term

	Bl.	Do.	Wa.
Black	[2]	22	5
Douglas		[2]	4
Warren			[0]
Clark			
Burton			
Reed			
Jackson			
Frankfurter			
Minton			
Total dissents this period	26	33	9

NOTE: For key to table, see table 5.3.
SOURCE: Schubert, *Quantitative Analysis*, table 3A.1 (p. 144).

The Fourth, Fifth, and Sixth Natural Courts: 1955, 1956, and 1957 Terms

The remaining three terms constitute three separate natural courts because of the retirements of Jackson, then Minton, and finally, Reed (tables 5.8–5.13). Throughout these three terms Black and Douglas remained the most closely aligned justices, and the individuals most prone to vote alone for review. Warren's voting pattern, on the other hand, changed. From the 1955 term on, he became more closely associated with Black and Douglas. At the same time, his propensity to vote for review increased, although he did not show the tendency to vote alone for review typical of other review-prone justices.

The infrequency with which Chief Justice Warren voted alone for review was probably a function of his position as chief justice. As I have discussed earlier, all chief justices during the Burton period had disproportionately few lone votes for or against review. Warren's behavior in two-vote cases may also be attributable to his position as chief justice. In all three terms, Warren participated in a disproportionate share of the two-vote cases. By voting as he did, one might conjecture, he amassed good will with individual justices, which could be used when needed. It should be noted, however, that Vinson evidenced no similar propensity to-

Cl.	Bu.	Re.	Ja.	Fr.	Mi.
2	0	0	2	4	5
4	8	0	3	3	10
6	3	3	1	0	2
[0]	5	3	2	1	2
	[0]	7	3	1	8
		[2]	2	0	4
			[0]	4	6
				[0]	3
					[0]
9	15	10	11	9	20

wards sociability in case selection.

Brennan joined the Black-Douglas-Warren combination in the 1956 term when he took Minton's place on the Court. Unlike Minton, Brennan voted frequently for review. Only Black and Douglas voted oftener for review. In 1957, Black, Douglas, and Brennan were closely enough associated to be deemed a bloc. Warren's association with any of the three, however, was never high enough to satisfy the bloc criterion used in this analysis, although the Black-Douglas-Warren combination came close in 1955.

Among more review-conservative members of the Court, the relationships approximated those of earlier years, except for some unusual patterns in the two-vote cases. Although the number of such cases is not large in these single-term natural courts, Reed's tendency to vote with various justices and Harlan's tendency to vote with Frankfurter are worth noting.

The on-the-merits parallels associated with earlier terms are largely absent in this three-year period. The propensity to dissent shows almost no tendency to match the propensity to vote for review. Likewise, lone dissents did not parallel lone votes for review in frequency. The clear association between Black and Douglas in case selection was also absent on the merits, although they did dissent together oftener than any other pair.

Table 5.8   Interagreement in favor of review and two-vote pairs, 1955 Term

	Do.	Bl.	Wa.
Douglas	[10]	35	28
		(31)	(7)
Black		[10]	29
			(3)
Warren			[1]
Clark			
Harlan			
Burton			
Reed			
Minton			
Frankfurter			

NOTE: For key to table see table 5.2.
STATISTICS: Total of 268 cases, 28 two-vote pairs; no prolonged absence cohesion = .16; criterion = .32; largest bloc satisfying criterion = Black Douglas (Black, Douglas, Warren = .31).

Table 5.9   Interagreement in dissent, 1955 Term

	Do.	Bl.	Wa.
Douglas	[2]	17	15
Black		[0]	15
Warren			[0]
Clark			
Harlan			
Burton			
Reed			
Minton			
Frankfurter			
Total dissents this period	25	17	15

NOTE: For key to table see table 5.3.
SOURCE: Schubert, *Quantitative Analysis,* table 3A.3 (p. 146).

Cl.	Ha.	Bu.	Re.	Mi.	Fr.
18	18	14	11	12	15
(0)	(2)	(2)	(2)	(0)	(5)
20	17	13	14	13	17
(0)	(2)	(2)	(7)	(0)	(5)
22	20	15	17	14	16
(4)	(6)	(5)	(7)	(0)	(2)
[1]	16	14	15	15	13
	(0)	(0)	(0)	(0)	(0)
	[1]	18	16	13	15
		(4)	(4)	(0)	(0)
		[3]	13	12	12
			(2)	(0)	(0)
			[5]	13	11
				(0)	(0)
				[0]	11
					(0)
					[1]

Cl.	Ha.	Bu.	Re.	Mi.	Fr.
4	3	2	2	0	3
4	0	0	0	0	1
4	0	0	0	0	1
[0]	1	1	4	4	1
	[4]	11	6	8	16
		[1]	14	14	7
			[1]	14	2
				[0]	4
					[1]

Cl.	Ha.	Bu.	Re.	Mi.	Fr.
9	27	22	18	18	22

Table 5.10   **Interagreement in favor of review and two-vote pairs, 1956 Term**

	Bl.	Do.	Wa.
Black	[8]	39 (19)	35 (6)
Douglas		[8]	38 (14)
Warren			[2]
Brennan			
Harlan			
Frankfurter			
Clark			
Burton			
Reed			

NOTE: For key to table see table 5.2.

STATISTICS: Total of 233 cases, 36 two-vote pairs; Reed absent for approximately one third of votes; cohesion = .20; criterion = .40; no bloc satisfy criterion (Black, Douglas = .39).

Table 5.11   **Interagreement in dissent, 1956 Term**

	Bl.	Do.	Wa.
Black	[0]	23	14
Douglas		[8]	13
Warren			[0]
Brennan			
Harlan			
Frankfurter			
Clark			
Burton			
Reed			
Total dissents this period	26	32	14

NOTE: For key to table see table 5.3.

SOURCE: Schubert, *Quantitative Analysis,* table 3A.4 (p. 147).

Br.	Ha.	Fr.	Cl.	Bu.	Re.
28	21	21	18	13	15
(0)	(6)	(2)	(0)	(2)	(5)
31	21	19	20	12	13
(0)	(0)	(2)	(0)	(0)	(2)
35	22	19	22	16	20
(4)	(0)	(0)	(0)	(4)	(5)
[1]	24	22	21	17	14
	(0)	(0)	(0)	(0)	(0)
	[1]	22	19	18	11
		(6)	(2)	(2)	(5)
		[0]	15	13	11
			(0)	(0)	(10)
			[1]	13	10
				(0)	(0)
				[1]	10
					(3)
					[3]

Br.	Ha.	Fr.	Cl.	Bu.	Re.
7	2	5	2	1	0
7	1	3	3	1	0
6	0	0	0	0	0
[0]	4	6	1	2	1
	[2]	22	2	15	6
		[4]	2	14	6
			[2]	9	3
				[2]	1
					[0]

Br.	Ha.	Fr.	Cl.	Bu.	Re.
12	29	33	18	27	9

Table 5.12   Interagreement in favor of review and two-vote pairs, 1957 Term

	Bl.	Do.	Br.
Black	[10]	33	27
		(27)	(0)
Douglas		[8]	31
			(7)
Brennan			[1]
Warren			
Harlan			
Frankfurter			
Burton			
Clark			
Whittaker			

NOTE: For key to table see table 5.2.
STATISTICS: Total of 222 cases, 26 two-vote pairs; no prolonged absence
cohesion = .15; criterion = .30; largest bloc satisfying criterion = Blac
Douglas, Brennan.

Table 5.13   Interagreement in dissent, 1957 Term

	Bl.	Do.	Br.
Black	[0]	29	14
Douglas		[5]	15
Brennan			[0]
Warren			
Harlan			
Frankfurter			
Burton			
Clark			
Whittaker			
Total dissents this period	32	38	16

NOTE: For key to table see table 5.3.
SOURCE: Schubert, *Quantitative Analysis,* table 3A.5 (p. 148).

Wa.	Ha.	Fr.	Bu.	Cl.	Wh.
25	16	13	11	15	16
(2)	(0)	(0)	(0)	(0)	(2)
27	14	10	10	15	9
(14)	(2)	(0)	(0)	(7)	(0)
24	21	20	15	15	12
(0)	(0)	(7)	(0)	(7)	(0)
[2]	15	11	12	15	10
	(0)	(0)	(0)	(0)	(2)
	[3]	19	14	13	15
		(7)	(0)	(0)	(5)
		[1]	12	10	10
			(0)	(2)	(0)
			[1]	11	7
				(2)	(0)
				[1]	9
					(0)
					[3]

Wa.	Ha.	Fr.	Bu.	Cl.	Wh.
26	0	0	3	1	2
26	1	2	2	0	1
12	2	2	2	0	0
[0]	1	0	1	0	2
	[0]	24	18	9	14
		[3]	12	6	11
			[0]	13	14
				[4]	7
					[2]

Wa.	Ha.	Fr.	Bu.	Cl.	Wh.
29	31	29	30	21	24

Overall Patterns of Association in the Burton Period

Taken together, the matrices depicted in tables 5.2–5.13 suggest the importance of multiple variables in case selection. Were a single variable the basis of disagreement, the justices would have tended to divide into opposing subgroups, at least in some terms.[8] Were that single variable merits-consciousness, the alignments in case selection would have resembled the patterns of association in dissent. Instead, the typical pattern throughout the Burton period was a single two-, three-, or four-man alignment of the most review-prone justices, with the remaining justices voting more frequently with each of the review-prone justices than with each other. This pattern is only partially reproduced in dissent. Again, the most review-prone justices tended to be the most closely associated. The pattern was different for the less review-prone justices. In dissent they associated with each other more, and with the review-prone justices less, than in case selection.

The pattern among review-conservative justices— dissociation in case selection and association in dissent— may be attributable to the desire of these justices to ration the amount of on-the-merits decision making the Court took on. It should be noted, of course, that in an analysis based on votes in favor of review, justices who tended to vote against review across the board could show their ideological similarity directly only in on-the-merits voting. The tendency of some justices to oppose review in most cases also masked ideological similarities between some review-prone justices and review-conservative justices. Such similarities were only evident on the merits in dissent, where obstacles to review were not so frequently an issue.

The patterns revealed in these analyses of preliminary and on-the-merits votes also suggest the absence of conscious coalition formation in case selection. In every natural court, even the most highly associated justices often voted in opposition to each other, as the large percentages of lone votes for review and the two-vote patterns show. Were vote manipulation common, such unsuccessful votes for review would have been less frequent, and tight-knit blocs containing more than two justices would have tended to develop.

The Burton-period block analyses thus suggest that case selection does not routinely involve deliberate strategies by subgroups to gain review. As we have seen, this seems to be true also of individual tendencies to take the probable majority decision on the merits into account in case selection. The negative evidence of coalitional behavior, however, does not eliminate the possibility that, in a confined segment of cases, some of the justices do form subgroups to maximize their power to effectuate their policy wishes. The overall analysis may simply have been insufficiently precise to show the operation of a certiorari bloc. If we narrow the scope of analysis sufficiently, it may be possible to determine whether the justices actually did form outcome-oriented blocs on occasion.

Do Justices Form Blocs in Certain Cases?

Two approaches can be taken to search for evidence of coalitions in case selection. The first is to compare the numbers of cases supported by one, two, three, up to all nine justices. Evidence of conscious bloc behavior in case selection is a disproportionate number of four- or five-vote grants of review. If opposing blocs were operating, cases in which one, two, or three justices cast unsuccessful votes for review should be relatively rare because they would indicate the failure of a bloc to control the outcome of the vote. Two blocs are likely because manipulation of the case-selection process would tend to encourage an opposing subgroup to form.

A second approach likely to reveal bloc behavior in case selection, if it exists, is to focus on the type of case most likely to elicit such behavior. Published dissents from the Court's negative certiorari and appeals decisions, because they often claim departures from the Court's usual review formula, provide a good means of isolating possible pockets of coalitional behavior.[9] If we use this criterion, FELA cases

appear to be the most likely candidates for coalition formation during the Burton period. These are the only cases in
which the justices repeatedly indicated serious disagreement over the proper standards for review.[10] It seems safe
to conclude that if the Burton-period justices did not bloc
to gain review in these cases, they never did.

Four-Vote Cases and Their Meaning

Patterns of case-selection voting remained fairly constant
over the Burton period. The proportion of cases receiving
one vote never rose above 27 percent, for example, and the
proportion of unanimous grants was consistently high.
Throughout the period, the most frequent pattern was for a
case to get one or, less often, two votes in favor of review
(see fig. 5.1). The high proportion of losing votes suggests
that coalitional behavior does not characterize case selection, although the percentage of four-vote grants of review
is slightly higher than might be expected if voting behavior
were entirely individualistic. Even more striking, however,
is the proportion of unanimous votes for review.

This high percentage deserves attention here because it
suggests that some factor unrelated to the substance of cases
may be relevant to voting behavior in certain circumstances.
Of course, some types of cases each term must clearly merit
review in the eyes of everyone, but this variable can hardly
account for the 10 percent jump from the eight- to the
nine-vote category. One explanation is that when almost the
whole Court desired to hear a case, the remaining justice
sometimes threw in his vote to make the decision unanimous. Such a practice would encourage group cohesion
by reducing the occasions of disagreement, and it would
evidence respect for the opinion of one's colleagues. Moreover, nothing important is lost to the justice who goes along
with his colleagues, because a losing vote against review
has little public significance, unlike a dissent on the merits.

The relatively high percentage of four-vote cases may be
another manifestation of the tendency of some members of
the Court to seek to maintain harmony where the personal
cost is small. In any natural court one or more justices sen-

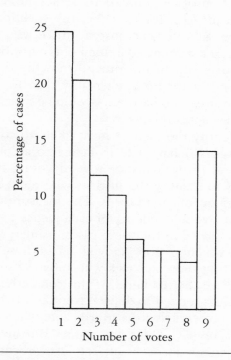

Fig. 5.1   Votes for review, 1945–57 Terms.

sitive to the importance of maintaining good feeling on a collegial court might have volunteered decisive votes to any trio of justices who wanted review. Such a justice would become the fourth member of the group not because he believed that review was appropriate but because of his desire to alleviate the harshness of the rule of four in close cases. This possibility, of course, directly conflicts with the coalitional hypothesis discussed earler.

The competing explanations can be tested by establishing who among the Burton period justices was more likely to vote for review in four-vote cases than otherwise. Knowing the identity of such a justice might help determine whether justices add their votes primarily to be sociable in four-vote cases, or whether they act as part of a coalition seeking review. If the major contributor of crucial fourth votes were known from other contexts to be among the more policy-oriented justices, for example, the coalitional explanation would be indicated, because a justice who is the marginal member of a winning coalition holds a position of power on the Court.[11] If, on the other hand, the contributor were better known for his congeniality than for his orientation toward power, the harmony-seeking explanation would appear more appropriate.

To identify the justices most likely to contribute crucial fourth votes, I have had to take into account the general inclination of each justice toward voting for review. The task was to identify the justices who tended to step out of character in four-vote cases. The measure used here compares the overall tendency of each justice to vote for review with his record in four-vote cases, using rank orders to determine which justices "moved up" in these cases (see table 5.14). Only those justices who moved up more than one position are charted here. As this comparison shows, only a few justices tended to depart from their overall voting propensities to contribute a fourth vote when that was necessary for review. Over the entire Burton period, during which sixteen justices sat, six justices contributed a disproportionate number of votes in cases receiving four votes.

The appearance of all three chief justices among the six suggests that many four-vote combinations were the result of attempts by the chiefs to build social stability on the Court. Like the tendency of the chief justices to suppress lone votes for or against review, the tendency to contribute the crucial fourth vote tends to increase overall good feelings on the Court. In both situations, harmony is enhanced at the expense of self-expression by the chief.

The repeated appearance of Burton and Clark in four-vote cases suggests another reason why a justice might contribute a fourth vote oftener than one would otherwise expect. Both men were affable and outgoing in their personal relationships. Chief Justice Warren described Burton as the "leavening agent" on the Court who was

gentle, kindly, self-effacing, but with complete dedication to the principles of justice, he strove diligently and

Table 5.14   Propensity to vote for review: Generally, and in four-vote cases

	Justice	Overall Ranking	Ranking in four-vote cases	Difference in rank
1945	Burton	4	1	3
	Stone	8	4	4
1947–48	(No one moved more than one place			
1949–52	Vinson	7	1	6
	Clark	8	6	2
1953–54	(No one moved more than one place)			
1955	Warren	5	1	2
	Clark	7	4	3
1956	Warren	3	1	2
	Clark	8	6	2
	Burton	9	7	2
1957	Brennan	3	1	2

understandingly always for that which he believed to be right. His one overwhelming desire was to be helpful to everyone, on and off the court.[12]

It is reasonable to assume that such a man would vote for review out of friendship when three fellow justices wanted to decide a case. Clark, who was alive when this research was conducted, was able to indicate his attitude toward these cases directly. When asked his position on contributing the crucial fourth vote, Clark stated that as a general rule, when three members of the Court wanted to hear a case, he did not mind supplying the additional vote necessary for review.[13]

The identity of the justices most frequently contributing the crucial fourth vote in case selection during the Burton period thus suggests that the desire to be agreeable and the leadership responsibility felt by chief justices are the primary reasons some justices vote oftener for review in four-vote cases than otherwise. The hypothesis that four-vote cases reflect the presence of coalitions seeking review on the merits, on the other hand, receives no support in this analysis. The question remains, however, whether coalitional behavior exists in a narrow class of volatile cases. The preceeding analysis using all four-vote cases during the Burton period might be too general to reveal such behavior. Narrowing our subject to the controversial FELA cases that so troubled the Court in Burton's day may help to determine whether coalitions did or did not exist.

Case Selection in FELA Cases

My examination of coalitional behavior in FELA cases relies upon an elaborate model of power-oriented case-selection voting presented by Glendon Schubert. To establish how a bloc on the Court, motivated to win on the merits whenever it could, might have voted at the review-granting stage, he applied game-theory principles to the grant-denial pattern, the only evidence of case-selection behavior available at that time.[14] Schubert hypothesized that one subgroup of justices, highly result-oriented and aware of its power to affect public policy through case selection, attempted to effectuate its policy goals in these cases:

> The Certiorari Game is another example of a power game: i.e., one in which it is assumed that the Supreme Court is a power group, with sub-groups whose organization, motivation, and behavior are political. By "political" it is meant that members of the Court are divided on various issues of public policy, and that there are "activists" within the group who consciously attempt to control the Court's decision-making.[15]

The Federal Employers' Liability Act. Congress enacted the Federal Employers' Liability Act (FELA) in 1908 to provide compensation for railroad workers injured on the job.[16] The statute replaced the exception-ridden common law remedy then available to injured railroad employees. Just how generous Congress intended to be with this legislation and its later amendments immediately became a matter of dispute among Supreme Court justices and others.[17] Instead of providing a fixed compensation for each type of injury, the statute gave the injured worker the right to a lawsuit. The plaintiff had a chance to receive a large settlement or nothing at all, depending on the jury, the judge, and the facts of the injury. Not surprisingly, disputes over recovery for these injuries immediately became a steady source of business for courts.[18]

During the first years of the new statute, jurisdiction was mandatory for those cases appealed to the Supreme Court, but after the 1916 amendments to the Judicial Code, FELA petitions have almost always come to the Court on certiorari. Even though the decision to review these cases has for over half a century been solely a matter of discretion, the Court until recently voted with some regularity to decide several of these cases on the merits each term.[19]

The number of petitions that reached the Court and the Court's willingness to continue to review FELA cases led Felix Frankfurter, then a Harvard Law School professor, to declare the statute a failure.[20] Frankfurter reasoned that Congress must have failed to communicate workable standards to the courts and that further Supreme Court attention wasted judicial time:

> Analysis of the individual cases compels the conclusion that the Supreme Court cultivates sterile soil in this field of litigation.[21]

The issue on appeal in FELA cases most often involves the sufficiency of the evidence necessary to permit a jury determination of liability. Juries, generally sympathetic to the injured, usually decide for the worker. The trial judge, however, sometimes directs a verdict for the railroad on the grounds that there is insufficient evidence for a jury determination. Occasionally the trial judge makes this determination after a jury verdict in favor of the injured worker. In these instances, the trial judge enters a judgment overriding the jury's decision on the grounds of insufficient evidence. Appellate judges can also overturn favorable jury verdicts by ordering that the trial judge should not have allowed the case to go before the jury. Thus the issue before the Supreme Court often concerns the permissible latitude for jury decision. In the period under analysis here, this issue was the one most frequently raised in FELA litigation and the one most frequently taken up by the Supreme Court on the merits.[22]

Although the Court has consistently decided a high proportion of FELA evidentiary cases, the litigant most likely to gain review shifted dramatically during the 1937 term, when other important changes (discussed in chapter 3) took place on the Court. During the 1921–37 terms the Court heard thirty-eight FELA cases and supported the worker's claim in only seven of these, whereas during the 1938–48 terms it heard twenty-nine cases and supported the worker in twenty-five.[23]

Most FELA evidentiary cases accepted for review are reversed by the Court,[24] so a change in the likelihood of review for one class of litigants tends to benefit the reviewed class. The Court, in other words, seems to have had a consistent "monitor policy" in this type of litigation, taking up cases that it believes have been wrongly decided below and readjudicating them in the appellant's favor.[25] The high proportion of summary reversals, nearly half of all FELA jury cases decided between 1949 and 1959, is further evidence of this policy.[26]

FELA Litigation in the Supreme Court. The post-1937 willingness of some members of the Court to review worker petitions and to reverse the decisions below can be interpreted in legal terms as the effect of concern for high standards of statutory interpretation in the lower courts, or in political terms as the expression of a bias in favor of workers. Supreme Court justices who usually vote for the worker on the merits have justified their position in legal terms. Justice Brennan, for example, justifies the Court's involvement in these cases by referring to congressional intent, which, he has argued, vested the power of decision in jury hands in these cases.[27] Justice Douglas has stressed the hostile interpretation of the act given by the Supreme Court and the lower courts in explaining why he favored review.[28] He believed it only appropriate that the Court should act to undo the damage to congressional intent done during this earlier period:

Since the condition was one created by the Court and beyond effective control by Congress, it was appropriate

and fitting that the Court correct it. In fact, a decision
not to correct it was to let the administration of this law
be governed not by the aim of the legislation to
safeguard employees but by a hostile philosophy that
permeated its interpretation.[29]

Justice Black cast the issue in constitutional terms in *Schultz
v. Pennsylvania Railroad Company:*

> I do not share the attitude that it is a waste of this
> Court's time to review cases where judges have de-
> prived litigants of their basic right to trial by jury. . . .
> No violation of a constitutional right is a minor thing in
> my judgment. It should never be beneath the dignity of
> this Court to protect those rights. I would grant cer-
> tiorari in this case and reverse, thereby restoring to this
> petitioner the right to trial by jury which I think has
> been wrongfully taken from her.[30]

Schubert, on the other hand, placed FELA cases squarely
within the liberal-conservative framework familiar to
analysts of the Court's work:

> Liberal Supreme Court justices cannot change the sys-
> tem, but they can be latitudinarian in their rulings on
> the sufficiency of the evidence necessary to establish
> negligence on the part of the Employer; conservative
> justices can cause claimants to lose merely by insisting
> that, in FELA cases, the same criteria of judgment apply
> as are used in other cases which raise the question of
> what is sufficient evidence to go to a jury.[31]

In non-FELA cases the Court has generally denied review
when the major issue was sufficiency of the evidence, on the
grounds that the issue was necessarily fact-based and
therefore not significant enough to warrant review.[32]
For Schubert, past hostile interpretations of the statute or
its periodic amendments are less important in explaining
voting behavior in FELA cases than the underlying liberal
and conservative attitudes of the justices. Schubert's position is buttressed by the fact that, with the exception of
Frankfurter, those justices generally considered to be most
liberal in civil liberties cases were also the most likely to

vote for review and for reversal in the FELA evidentiary cases workers brought to the Supreme Court.[33]

The Certiorari Game. Schubert theorized that Supreme Court justices who favored vigilance in FELA jury issue cases could, for the years he analyzed (1942–60), be conceptualized as a bloc with a strategy to effectuate its concerns. Frankfurter represented an opposing player in this certiorari game. Others on the Court were uncommitted "pawns" to be "coopted" in the conflict between the two activist sides.[34]

Schubert postulated that the certiorari bloc, which varied in size and membership over the years, consistently attempted to maximize the number of Supreme Court judgments favorable to worker claims in order to encourage the lower courts to look more favorably upon worker petitions. To effectuate this objective, the bloc would vote against review in all cases brought by railroads, because in those cases the injured worker had been successful below. For worker petitions, the best strategy was for the bloc to vote for review only when a majority of the whole court could be expected to reverse on the merits.

In the absence of any simple method for separating strong worker petitions from those too weak to win reversal on the merits, Schubert assumed that the strongest candidates were those in which the worker had won at the trial court level but lost on appeal:

> Such cases would be the best bets to bring before the Supreme Court for two reasons: a case in which a trial court and jury had both found for the plaintiff could rarely be characterized as frivolous; and the fact that these cases had resulted in disagreement among the justices of lower courts indicated that it would not be unreasonable for the Supreme Court to decide them in favor of the plaintiff.[35]

Tanenhaus and his associates, it will be recalled, made a similar differentiation in their research. These authors deemed dissension among the lower courts which hear a case a cue in the selection process, and they showed that its presence in a petition was positively correlated with the decision to grant review.[36]

Using on-the-merits voting as an indicator of probable certiorari voting, Schubert hypothesized that the certiorari bloc was composed of those members of the Court who voted 90 percent of the time or more for the worker on the merits. Black, Douglas, Rutledge, and Murphy formed the bloc until 1949 when Rutledge and Murphy died. Clark became a replacement member of the bloc soon after he joined the Court. Clark, however, was a marginal member because his on-the-merits votes did not quite satisfy Schubert's criterion, although his comments about the Court's duty in FELA evidentiary cases put him squarely within the bloc.

The bloc had a strength of three until 1953 when Warren joined the Court as chief justice. Because other evidence indicates that Warren did not immediately become one of the more liberal members of the Court, and because the number of cases taken on the merits did not dramatically increase in 1953, Schubert was unsure whether or not Warren immediately joined the bloc. Certainly he had by the 1954 term, thereby raising the bloc's strength to four, which was enough to assure review in any case the bloc desired. In 1956, when Brennan was appointed, the bloc gained a fifth member and the ability to get the on-the-merits decisions it desired.[37] Tabulation of the shifting proportion of FELA cases accepted for review in these periods bears out Schubert's argument (table 5.15).

Table 5.15   Case selection in the certiorari game, 1949–59 Terms

	Certiorari grants per term (average)	Certiorari grants/ total worker petitions	Pro-worker/total decisions on the merits
1949–52	.75	.16	.80
1953–55	3.00	.53	.83
1956–59	5.60	.62	.91

SOURCE: Schubert, "Policy Without Law," table 14 (p. 318).

The aggressiveness of a certiorari bloc should, of course, vary with its strength. When the bloc numbers only three, for example, the likelihood of gaining the two additional votes to win on the merits would be less than when the bloc had more members. Similarly, if those who favored worker claimants became a majority of the Court, the only bounds to review would be those necessary to keep bloc members within the fold.[38]

The strategy for Frankfurter, the lone opposing player in the game, was simple—to vote against certiorari in all cases. The plaintiff in each case was theoretically irrelevant for Frankfurter since the issues raised by either side on evidentiary matters were not suitable for readjudication at the Supreme Court level.[39] In published comments Frankfurter made it clear that whether or not the result below seemed wrongly decided on the facts was also irrelevant:

> For this Court to take a case which turns merely on appraisal of evidence, however much hardship in the fallible application of an archaic system of compensation for injuries to railroaders may touch on our private sympathy, is to deny due regard to considerations which led the Court to ask and Congress to give the power to control the Court's dockets.[40]

After 1949, Frankfurter carried this approach to FELA evidentiary cases to the merits of these cases. Thus when the Court did take a case on the merits, Frankfurter usually refused to vote on the merits, issuing a jurisdictional dissent instead.[41]

Schubert found that the certiorari bloc was not always successful in implementing its goal of achieving a judicial gloss on the FELA maximally favorable to workers. Its failures to win reversals in as many worker petitions as possible stemmed in part from its failure to follow what Schubert conceived to be its optimal or "pure" strategy:

> A's [the certiorari bloc's] most serious mistake in play, therefore, resulted from his departure from Rule II [requiring the bloc to distinguish between unanimous and nonunanimous decisions below] of his pure strategy; and

A was penalized for his irrational play by a less successful realization of his policy goal than a completely ra-
tional player would have been able to attain.[42]

Schubert's theory is not seriously damaged by the failure
of the certiorari bloc to adhere to its optimal strategy.
Whether or not the justices behaved rationally at all times,
the implications of the hypothesis are profound: the behavior of at least some members of the Court in certain
cases can be understood in the language of power politics.
Schubert's argument, in other words, is that a subgroup of
the Court, always desirous of controlling the Court's decision making to effectuate preferred policies, made use of
the opportunity afforded by the rule of four to manipulate
the will of the majority.

Actual Votes and Game-Theory Propositions. Selecting the
pool of cases to which the certiorari game purports to apply
is somewhat hazardous because Schubert failed to specify
his selection criterion, and other compilers do not agree
completely on which FELA cases raise the question of sufficiency of evidence for the jury as their principal issue.
Schubert, Justice Frankfurter, Justice Douglas, and a *Harvard Law Review* note writer all made separate lists of the
relevant cases, none of which are in complete agreement.
The problem is complicated by the failure of three of the
authors (Douglas is the exception) to name, rather than
simply count, the cases in which certiorari was denied. The
following analysis relies upon an independent review of the
petitions in which I have attempted to draw the lines for
inclusion and exclusion as closely to Schubert's as possible.
Unfortunately, Schubert gave no guidelines for selecting
relevant cases, and there are minor variations in the number
of cases included in some periods.

Schubert stated three rules for certiorari voting by bloc
members, and one rule for voting by the opposition player.
Other testable hypotheses can also be generated from these
game theory propositions. The conformity of actual votes
to these hypothesized rules can then be tested with the
Burton data.

The rule for the opposition player in the certiorari game was simple: to vote against review in every FELA case. Frankfurter actually followed this rule in all but two instances, where he voted with the majority to hear worker petitions.[43] These exceptions probably indicate the influence of other issues in the petitions, and therefore should be ignored. It seems fair to conclude that Frankfurter's actual voting behavior conformed to Schubert's expectations, and, it should be noted, to Frankfurter's public position on FELA evidentiary cases.

These are the rules Schubert established for members of the certiorari bloc:

1. Never vote in favor of granting review to employer petitions.

2. Vote for review in all cases brought by workers who won at trial.

2a (as revised in his second article). When the bloc has three members, vote to deny in all cases where the worker lost at trial. If there are four members, vote against review in a majority of these cases. If the bloc numbers five, vote for certiorari in a majority of these cases.[44]

Throughout the period covered by the Burton data, the whole Court, not just the certiorari bloc, almost always followed Rule 1. Of the forty-four railroad petitions in the period, only five cases received any votes for review. Contrary to Schubert's predictions, members of the certiorari bloc cast most of these pro-railroad votes, Douglas voting for review in three cases, Rutledge joining him in one.[45] Sixty percent of the time, however, railroad petitions were special-listed.

The justices varied in their compliance with Schubert's second rule. Whereas the rule states that all bloc members should vote for review in all worker-brought petitions where the worker won at the trial level, the bloc members ranged from 33 percent to 100 percent in their support in these cases (table 5.16). For Murphy, Rutledge, Black, and Douglas, Schubert's rule seems to apply. The variation among these four and Clark, Warren, and especially Brennan, suggests, however, that not all bloc members were

Table 5.16   The certiorari bloc's conformity to Rule 2, 1945–57 Terms

Bloc member	Petitions satisfying conditions of Rule 2	Cases in which justice followed Rule 2
Murphy	9	9
Rutledge	10	8
Douglas	46	9
Black	47	40
Clark	37	23
Warren	24	15
Brennan	9	3

following Rule 2 with consistency. Nevertheless, all of these justices clearly favored the worker complaints, and their behavior is much more favorable to workers than the rest of the Court's. Schubert, in other words, correctly identified the members of the Court most likely to vote for review from his knowledge of those justices most likely to favor the worker on the merits. The justices were, as Schubert assumed, adhering to a monitor policy: they voted to review the cases they desired to reverse.

Although Rule 2a is more precisely gauged to differences in bloc strength, and therefore seems easier to satisfy, it corresponds to the voting patterns only half the time (table 5.17). Rule 2a thus appears to have been incorrect, possibly because the key Schubert used to differentiate "strong" from "weak" cases was not the criterion employed by the Court. This mistake is not crucial to the validity of the basic hypothesis, however.

The more significant problem with Schubert's rules as a valid test of his certiorari game hypothesis is that Rules 1 and 2, propositions to which the actual votes do conform, fail to differentiate power-motivated from non-power-motivated voting behavior. Schubert's decision-making theory, however, is unequivocal on this point. As noted earlier, Schubert described the certiorari game as an example of a "power" game in which certain justices "consciously attempt to control the Court's decision-making." His use of a term like "pawn" to describe nonaligned justices is

Table 5.17   **Bloc conformity to Rule 2A, 1945–57 Terms**

Rule 2A satisfied?	Period	Number of bloc members	Condition to satisfy rule	Proportion of bloc members' votes cast for review
No	I (1945–48)	4	Vote against review in majority of cases	50/68
No	II (1949–52)	3	Vote against re- in all cases	1/12
Yes	III (1953–55)	4	Vote against review in majority of cases	5/28
Yes	IV (1956–57)	5	Vote for review in majority of cases	34/50

another indication that he was presenting a theory of power-oriented voting in case selection.

Rules 1 and 2 provide an inadequate test of the power hypothesis because an alternative hypothesis just as easily explains case selection behavior that conforms to his rules. If the justices whom Schubert identified as bloc members were convinced that the lower courts were significantly unfair in their interpretation of worker rights under the federal legislation, then their votes would approximate the pattern Schubert predicted, even if they were oblivious to power considerations. Whenever a lower court appeared to have made a serious error, these justices would vote to review and to reverse because they believed the Supreme Court had a responsibility to educate the lower courts in these instances.

Such a non-power-oriented explanation is the more plausible when these three other voting patterns in FELA cases are considered:

1. In five cases that were denied review, the vote of one bloc member prevented review on the merits desired by the remainder of the bloc. Such behavior would not be expected if power considerations were paramount in case selection.

2. In five cases that were granted review, the case won review despite a bloc member's vote to deny. Non-bloc justices cast the necessary votes. This behavior also runs directly counter to Schubert's theory.

3. The overall voting pattern in worker-brought cases does not match the pattern a theory of power-orientated voting would predict. Schubert's hypothesis implies that certiorari voting patterns should tend to clump around zero votes and four votes. Only during the brief period when the certiorari bloc had a fifth member should five-vote grants be common. A consistent pattern of five or more votes would indicate that the bloc had more members than Schubert hypothesized. Frequent instances of fewer than four votes would indicate that conscious manipulation of case selection was absent. Bloc members intent upon persuading the un-committed members of the Court to vote for workers on the merits would, at least ordinarily, be ill-advised to throw away votes on losing cases because such behavior would expose the true extent of their proworker bias. Of course, occasional instances of three votes would be understandable as mistakes, but even these should be rare.

When the worker cases are subdivided by the number of votes they received, however, it is clear that a tightknit power bloc was not operating in these cases during the Burton period (see table 5.18). Even though a power bloc was absent in these cases, it should be noted that the dis-tribution of votes in FELA cases does not correspond very precisely to the distribution of case-selection votes overall, as the low Pearson's correlation between the two dis-tributions, .288, indicates. The most likely explanation for the deviation of FELA cases from the overall pattern is that the issues raised by FELA evidentiary cases encouraged the justices either to favor review in most cases or to oppose review in most. One might expect such limited variation in the midrange of voting response patterns in these cases be-cause they revolved around a single legal issue in which the gradations produced by diverse factual patterns were largely irrelevant.

A Guttman scale of the voting in these cases supports this

Table 5.18   Vote totals in worker petitions compared to totals overall,
               1945–47 Terms

Number of votes cast	Number of worker petitions	Percentage of total worker petitions	Percentage overall[a]
1	7	10	24%
2	12	17	20
3	9	13	12
4	16	23	10
5	16	23	6
6	8	11	5
7	1	1	5
8	0	—	4
9	1	1	14
No vote shown	1	1%	0%
Total	71	100%	100%

NOTE: Correlation between Distribution of Worker Petitions and Overall: $r_p = .288$.
[a] From fig. 5.1.

interpretation. It shows that the middle range of disagreement among the justices was quite narrow (table 5.19). Murphy, Douglas, Rutledge, and Black seldom voted against the worker evidentiary cases that were strong enough to win at least one positive vote. In these same cases, Reed, Vinson, Jackson, Harlan, Burton, and Frankfurter seldom found reason to vote for review. Over the whole Burton period, only Clark, Warren, Brennan, and Minton were middlemen, and for Brennan and Minton, this position may have been partly attributable to the infrequency with which they participated in FELA cases.

Conclusion

It seems clear from the foregoing analysis of alignments among justices that considerations other than the consolidation of power operate in their case-selection decisions. The crucial variable in the FELA cases examined here could be described either as a feeling of special re-

Table 5.19   **A Guttman Scale of voting in FELA evidentiary cases, 1945–57 terms**

Case no.	MU	DO	RU	BL	CL	WA	BR	MI	RE	VI	JA	HA	BU	FR	Vote	# Incon-sistent
68,69		−		⊕	−	−	−	−				−	−	−	1-8	1
42		−		⊕	−			−	−	−	−	−	−	−	1-8	1
47,52		+	−	−	−			−	−	−	−		−	−	1-8	0
28,43		+	−					−	−	−	−		−	−	1-8	0
33		+	−	−				−	−	−	−		⊕	−	1-8	0
70		+		−	−	−	⊕		−	−	−		−	−	2-7	1
80		+		+	−	−	−					−	−	−	2-7	1
49,50		+		+	−		−					−	−	−	2-6	0
34,35,36,37,48		+		+	−			−	−	−	−		−	−	2-7	0
6	+	⊖	⊖	+				−	−	−	−		−	−	2-7	0
58		+		+	+	−		−	−	−	−		−	−	2-7	2
29,30,38,44		+		+	+	+		−	−	−	−		−	−	3-6	0
12,13,14	+	⊖	+	+					−	−	−		−	−	3-6	0
1	+	+	⊖	+					−	−	−		−	−	3-6	1
72		+		+	+	−			−	−	−		−	−	3-5	1
71		+		+	+	+	−		−			−	−	−	3-5	0
59,60,61,62		+		+	+	+		−				−	−	−	4-5	0
53		+		+	+	+		−				−	−	−	4-5	0
7,15-6,21-3	+	+	+	+					−	−	−		−	−	4-5	0
3		+	+	+					−	−	−	⊕		−	4-2	1
2	+	+	+	+				−					−	−	4-3	0
81,82,83		+		+	+	+	+		−			−	−	−	5-3	0
8	+	+	+	+				−	−	⊕		−	−	−	5-4	1
75		+		+	+	+	+		−			−	−	−	5-4	0
73		+		+	+	+	⊖		−			⊕	−	−	5-4	2
63,64		+		+	+	+		+	−			−	−	−	3-4	0
31		+		+	+			+				−			4-3	0
24,25	+	+	+	+					−	⊕	−		−	−	5-4	1
39		+		+	+			+	+	−			−	−	5-4	0
17	+	+	+	+				+	+	−			−	−	5-4	0
18	+	⊖	+	+				+	+	−			−	−	5-4	1
74		+		+	⊖	+	+		+			−	−	−	5-4	1
9	+	+	+	+				+	+	−			−	−	5-4	1
84		+		+	+	+	+		+			−	−	−	5-3	0
45		+		+	+			−	+			−	−	−	4-4	1
76,77		+		+	+	+	+	+				−	−	−	6-3	0
54		+		+	+	+	⊖	⊖		+		−	⊕		6-3	3
26	+	+	+	+				⊖	+	+			−		6-3	1
55		+		+	+	+	⊖	+		⊖			+	−	6-3	1
19	+	+	+	+				+	⊖	⊖			+	−	6-3	2
4	+	+	+	+				⊖		+		+	+	−	6-3	2
65		+		+	+	+		+	⊖			+	+	−	6-2	1
27	+	+	+	+					+	+	+		+	+	7-2	1
									+	+	+		+	+	9-0	0
Incons.	0	5	2	3	1	0	2	2	5	3	3	1	2	1	= 30 Incons.	
Votes	22	69	23	69	46	28	17	30	61	35	46	22	68	69	= 605 Votes	

Cases included in computation of coefficient of reproducibility

Note: $R = 1 - \dfrac{27}{533} = .949$

$S = \dfrac{69}{99} = .697$

sponsibility toward correcting one species of lower-court error or, more generally, as a liberal attitude favoring workers in disputes with their employers. The principal reasons for slightly more four-vote cases than one might expect appear to have been the perceptions by the various chiefs of their leadership responsibilities, and the affability of a few associate justices. In overall voting patterns the leadership variable and a mix of considerations (discussed in chapter 4) seem to have been determinative. In each of these three different types of alignment analysis, the possibility that power politics determined case-selection votes can be rejected. The relevance of the leadership variable in explaining patterns of association involving chief justices—both overall and in four-vote cases—does not detract from this conclusion. The evidence suggests that the Burton-period chief justices simply responded to the need to maintain social harmony on the Court in voting for reviews as they did.

The evidence that power politics was not central in case selection, where such behavior could have been highly effective, suggests that Supreme Court justices deem outcome-oriented voting inappropriate. It seems likely that a shared conception of the proper role of a judge prevents the justices from exploiting the possibilities for power-oriented voting in case selection.

The patterns of association among the justices also suggest that even though they agree fundamentally on their conceptions of the proper role of a justice, they may vary significantly in their conception of the proper work of the Court on the merits, and in their resolution of disputes. Apparently a justice's view of the proper role of a judge is quite separate from his interpretation of the proper work of the Court.

Conclusion. The Political Implications of Court-Controlled Case Selection

Contradictory interpretations of how the Supreme Court reaches decisions abound. At one end of the spectrum is the view that the Supreme Court, along with other agencies of government, makes decisions primarily in response to external pressures or to internal policy preferences. At the other extreme is a legalistic interpretation of Supreme Court decision making which emphasizes neutral reasoning based on legally relevant issues, and which assumes that whatever political power the Court has is the unavoidable by-product of its dispute-resolving responsibility.

This clash of views about judicial decision making resounds in the scholarly literature on case selection in the Supreme Court. The "political-agency" interpretation underlies Schubert's work adapting game theory to case selection. Schubert assumed that a group of the justices see case selection as an opportunity to implement their liberal or conservative political views. Treatises for lawyers on Supreme Court jurisdiction, on the other hand, take the legalistic view. They either ignore or downplay the judgmental aspect of case selection. Like the Court's own Rule 19, these works treat case selection as a matter of rules which exist without reference to the particular justices sitting or the political climate in which they function.

The evidence presented in this book suggests that neither of these extreme approaches is satisfactory for describing Supreme Court decision making in general, or case selection in particular. The view that downplays the individuality of judgment and treats case selection as a mechanical screening process misses much that is important. It ignores, for example, the selectivity of justices concerning the types of cases they believe deserve review. But as we have seen, some subject matters are almost never granted review, whereas others are reviewed more frequently than not. What cases receive favored treatment depends in large part on the views of the justices about what kinds of issues the Supreme Court should tackle on the merits. These conceptions of the appropriate role of the Court are subject to change, as the evolving attitude of the Court toward hearing civil rights and civil liberties petitioners indicates. The analysis of case selection presented in this book thus supports Frankfurter's observation:

> As is true of so many matters that come before us, one's view of the appropriate treatment of these cases derives from one's attitude toward the true functions of the Court and the best way to discharge them.[1]

Analysis suggests that the mechanical view is incomplete in another way: it does not take account of individual differences among justices. The justices are bound to disagree somewhat on which cases are most worthy of resolution on the merits, and they are also likely to disagree about how many cases should be resolved in a term. Differences among justices in their sensitivity toward various litigants and causes also plays a part in creating voting differences, because the perception that a lower court has erred influences review decisions. Changes in membership on the Court, therefore, can be expected to create significant changes in the cases accepted for review.

To accept the importance of individual judgment in Supreme Court decision making is not, however, to embrace the view that equates judicial decision making with decision making by a nonjudicial political body. The Burton data suggest that Supreme Court justices are not ordinary political decision makers, because members of the Supreme Court share a conception of their role which prevents them from using their votes simply to achieve policy preferences. Thus we have seen that none of the Burton-period justices either combined forces to achieve the results they preferred on the merits, or voted individually in a way that would suggest routine calculation of probable outcomes in the case selection process. Nor did the Court as a whole appear to make the calculation of political harm to itself central in even the most politically volatile case selection decisions. The concept Supreme Court justices share of the scope of behavior suitable to a judge seems to filter judicial attitudes toward desirable outcomes. Political scientists, Pritchett has noted, sometimes fail to appreciate this intervening variable:

> Political scientists who have done so much to put the "political" in "political jurisprudence" need to emphasize that it is still "jurisprudence." It is judging in a political context, but it is still judging; and judging is something different from legislating or administering. . . . Any accurate analysis of judicial behavior must have as a major purpose a full clarification of the unique limiting conditions under which judicial policy making proceeds.[2]

In the context of case selection, role conceptions serve both a limiting and a liberating function. Although judicial conceptions of appropriate behavior limit individual result orientation and conscious bloc formation, they also operate to free the justices from ideological isolation, permitting them to vote for review routinely with ideologically dissimilar justices.

The self-imposed limits of role conceptions, it is important to note, are essentially the only limits upon judicial discretion in case selection. Case selection approximates and even exceeds plenary decision making in the scope it provides for the exercise of unfettered judicial judgment. The question for policy makers is whether the Court should be permitted to maintain complete control in setting its agenda, limited only by the conceptions the justices hold of the proper way to perform this function.

My analysis points to one troubling feature of the current structure of case selection. In the justices' persistent campaign to maximize their discretion to select cases, they have given an advantage to sophisticated and experienced petitioners, especially the U.S. government. Both the failure of the Court to establish clear rules for the exercise of its discretion and its preference for choosing conflicts among lower courts operate to favor frequent litigators. The strategies frequent litigators have devised for exploiting these opportunities to achieve review deserve more attention than they have yet received from scholars concerned with the power of interest groups in American society.

It is difficult to imagine how any body invested with the responsibility to select only significant cases could easily remain invulnerable to the ability of seasoned petitioners to make their cases seem important. The self-imposed constraints provided by role perceptions do not provide a solution for this problem. Although role perceptions differentiate Supreme Court justices from other political decision-makers, they do not endow the justices with any unusual degree of wisdom concerning how the Court actually should use its decision-making authority.

If Court-controlled case selection has as its by-product unavoidable differences in access to review, the policy issue raised earlier can be restated in terms of competing considerations. The reasons for maintaining case selection as it is must be weighed against the problems raised by differential access to review in a democratic political system. My analysis suggests that the dilemma should be resolved in favor of maintaining Court-controlled case selection.

That the reality of access to the Court does not match the popular image does not appear to be crucial to citizens. The idea that the legal merits of a case is the only consideration in case selection has been incorrect almost since the advent of discretionary review. As Frankfurter and Landis pointed out long ago, the government's expertise has always helped it gain frequent review. The survival of the popular perception that cases can go "all the way to the Supreme Court" must mean that the Court takes on enough disputes of concern to the public to sustain its image as an available forum.

Were the Court to lose its wide discretion to select cases, on the other hand, it would be weakened in several important respects. Its ability to choose the most appropriate cases for the announcement of new doctrine would be adversely affected, as would its capacity to sidestep or postpone litigation that might damage its prestige. Perhaps even more significantly, the Court's image among laymen as the ultimate source of relief for legal wrongs would be damaged. Case selection, in short, is an important aspect of the Supreme Court's institutional power. Were this not true, the work of justices from Taft to the present to protect and extend the Court's authority to select cases without interference would be incomprehensible.

The importance of Court-controlled case selection to the institutional power of the Supreme Court does not require that it remain as secret as it has been in the past, however. Studies based on fragmentary evidence have, not surprisingly, misinterpreted case selection in significant ways. More generally, the paucity of data on case selection has limited understanding of the work of the Supreme Court and has contributed to the tendency to view the Court solely in terms of its decisions on the merits.[3]

Interested persons should have access to voting data that will enable them to piece together the considerations the Court takes into account in deciding cases. Publication of votes might indeed encourage some justices to write opinions justifying their case-selection votes, but this is an insufficient argument against any disclosure at any time. If case selection is an important dimension of Supreme Court power, as I argue that it is, the public deserves the opportunity to learn more about how that process proceeds.

Notes

1. Act of February 13, 1925, ch. 229, 43 Stat. 936.

2. See Pamela R. Winnick, "Comment: The Precedential Weight of a Dismissal by the Supreme Court for Want of a Substantial Federal Question," *Columbia Law Review* 76 (1976): 508–33.

3. See Annual Report, Director of the Administrative Office of U.S. Courts. See also the Federal Judicial Center, *Report of the Study Group on the Case Load of the Supreme Court* (Washington, D.C.: Administrative Office of U.S. Courts, 1972).

4. *Federalist Papers,* no. 78, p. 465 in the New American Library edition (1961).

5. The rule is quoted and discussed fully in chap. 1, in the section entitled "The Court's Published Decision Criterion: Rule 19."

6. Arlene Fickler recently prepared an exhaustive analysis of the Court's reasoning in dissenting from denials of certiorari for the Commission on Revision of the Federal Court Appellate System. It appears without attribution in *Structure and Internal Procedures: Recommendations for Change,* (Washington, D.C. 1975). Appendix B III, pp. 111–33. See also S. Sidney Ulmer, "Changing Patterns of Conflict: Dissent to Denials of Review in the Burger Court," a paper prepared for delivery at the Southern Political Science Association Meeting, Atlanta, November 9–11, 1978.

7. Handwritten note, October 16, 1943, Murphy Papers, Bentley Historical Library, Ann Arbor, Michigan. For Frankfurter's views, see *Bondholders Inc. v. Powell,* 342 U.S. 921 (1952), separate opinion by Frankfurter.

8. The only other Supreme Court justice who made the Court's voting records available to the public was Chief Justice Morrison Waite, who served in the late 1800s.

9. The major critical articles all have Fowler Harper as their principal author. They appear in the *Pennsylvania Law Review*

under the title: "What the Supreme Court Did Not Do in the 1949, [1950, 1951, 1952] Term." Coauthor for the 1949 term was Alan Rosenthal (vol. 99 [1950], pp. 293–325); for the 1950 term, Edwin Etherington (vol. 100 [1951], pp. 354–409); for the 1951 term, George C. Pratt (vol. 101 [1953], pp. 439–79); and for the 1952 term, Arnold Leibowitz (vol. 102 [1954], pp. 427–63).

10. Jerome J. Hanus, "Denial of Certiorari and Supreme Court Policy-Making," *American University Law Review* 17 (1967): 41–53; Stephen W. Earp, "Sovereign Immunity in the Supreme Court: Using the Certiorari Process to Avoid Decision Making," *American Journal of International Law* 16 (1976): 903–29.

11. Joseph Tanenhaus, Marvin Schick, Matthew Muraskin, and Daniel Rosen, "The Supreme Court's Certiorari Jurisdiction: Cue Theory," in Glendon Schubert, ed., *Judicial Decision Making* (New York: Free Press, 1963), pp. 111–32.

12. Glendon Schubert, "The Certiorari Game," chap. 4 of his *Quantitative Analysis of Judicial Behavior* (New York: Free Press, 1959), and "Policy without Law: An Extension of the Certiorari Game," *Stanford Law Review* 14 (1962): 284–327.

13. Although Ulmer is the only scholar who has examined the Burton docket books in depth, at least one other person has sampled the docket books for a limited purpose. Saul Brenner examined a sample of votes in which review was granted to suggest that pro-affirmance and pro-reversal justices calculate their probabilities of success differently in case selection. Saul Brenner, "The New Certiorari Game," *Journal of Politics* 41 (1979): 649–55.

14. S. Sidney Ulmer (with William Hintze and Louise Kirklosky), "The Decision to Grant or Deny Certiorari: Further Consideration of Cue Theory," *Law and Society Review* 7 (1972): 637–43; "Revising the Jurisdiction of the Supreme Court: Mere Administrative Reform or Substantive Policy Change?" *University of Minnesota Law Review* 58 (1973): 121–55; "Selecting Cases for Supreme Court Review: An Underdog Model," *American Political Science Review* 72 (1978): 902–10; "Supreme Court Justices as Strict and Not-So-Strict Constructionists: Some Implications," *Law and Society Review* 8 (1973): 13–31; "The Decision to Grant Certiorari as an Indicator to Decision 'On the Merits,'" *Polity* 4 (1972): 429–47; "Voting Blocs and 'Access' to the Supreme Court: 1947–1956 Terms," *Jurimetrics Journal* 16 (1975): 6–13.

15. Lawrence Baum, "Decisions to Grant and Deny Hearings in

the California Surpreme Court: Patterns in Court and Individual Behavior," *Santa Clara Law Review* 16 (1976): 713–44; "Judicial Demand-Screening and Decisions on the Merits: A Second Look," *American Politics Quarterly* 7 (1979): 109–19; "Policy Goals in Judicial Gatekeeping: A Proximity Model of Discretionary Jurisdiction," *American Journal of Political Science* 21 (1977): 13–35.

16. For a sample of analyses of the same issue on the merits, see Joel Grossman, "Role-Playing and the Analysis of Judicial Behavior: The case of Mr. Justice Frankfurter." *Journal of Public Law* 11 (1962): 285–309, and "Dissenting Blocs on the Warren Court: A Study in Judicial Role Behavior," *Journal of Politics* 30 (1968): 1068–90; J. Woodford Howard, "Role Perceptions and Behavior in Three U.S. Courts of Appeals," *Journal of Politics* 39 (1977): 916–38; and James L. Gibson, "Judges' Role Orientations, Attitudes and Decisions," *American Political Science Review* 72 (1978): 911–24.

17. 408 U.S. 238 (1972), at 405–6, Blackmun dissenting.

One

1. See, for example, Supreme Court of the United States, Office of the Clerk, "October Term 1975: Statistical Sheet No. 28 (Final)," reprinted in *U.S. Law Week* 45 (July 27, 1976): 3083. A total of 3,939 review requests included 1,921 paid cases, 2,013 *in forma pauperis* petitions, and 5 Original Docket cases.

2. *Report of the Study Group on the Caseload of the Supreme Court* (Washington, D.C.: Administrative Office of the U.S. Courts, 1972), p. 5.

3. Act of February 13, 1925, ch. 229, 43 Stat. 936. The relevant constitutional provision is in Article III, Sec. 2, of the U.S. Constitution.

4. An excellent account of the Court's entire jurisdictional history through 1925 is Felix Frankfurter and James Landis's *The Business of the Supreme Court: A Study of the Federal Judicial System* (New York: Macmillan, 1928).

5. Act of March 3, 1891, ch. 517, 26 Stat. 826.

6. For a history of the writ, see Jerome J. Hanus, "The Writ of Certiorari as a Political Instrument" (Ph.D. diss., University of Maryland, 1966). See also Hanus, "Certiorari and Policy-making in English History," *American Journal of Legal History* 12 (1968): 63–94.

7. *American Construction Co. v. Jacksonville Ry.,* 148 U.S. 372 (1893) at 383. Statistics for the 1891–1925 period are in Felix

Frankfurter and Henry Hart, Jr., "The Business of the Supreme Court at October Term, 1933," *Harvard Law Review* 48 (1934): 260–61, n.50. The legislative history of this period can be found in Frankfurter and Landis, *Business of the Supreme Court,* chaps. 4, 5, 7.

8. Felix Frankfurter and James Landis, "The Supreme Court under the Judiciary Act of 1925," *Harvard Law Review* 42 (1928): 10, table 3.

9. Harold H. Burton, "Judging Is Also Administration: An Appreciation of Constructive Leadership," *American Bar Association Journal* 33 (1947): 1099. See the concise history of this period in the first section of James C. Conner, "Supreme Court Certiorari Policy," *Cornell Law Quarterly* 43 (1958): 451–68.

10. Act of February 13, 1925, ch. 229, 43 Stat. 936.

11. See Alpheus T. Mason, *William Howard Taft: Chief Justice* (New York: Simon & Schuster, 1964), chap. 5.

12. William Howard Taft to J. B. Woodward, March 3, 1924. Quoted ibid., p. 111.

13. Jurisdiction of Circuit Courts of Appeal and of the Supreme Court of the United States, Hearing before the Committee of the Judiciary, House of Representatives, 68th Congress, 2d Session, on H.R. 8206, December 18, 1924, Serial 45 (Washington, D.C.: U.S. Government Printing Office, 1924), testimony of Justice McReynolds, p. 22. See also William Howard Taft, "The Jurisdiction of the Supreme Court under the Act of February 13, 1925," *Yale Law Journal* 35 (1925): 2: "The function of the Supreme Court is conceived to be, not the remedying of the particular litigant wrong, but the consideration of cases whose decision involves principles, the application of which are of wide public or governmental interest."

14. Frankfurter and Landis, *Business of the Supreme Court,* p. 275.

15. Ibid., p. 1. In a 1931 article the same authors state: "The reversal of the sources of the Court's business as between obligation and discretion, during the five year period which covers substantially the full life of the Judiciary Act of 1925, is perhaps the most significant fact in the Court's recent history" ("The Business of the Supreme Court at October Term 1930," *Harvard Law Review* 45 [1931]: 288).

16. Frankfurter and Landis, "The Supreme Court under the Judiciary Act," p. 11.

17. Frankfurter and Landis, *Business of the Supreme Court,* p. 1.

18. Review remains obligatory when a federal statute is held unconstitutional (28 *U.S.C.* 1252) and when a state statute is held unconstitutional (28 *U.S.C.* 1254 (2)). Only 12 of the 311 appeals filed in 1971 came from courts of appeals (*Report of the Study Group,* table 7b, p. A12).

19. 28 *U.S.C.* 1257.

20. Certified question jurisdiction: 28 *U.S.C.* 1254 (3) and 1255 (2). See Robert L. Stern and Eugene Gressman, *Supreme Court Practice,* 2d ed. (Washington, D.C.: Bureau of National Affairs, 1954) pp. 257–63. The authors also discuss the other types of Supreme Court jurisdiction in detail. The provision in the Constitution for original jurisdiction reads: "In all cases affecting Ambassadors, other public Ministers and Consuls, and those in which a State shall be a Party, the Supreme Court shall have original Jurisdiction."

21. Eugene Gressman, "Requiem for the Supreme Court's Obligatory Jurisdiction," *American Bar Association Journal* 65 (1979): 1325–31.

22. *U.S. Law Week* and the *Harvard Law Review* annually publish statistical summaries containing some of this information. See also *Report of the Study Group,* table V.

23. Stern and Gressman, *Supreme Court Practice,* p. 234.

24. For the history of the development, see Felix Frankfurter and Adrian S. Fisher, "The Business of the Supreme Court: 1935 and 1936 terms," *Harvard Law Review* 51 (1938): 582–92.

25. See the anonymous "Note: The Insubstantial Federal Question," *Harvard Law Review* 62 (1949): 488–96. Frankfurter and Fisher describe this procedure in glowing terms: "It proves in striking fashion how much opportunity for creativeness in judical administration remains even with a jurisdictional orbit defined by the legislature" ("The Business of the Supreme Court: 1935 and 1936 Terms," p. 582).

26. The Supreme Court's Rule 15 governs jurisdictional statements. For certiorari petitions, the applicable provision is Rule 23. See also Stern and Gressman, *Supreme Court Practice,* p. 238. Studies of the Court's work often ignore the technical differences in the two types of jurisdiction. Even the Freund Commission, which distinguished certiorari and appeals jurisdiction in its recommendations, stated that "The discretionary-mandatory distinction between certiorari and appeal has been largely eroded" (*Report of the Study Group,* p. 25). But cf. William O. Douglas, "The Supreme Court and Its Case Load," *Cornell Law Quarterly* 45

(1960): 410. For a caveat on lumping dissimilar types of cases see Roger Cramton and Hans Zeisel, review of Glendon Schubert's *Quantitative Analysis of Judicial Behavior* in *University of Chicago Law Review* 28 (1960): 182–87.

27. See, for example, William J. Brennan, Jr., "Working at Justice," in Alan F. Westin, ed., *An Autobiography of the Supreme Court* (New York: Macmillan, 1963), p. 301; Harold H. Burton, "Judging Is Also Administration," *American Bar Association Journal* 33 (1947): 1102; Tom C. Clark, "Internal Operations of the United States Supreme Court," *Journal of the American Judicature Society* [now *Judicature*] 43 (1958–60): 50; William O. Douglas, *Farr v. Pitchess,* 409 U.S. 1243 (1973); Frankfurter dissenting, in *Darr v. Burford,* 339 U.S. 200, at 226; John M. Harlan, "Manning the Dikes," 1958 speech before the bar of the city of New York, *Benjamin N. Cardozo Memorial Lectures* (New York: Matthew Bender, n.d.), vol. 2, p. 683; John Paul Stevens, commenting upon the denial of certiorari in *Singleton v. Commissioner of Revenue* (#78–78), cert. denied, *Law Week* 47:3299 (October 31, 1978), at 3300.

28. *Maryland v. Baltimore Radio Show,* 338 U.S. 912 (1950), at 917–18.

29. Ibid., p. 917.

30. Cf. Justice Blackmun's statement, *U.S. v. Kras,* 409 U.S. 434 (1972), at 443.

31. 422 U.S. 332 (1975), at 343–44. For a discussion of this case and its implications, see Pamela R. Winnick, "Comment: The Precedential Weight of a Dismissal by the Supreme Court for Want of a Substantial Federal Question," *Columbia Law Review* 76 (1976): 508–33. See also David W. Brown, "Note: Summary Disposition of Appeals: The Significance of Limited Discretion and a Theory of Limited Precedent," *Boston University Law Review* 52 (1972): 373–425.

32. *Hogge v. Johnson,* 526 F2d 833 (4th Cir. 1975), at 836.

33. See *Report of the Study Group,* table 6, p. A10, and Douglas, "The Supreme Court," p. 411. See also A. Leo Levin and Arthur D. Hellman, "The Many Roles of the Supreme Court and the Constraints of Time and Case Load," *University of Toledo Law Review* 7 (1976): 399–430.

34. *Ohio v. Wyandotte Chemical Co.,* 401 U.S. 493 (1971), at 497.

35. Richard L. Williams, "The Supreme Court of the United States: The Staff that Keeps It Operating," *Smithsonian* 7 (1977): 38–48.

36. For the origins of the Miscellaneous Docket, see B. B., "Note: The Supreme Court's Miscellaneous Docket," *Harvard Law Review* 59 (1946): 604–6.

37. The proportion of criminal Appellate Docket cases approximated 12 percent during the Burton period. The proportion of criminal Miscellaneous Docket petitions was about 80 percent.

38. According to the Supreme Court Clerk, responses are filed in 90 to 95 percent of all paid cases and in 60 to 70 percent of the *in forma pauperis* cases. Reply briefs are filed about 25 percent of the time, and one of the parties files a copy of the record about 20 percent of the time. If justices desire any of these items, the Court routinely delays its review decision and requests the missing material. For a more general discussion of the Court's procedures, see John M. Harlan, "Some Aspects of the Judicial Process in the Supreme Court of the United States," *Australian Law Journal* 33 (1959): 112.

39. Stern and Gressman discuss these requirements fully in *Supreme Court Practice,* secs. 6 and 7. For a different perspective, see E. Barrett Prettyman, "Opposing Certiorari in the United States Supreme Court," *Virginia Law Review* 61 (1975): 197–209.

40. "Note: The Court, the Bar, and Certiorari at October Term 1958," *University of Pennsylvania Law Review* 108 (1960): 1160–1217.

41. Burton Collection, Box 235, "Memorandum by Mr. J. Frankfurter for the Conference," November 23, 1951, p. 1.

42. Felix Frankfurter and Henry M. Hart, Jr., "The Business of the Supreme Court at October Term, 1933," pp. 244–46.

43. Edwin McElwain, "The Business of the Supreme Court as Conducted by Chief Justice Hughes," *Harvard Law Review* 63 (1949): 21.

44. Ibid., p. 22.

45. Interview with Justice Tom Clark (retired) at Supreme Court, February 8, 1977.

46. "The Supreme Court: Deciding Whether to Decide," *Time,* December 11, 1972, p. 72.

47. J. Harvie Wilkinson III, *Serving Justice: A Supreme Court Clerk's View* (New York: Charterhouse, 1974), pp. 22–23.

48. W. B. M. to Justice Harold Burton, #279, *Sawyer v. Wisc.,* p. 3. Found in Box 271, Certs. Denied and Appeals Dismissed, 1954 term. See published examples of clerk memos for Justice Black in Walter F. Murphy and C. Herman Pritchett, *Courts, Judges and Politics* (New York: Random House, 1974), pp. 498–500. Some clerk memos are also available in Justice Frank Mur-

phy's papers, Michigan Historical Collections, University of Michigan, Ann Arbor, Michigan.

49. Wilkinson, *Serving Justice,* p. 48.

50. Telephone interview with the Supreme Court Clerk, March 14, 1979.

51. In addition to Wilkinson's book, which includes a description of how he got the job, see Paul R. Baier, "The Law Clerks: Profile of an Institution," *Vanderbilt Law Review* 26 (1973): 1125–77, and Alexander Bickel, *Politics and the Warren Court* (New York: Harper & Row, 1965), chap. 10, "The Law Clerks."

52. 335 U.S. 464 (1948).

53. J. L. to Justice Harold Burton, p. 3. In Box 189, Argued Cases, 1948 Term, Notebook for cases 25–49.

54. See the discussion of this issue in Clark, "Internal Operations" (n.27 above), p. 48; Wilkinson, *Serving Justice,* esp. pp. 56–63; Bickel, *Politics,* pp. 139–41; and Lewis F. Powell, Jr., "Myths and Misconceptions about the Supreme Court," *American Bar Association Journal* 6 (1975): 1347.

55. A. E. D. Howard and George Freeman, "Justice Hugo Black," interview in *Richmond Times-Dispatch,* December 12, 1971, cited in Wilkinson, *Serving Justive,* p. 19.

56. Interview with Justice Clark, February 8, 1977.

57. William Brennan, "Justice Brennan Calls National Court of Appeals Proposal 'Fundamentally Unnecessary and Ill-Advised,'" *American Bar Association Journal* 59 (1973): 835–40.

58. *New York Times,* October 14, 1957, p. 29.

59. A 1957 article by William Rehnquist, formerly a clerk to Justice Jackson and now a justice, started a debate on this subject among former clerks. Rehnquist claimed that the law clerks' responsibilities and their political orientation might bias the justices toward "the political left." Even Rehnquist, however, described the clerk's role as "primarily a trusted subordinate" ("Who Writes Decisions of the Supreme Court?" *U.S. News and World Report,* December 13, 1957). For a sample of the reaction to Rehnquist's article, see William D. Rogers, "Do Law Clerks Wield Power in Supreme Court Cases?" ibid., and Bickel, *Politics,* chap. 10.

60. Hearings before the Senate Committee on the Judiciary, 75th Cong., 1st Sess., on S. 1392, "A Bill to Reorganize the Judicial Branch of Government," March 10, 1937, p. 78.

61. Philip Kurland, "Jurisdiction of the United States Supreme Court: Time for a Change?" *Cornell Law Quarterly* 59 (1974): 627. On the precise subject of law clerk influence, from a justice's point of view, Justice Goldberg has stated: "Law clerks are helpful

and, indeed, indispensable aides to the justices, but law clerks do not make decisions for a justice" ("The Case Against the National Court of Appeals," *Washington Post,* January 6, 1973, A-14).

62. Wilkinson, *Serving Justice,* p. 20.

63. "An Overburdened Supreme Court," an address to the 4th Circuit Judicial Conference, June 30, 1972. Quoted in Wilkinson, p. 16. Justice Clark also noted the dramatic shift in staff support upon leaving his post as attorney general, where he had over one hundred employees working directly under him, including several secretaries and aides and a limousine on call at all times. At the Court he was entitled at that time to a single secretary and two law clerks, who, he said, "couldn't get much done" (interview cited above, n.45). N. O. Stockmeyer, Jr., recommended changing this aspect of the Court's work in "Rx for the Certiorari Crisis: A More Professional Staff," *American Bar Association Journal* 59 (1973): 846.

64. Until the 1955 term, the regular meeting day was Saturday.

65. Warren Weaver, "The Supreme Court at Work: A Look at the Inner Sanctum," *New York Times,* February 6, 1975, pp. 35, 65.

66. Justice White, dissenting from the denial of review in *Brown Transport Corp. v. Atcon,* 47 *Law Week* 3388 (December 5, 1978).

67. McElwain, "The Business of the Supreme Court," p. 15. Even under Stone, a notoriously slow worker, these conferences disposed of many cases. A typical fall entry in Justice Burton's diary in the period when Stone was Chief Justice indicates that in a six-hour conference the justices "cleared up the conference list," consisting of twenty-nine petitions for certiorari, two statements on jurisdiction, thirty-five motions to proceed *in forma pauperis,* and forty petitions for rehearing (October 6, 1945, diary entry, Box 1).

68. Richard L. Williams, "Supreme Court of the United States: The Staff that Keeps It Operating," *Smithsonian* 7 (1977): 46. Chief Justice Hughes's autobiography also describes the considerable lengths to which he went to keep up with summer petitions; see *The Autobiographical Notes of Charles Evans Hughes,* edited by David J. Danelski and Joseph Tulchin (Cambridge: Harvard University Press, 1973).

69. For a description of Hughes's unusual ability to shape Court procedures toward greater efficiency, see McElwain, "The Business of the Supreme Court."

70. Justice Burton records in his diary (Box 1) a visit with

Hughes on Saturday, October 12, 1946, in which they discussed his introduction of dead listings.

71. Burton recorded in his diary that Hughes recalled only about six changes from the dead list to the regular (discussion) list had been requested during his chief justiceship, and these were toward the end of his service (ibid).

72. Requests for changes in the special lists in the Burton papers are either typed notes from the deleting justice to the members of the Court, or simply circled changes in the special lists themselves, presumably made by Burton. Deletions averaged twelve per year, and 16 percent of them resulted in the Court's acceptance of the case for review on the merits. The deleter voted for his case in at least 61 percent of the instances (some are anonymous), and 17 percent of the time this was the only vote for review.

73. In the 1947–49 terms an average of 67 percent of the Miscellaneous Docket cases were special-listed. The proportion rose to 78 percent in 1950, and averaged 82 percent in the 1951–57 terms. In 1950, it may be noted, the Court replaced the Special List with a Discussion List for Miscellaneous Docket Cases.

74. Brennan, "Justice Brennan Calls," pp. 836–37. See also Weaver, "The Supreme Court," p. 35.

75. Burton's diaries, for example, contain diagrams of the various seating arrangements during his tenure.

76. Voting used to occur in reverse order—from the junior to the senior justice. According to Weaver, "The Supreme Court," p. 35, this practice is no longer followed.

77. Brennan, "Justice Brennan Calls," p. 837.

78. Of the 1,513 cases granted review, 438 received unanimous votes.

79. Joan M. Leiman, "The Rule of Four," *Columbia Law Review* 57 (1957): 981. In Justice Burton's conversation with Hughes (n.71), Hughes says that as a justice, Cardozo had suggested a rule of five but that Justice Van Devanter had replied that the Court had already practically committed itself to the rule of four by that time.

80. Testimony of Justice Van Devanter in Hearings before the Senate Committee on the Judiciary on S. 2060 and 2061, 68th Cong., 1st. Sess., p. 29 (Washington, D.C.: U.S. Government Printing Office, 1924).

81. Hughes mentioned this to Burton (n.71) and to Senator Wheeler (Hughes to Wheeler, March 23, 1937, reprinted in *Congressional Record* 81 [1937]: 2814).

82. See figure 5.1 and accompanying discussion in chap. 5.

83. "The Supreme Court: Deciding Whether to Decide," *Time,* December 11, 1972, p. 73. The justice who made this statement did so anonymously.

84. See Leiman, "Rule of Four," also David Berman, "The Case of Mr. Justice Frankfurter," *New Jersey State Bar Journal* 2 (1958): 168–89, and the dissenting opinions of Frankfurter and Harlan in *Rogers v. Mo. Pac. Ry.,* 352 U.S. 500 (1956), at 512, 518, 521.

85. Charles Evans Hughes, *The Supreme Court of the United States* (New York: Columbia University Press, 1936), p. 58.

86. David J. Danelski, "The Influence of the Chief Justice in the Decision Process of the Supreme Court," Paper delivered at the 1960 meeting of the American Political Science Association and published in Sheldon Goldman and Thomas P. Jahnige, eds., *The Federal Judicial System: Readings in Process and Behavior* (New York: Holt, Rinehart, & Winston, 1968), pp. 147–60, and excerpted in Joel B. Grossman and Richard S. Wells, *Constitutional Law and Judicial Policy Making* (New York: John Wiley & Sons, 1972), pp. 170–75.

87. This was the 1927 term, and there were 228 accumulated applications for certiorari. Justice Harlan Fiske Stone, "Fifty Years of Work on the United States Supreme Court," *American Bar Association Journal* 14 (1928): 436.

88. As William O. Douglas said diplomatically: "The conference never assumed more importance than it did under Chief Justice Stone. Petitions for certiorari and jurisdictional statements were never more fully or carefully considered and there was no cloture in discussing argued and submitted cases. Frequently the Saturday conference would continue over into Monday, Tuesday, or even Wednesday of the following week" ("Chief Justice Stone," *Columbia Law Review* 46 [1946]: 695). Others have also noted Stone's slowness; see Bennett Bosky, "Mr. Chief Justice Stone," *Harvard Law Review* 59 (1946): 1200, and Alfred McCormack, "A Law Clerk's Recollections," *Columbia Law Review* 49 (1949): 716.

89. McElwain, "The Business of the Supreme Court," p. 14.

90. David J. Danelski, "Conflict and Its Resolution in the Supreme Court," *Journal of Conflict Resolution* 11 (1967): 78.

91. Brennan, "Justice Brennan Calls," p. 837.

92. Interview with Justice Clark, February 8, 1977.

93. Clark remembered, for example, that Frankfurter would each term reproduce and circulate the same memo encouraging the Court to be more careful in selecting cases.

94. Supreme Court of the United States, Revised Rules (1967), 28 *U.S.C.* Appendix.

95. Stern and Gressman, *Supreme Court Practice,* p. 110.

96. Felix Frankfurter and Henry M. Hart, Jr., "The Business of the Supreme Court at October Term, 1933," p. 267.

97. Joseph Tanenhaus, Marvin Schick, Matthew Muraskin, and Daniel Rosen, "The Supreme Court's Certiorari Jurisdiction: Cue Theory," in Glendon Schubert, ed., *Judicial Decision-Making* (New York: Free Press, 1963), p. 116.

98. A 1975 study by Floyd Feeney for the Commission on the Revision of the Federal Court Appellate System (CRFCAS) shows this dramatically. He found that about one-third of the cases in the sample claimed conflict but that in 708 of the 966 cases in which conflicts were claimed there was no genuine conflict, direct or indirect. See "Conflicts and the Supreme Court: A Study in Petitions for Certiorari," in CRFCAS, "Structure and Internal Procedures: Recommendations for Change" (mimeographed), table 9, p. A67.

99. Ibid. Compare table 3, p. A55 (omitting argued cases), and table 9, p. A67. Early controversy on this subject is more impressionistic. It is directed toward the question of whether cases of genuine conflict are *ever* refused by the court. See Edward Roehner and Sherla Roehner, "Certiorari: What Is a Conflict between Circuits?" *University of Chicago Law Review* 20 (1953): 656, and Robert L. Stern, "Comment: Denial of Certiorari despite a Conflict," *Harvard Law Review* 66 (1953): 465–72.

100. CRFCAS, Hearings, 2d Phase, 1974–75, vol. 1, 1974 Hearings, Pursuant to P.L. 92-489, as amended P.L. 93-420. Testimony of Melvin L. Wulf, legal director, American Civil Liberties Union, p. 331.

101. The Commission (CRFCAS), for example, came to this conclusion.

102. Opinion of Justice White, with whom Justice Blackmun joined, dissenting from the denial of review in *Brown Transport Corp. v. Atcon* (#77-1581), *Law Week* 47:3387 (December 5, 1978), at 3389. Chief Justice Burger filed a separate opinion in support of this view.

103. The major critical articles all have Fowler Harper as their principal author. They appear in the *Pennsylvania Law Review* under the title: "What the Supreme Court Did Not Do in the 1949 [1950, 1951, 1952] Term." Coauthor for the 1949 terms was Alan Rosenthal (99 [1950]: 293–325); for the 1950 term, Edwin Etherington (100 [1951]: 354–409); for the 1951 term, George

C. Pratt (101 [1953]: 439–79), and for the 1952 term, Arnold Leibowitz (102 [1954]: 427–63).

104. This issue is discussed in Stern and Gressman, *Supreme Court Practice,* pp. 121–27.

105. Address before the American Bar Association, September 7, 1949, *St. Louis Daily Record,* September 8, 1949, p. 1, reprinted in Stern and Gressman, *Supreme Court Practice,* p. 107.

106. For example, Reynolds Robertson and Francis R. Kirkham, *Jurisdiction of the Supreme Court of the United States* (New York: Matthew Bender, 1951), p. 662.

107. Opinion of Mr. Justice Stevens respecting the denial of certiorari in *Singleton v. Commissioner of Internal Revenue* (#78-78) *Law Week* 47:3300 (October 31, 1978).

108. Tanenhaus, "Certiorari Jurisdiction," table 1, p. 115.

109. Harlan, "Manning the Dikes," p. 675. This problem is not a new one. Hughes complained of the burden in an address to the American Law Institute (*American Bar Association Journal* 20 [1934]: 341). Taft also complained about this. He claimed that 80 percent of petitioners apparently did not understand the meaning of the writ of certiorari (*Magnum Co. v. Coty,* 262 U.S. 159 [1923], at 163).

110. Felix Frankfurter and James Landis, "The Business of the Supreme Court at October Term 1931," *Harvard Law Review* 46 (1932): 240. Even Frankfurter was not wholly satisfied with the Court's rule on decision criteria: "Nor does Rule 38 unambiguously prescribe the requisites of a proper petition" (Frankfurter and Hart, "The Business," [note 96], p. 265).

111. Harper and Pratt, "What the Supreme Court," (1951 term article), p. 456.

112. See "Note: Penalties for Frivolous Appeals," *Harvard Law Review* 43 (1929): 113.

1.13. See Harper and Leibowitz, "What the Supreme Court," (1952 term article).

114. Frankfurter and Hart suggest this (1933 term article "The Business," [Note 96], p. 276). Harper and Leibowitz (1952 term "What the Supreme Court," p. 456) repeat the suggestion. So does Bennet Bosky, less directly, in "Mechanics of the Supreme Court's Certiorari Jurisdiction," *Columbia Law Review* 46 (1946): 262.

115. Opinion of Justice White, dissenting from the denial of review in *Brown Transport Corp. v. Atcon* (#77-1581) *Law Week* 47: 3387 (December 5, 1978), at 3389.

Two   1. Federal Judicial Center, *Report of the Study Group on the Caseload of the Supreme Court* (Washington, D.C.: Administrative Office of U.S. Courts, 1972).

2. For example, S. Sidney Ulmer, "Supreme Court Justices as Strict and Not-So-Strict Constructionists: Some Implications," *Law and Society Review* 8 (1973): 13–31, esp. 15.

3. Fowler Harper and Alan Rosenthal, "What the Supreme Court Did Not Do in the 1949 Term," *University of Pennsylvania Law Review* 99 (1950): 293.

4. *Ratchford v. Gay Lib* (#77-477), cert. denied, "Supreme Court Proceedings," *Law Week* 46:3524 (February 21, 1978).

5. Dan T. Carter, *Scottsboro: A Tragedy of the American South* (New York: Oxford University Press, 1969), p. 165.

6. Henry M. Hart, Jr., and Albert M. Sacks, *The Legal Process: Basic Problems in the Making and Application of Law* (Cambridge University Press, 1958), pp. 185–86. See also Carl A. Auerbach, et al., *The Legal Process: An Introduction to Decision-Making by Judicial, Legislative, Executive, and Administrative Agencies* (San Francisco: Chandler, 1961), p. vi.

7. Hart and Sacks, *The Legal Process,* p. 186. The literature on such attempts is enormous. See Clement E. Vose, *Constitutional Change: Amendment Politics and Supreme Court Litigation Since 1900* (Lexington, Mass.: Heath, 1972). His substantial bibliography is particularly helpful. For a more general view, see Gerhard Casper and Richard Posner, "A Study of the Supreme Court's Caseload," *Journal of Legal Studies* 3 (1974): 339–75. These authors argue that uncertainty in the law is an important factor in recent overall litigation increases. See also their more recent article "The Workload of the Supreme Court: 1975 and 1976 Terms," *Supreme Court Review* (1977): 87–98.

8. Felix Frankfurter and Henry M. Hart, Jr., "The Business of the Supreme Court at October Term 1933," *Harvard Law Review* 48 (1934): 257.

9. For example, Richard Kluger, *Simple Justice* (New York: Knopf, 1976) and Vose, *Constitutional Change.*

10. See Hayden C. Covington, *Defending and Legally Establishing the Good News* (Brooklyn: Watchtower Bible and Tract Society, 1950).

11. Leon Friedman, "Up against the Burger Court," *Civil Liberties Review* 156 (1973): 161.

12. See Richard Kluger, *Simple Justice.*

13. On the relationship between new legislation and the Court's caseload, see Casper and Posner, "A Study."

14. *Roe v. Wade,* 410 U.S. 113 (1972) and *Doe v. Bolton,* 410 U.S. 179 (1972).

15. Barbara A. Babcock, Ann E. Friedman, Eleanor H. Norton, and Susan C. Ross, *Sex Discrimination and the Law: Causes and Remedies* (Boston: Little, Brown, 1975), p. 975.

16. Alexis de Toqueville, *Democracy in America* (New York: Random House, 1945), 1:290.

17. See Walter F. Murphy, *Congress and the Court* (Chicago: University of Chicago Press, 1962).

18. Ibid., p. 2. An analogous discussion of the problem is in John P. Frank, *Marble Palace: The Supreme Court in American Life* (New York: Knopf, 1958), chap. 2: "The Practicalities of Power."

19. *Korematsu v. U.S.,* 323 U.S. 214 (1944).

20. Lawrence Baum calls these "gatekeeping powers." He notes that all courts have such powers over their business, and that the power of courts to limit decisions of the merits significantly limits the power of litigants. ("The Judicial Gatekeeping Function: A General Analysis and a Study of the California Supreme Court," prepared for delivery at the 1975 meeting of the American Political Science Association, San Francisco, September 25, 1975. See also: Karen Orren, "Standing to Sue: Interest Group Conflict in the Federal Courts," *American Political Science Review* 70 (1976): 723–41.

21. Certiorari denied, 389 U.S. 934 (1967).

22. 416 U.S. 312 (1974).

23. Alexander M. Bickel, *The Least Dangerous Branch: The Supreme Court at the Bar of Politics* (Indianapolis: Bobbs-Merrill, 1962).

24. Ibid., p. 128.

25. Chapter 5 discusses a related issue, the propensity of justices to calculate the final outcome in casting case selection votes.

26. Arthur Goldberg, "High Court Strength," *New York Times,* November 17, 1971, p. 47.

27. Norman Dorsen, "The Court of Some Resort," *Civil Liberties Review,* Spring 1974, p. 99.

28. See Jerome J. Hanus, "Denial of Certiorari and Supreme Court Policy-Making," *American University Law Review* 17 (1967): 41–53, and Stephen W. Earp, "Sovereign Immunity in the Supreme Court: Using the Certiorari Process to Avoid Decision Making," *American Journal of International Law* 16 (1976): 903–29.

29. Ibid., p. 53.

30. Jan G. Deutsch, "Neutrality, Legitimacy, and the Supreme

Court: Some Intersections between Law and Political Science," *Stanford Law Review* 20 (1968): 217. Similarly, see Gerald Gunther, "The Subtle Vices of the 'Passive Virtues'—A Comment on Principle and Expediency in Judicial Review," *Columbia Law Review* 64 (1964): 1–25.

31. See, for example, Donald B. Ring and Charles W. Quick, eds., *Legal Aspects of the Civil Rights Movement* (Detroit: Wayne State University Press, 1965).

32. For example, Clement E. Vose, *Caucasians Only: The Supreme Court, the NAACP, and the Restrictive Covenant Cases* (Berkeley: University of California Press, 1959), chap. 7: "Preparations for the U.S. Supreme Court."

33. Kluger, *Simple Justice* pp. 536–37.

34. Ibid., p. 537.

35. F. A. A. to Burton, *Shelley v. Kraemer,* #268, 1946 Term (renumbered #72, 1947 Term). Box 174, Argued Cases: 1947 Term, p. 4.

36. A different recommendation, but with similar reference to public attitudes, occurs in J. L.'s memo to Burton in *McLaurin v. Oklahoma,* #34, 1949 Term (renumbered #614 1948 Term), Box 24, Argued Cases: 1948 Term.

37. A. J. M. to Burton, *Holmes v. City of Atlanta,* #396, 1955 Term, Box 282. Another example is J. R. R. to Burton, *Housing Authority of San Francisco v. Banks,* #583, 1953 Term, Box 261, Certs. Denied and Appeals Dismissed: 1953 Term.

38. On the significance of technical defects in preventing review see chap. 3.

39. A. J. M. to Burton, #366, 1955 Term, Box 283, Certs. Denied and Appeals Dismissed: 1955 Term.

40. 350 U.S. 891 and 985 (1956).

41. Interview with Justice Tom Clark (retired) at Supreme Court, February 8, 1977.

42. 388 U.S. 1 (1967). For a good description of this history, see Robert J. Sickels, *Race, Marriage and the Law* (Albuquerque: University of New Mexico Press, 1972).

43. Felix Frankfurter, January 25, 1956, memorandum concerning *South Carolina Electric and Gas v. Fleming* #511, 1955 Term, Box 283. p. 2.

44. Harry Kalven, Jr., "Forword to the 1970 Term: Even When a Nation Is at War," *Harvard Law Review* 85 (1971): 3.

45. Douglas, "The Supreme Court," p. 412.

46. Brennan, "Justice Brennan Calls," p. 839.

47. Felix Frankfurter and Adrian S. Fisher, "Business of the Supreme Court, 1935 and 1936 Terms," *Harvard Law Review* 51 (1938): 598.

48. Complaints about all-male juries are an example of this type of case. Libel cases raising strong First Amendment issues are another type of case which was special-listed in Burton's time, but which would be reversed today.

49. 335 U.S. 464 (1948). See chap. 1 for a discussion of this case.

50. 339 U.S. 629 (1950).

51. The following year, as table 2.1 indicates, the Court voted unanimously to decide the case.

52. 372 U.S. 335 (1963). Anthony Lewis described the case and its development in detail in *Gideon's Trumpet* (New York: Random House, 1964).

53. Nathan Lewin, "A Response to Goldberg and Bickel: Helping the Court with Its Work," *New Republic*, March 3, 1973, p. 18.

54. Remarks of Justices Powell and Brennan to members of the Commission on Revision of the Federal Court Appellate System, May 8, 1975, and March 14, 1974, confidential draft prepared for the Commission, pp. 4 and 8.

55. Federal Judicial Center, *Report*, pp. 16, 18. Similarly, the Study Group described a means by which the Court might "manage to administer its docket" as opposed to meeting "its essential responsibilities" (p. 9).

56. Ibid., p. 1. In defense of the report Freund stated: "All the members of our group are persuaded that our proposals would not fetter the Supreme Court but would help to emancipate it for the highest performance of its essential functions" ("Why We Need the National Court of Appeals," *American Bar Association Journal* 59 [1973]: 252).

57. Federal Judicial Center, *Report*, p. 1.

58. Ibid., p. 5.

59. Ibid., pp. 18–24.

60. Paul A. Freund, *The Supreme Court of the United States: Its Business, Purposes, and Performance* (Cleveland: World Publishing Co., 1961), p. 183.

61. Earl Warren and Warren Burger, "Retired Chief Justice Warren Attacks, Chief Justice Burger Defends Freund Study Group's Composition and Proposal," *American Bar Association Journal* 59 (1973): 721–30. Warren, "Retired Chief Justice Earl

Warren, 'Let's Not Weaken the Supreme Court,'" *American Bar Association Journal* 60 (1974): 677–80. Arthur J. Goldberg, "It Doesn't Need Its Cases 'Screened': One Supreme Court," *New Republic,* February 10, 1973, p. 14; Brennan, "Justice Brennan Calls."

62. See Warren, "Retired Chief Justice Warren Attacks" and the annual reports on the judicial branch prepared by Chief Justice Burger (published yearly in the *American Bar Association Journal*); William Rehnquist, "The Supreme Court: Past and Present," *American Bar Association Journal* 59 (1973): 361–64; and Rehnquist, "Whither the Courts?" *American Bar Association Journal* 60 (1974): 787–90.

63. The Association's disclaimers in its 1974 testimony before CRFCAS clearly revealed the lack of full organizational support or concrete proposals. See the remarks of Chesterfield Smith, president of the Association, Judge Shirley Hufstedler, and Frank Reifsnyder on April 1, 1974, reprinted in Commission on Revision of the Federal Court Appellate System, *Hearings,* Second Phase, vol. 1 (1974), pp. 4–48.

64. For example, Paul A. Freund, "Why We Need the National Court of Appeals," *American Bar Association Journal* 59 (1973): 247–52. No one in the prestigious Cornell Law School series of lectures on federal appellate justice, for example, unqualifiedly endorsed the Freund Committee proposal. See *Cornell Law Review* 59 (1974), articles (from the lectures) by Maurice Rosenberg, Clement F. Haynsworth, Philip B. Kurland, and Henry J. Friendly.

65. In his November 2, 1974, Cornell Law School lecture, Professor Henry J. Friendly concluded: "The proposal has been talked to death and, if I may say so with deference, I hope literally as well as figuratively" ("Averting the Flood by Lessening the Flow," *Cornell Law Review* 59 [1974]: 635).

66. Commission on the Revision of the Federal Court Appellate System, *Structure and Internal Procedures: Recommendations for Change* (Washington, D.C., June 1975).

67. For the argument of overwork due to case selection as a justification for increasing the membership of the Supreme Court see the testimony of Attorney General Homer Cummings in *Reorganization of the Federal Judiciary,* Hearings before the Committee on the Judiciary, U.S. Senate, 75th Cong. 1st Sess. on S. 1392, pt. 1, March 10, 1937, p. 25.

68. Henry M. Hart, Jr., "The Supreme Court, 1958 Term.

Foreword: The Time Chart of the Justices," *Harvard Law Review* 73 (1959): 100.

69. Philip B. Kurland, "The Court Should Decide Less and Explain More," *New York Times*, June 9, 1968, p. 124 (magazine section).

70. Douglas's views are reprinted from a letter to CRFCAS (*Structure and Internal Procedures*, p. 180).

71. Warren, "Retired Chief Justice Earl Warren, 'Let's Not Weaken,'" pp. 677–78.

72. Testimony of Melvin L. Wulf before CRFCAS, May 21, 1974 (*Hearings*, pp. 313–33), p. 317.

73. The chairman, Paul A. Freund, was clerk for Justice Brandeis, Alexander Bickel clerked for Justice Frankfurter, and Peter Ehrenhaft clerked for Chief Justice Warren. All members of the Study Group are distinguished men in the field of Supreme Court procedure. See appendix: Biographies of Members of the Study Group (Federal Judicial Center, *Report*, pp. A15–A17).

74. Warren, "Retired Chief Justice Warren Attacks," p. 728.

75. Judge James L. Oakes to Frank Reifsnyder, reprinted in CRFCAS, *Hearings*, p. 53.

76. S. Sidney Ulmer "Revising the Jurisdiction of the Supreme Court: Mere Administrative Reform or Substantive Policy Change?" *Minnesota Law Review* 58 (1973): 121–55.

77. Nathan Lewin chides Bickel for his stance in "A Response to Goldberg and Bickel: Helping the Court with Its Work," *New Republic*, March 3, 1973, p. 17.

Three   1. Felix Frankfurter and Adrian S. Fisher, "The Business of the Supreme Court at October Term, 1935 and 1936," *Harvard Law Review* 51 (1938): pp. 578–79.

2. "Appeals from Federal Courts," Hearings before the Committee on the Judiciary, U.S. Senate, 74th Cong., 1st Sess. (on S. 2176), March 25, 1935 (Washington, D.C.: U.S. Government Printing Office, 1935), p. 7.

3. Information on the Court's weighing of conflicts in its review decisions is contained in a report prepared by Floyd Feeney for the Commission on the Revision of the Federal Court Appellate System, entitled "Conflicts involving Federal Law: A Review of Cases Presented to the Supreme Court." It is reprinted in an appendix to the Commission's *Structure and Internal Procedures: Recommendations for Change* (Washington, 1975). On the severity of penalties, see Robert W. Dickey, "An Empirical Analysis of

Death and the Supreme Court: The Impact of Death upon the Court's Decision to Make a Decision," unpublished paper prepared for David Danelski, February 28, 1962.

4. Felix Frankfurter and James Landis, *The Business of the Supreme Court* (New York: Macmillan, 1928), chap. 8: "The Future of Supreme Court Litigation." See also Eugene Gressman, "Much Ado about Certiorari," *Georgetown Law Journal* 52 (1964): 756–58.

5. Every year the *Harvard Law Review* publishes a statistical summary of the subject matter of the cases that came before the Court that term. Except for the period when Felix Frankfurter prepared the accompanying commentary, the law review articles have ignored trends in subject-matter interests of the Court over time. For a nonempirical historical treatment of changes in the Court's concerns see Robert McCloskey, *The American Supreme Court* (Chicago: University of Chicago Press, 1960).

6. Fowler Harper and Arnold Leibowitz, "What the Supreme Court Did Not Do in the 1952 Term," *University of Pennsylvania Law Review* 102 (1954): 427.

7. See, for example, Richard Wolfson, Philip Kurland, Reynolds Robertson, and Francis Kirkham, *Jurisdiction of the Supreme Court of the United States* (Albany: Matthew Bender, 1951).

8. The study by Radek and Spaniol is unpublished, but is discussed in Curtis R. Reitz, "Federal Habeas Corpus: Postconviction Remedy for State Prisoners," *University of Pennsylvania Law Review* 108 (1960): 477.

9. Robert Stern and Eugene Gressman, *Supreme Court Practice,* 2d ed. (Washington, D.C.: Bureau of National Affairs, 1954); "Supreme Court Certiorari Policy in Cases Arising under the Federal Employers' Liability Act," *Harvard Law Review* 69 (1956): 1441; E. Barrett Prettyman, Jr., "Opposing Certiorari in the United States Supreme Court," *University of Virginia Law Review* 61 (1975): 197.

10. See Stern and Gressman, *Supreme Court Practice,* and the discussion of the Tanenhaus research to follow.

11. See the work of Lawrence Baum and S. Sidney Ulmer, especially Baum's "Policy Goals and Judicial Gatekeeping: A proximity Model of Discretionary Jurisdiction," *American Journal of Political Science* 21 (1977): 149–69, and Ulmer's "The Decision to Grant or Deny Certiorari as an Indicator to Decision 'On the Merits,'" *Polity* (1972): 429–47 and "Supreme Court Justices as Strict and Not-So-Strict Constructionists: Some Implications," *Law and Society Review* 8 (1973): 13–31.

12. Glendon Schubert, "The Certiorari Game," chap. 4 of his *Quantitative Analysis of Judicial Behavior* (New York: Free Press, 1959), and Schubert, "Policy without Law: An Extension of the Certiorari Game," *Stanford Law Review* 14 (1962): 284–327.

13. Joseph Tanenhaus, Marvin Schick, Matthew Muraskin, and Daniel Rosen, "The Supreme Court's Certiorari Jurisdiction: Cue Theory," in Glendon Schubert, ed., *Judicial Decision-Making* (New York: Free Press, 1963), pp. 111–32. (Hereafter cited as "Tanenhaus.")

14. Tanenhaus, pp. 119, 121–22.

15. Ibid., tables 4–6, pp. 123–26.

16. Ibid., p. 118. What part the law clerks play in this review is unclear because the authors omit any discussion of their role.

17. The authors derived one cue from an apparent misunderstanding of the relevant literature. They interpreted Chief Justice Vinson's statement that the Court most often hears cases where "there is a conflict among the lower courts" to mean the lower courts involved in each specific case. In keeping with his other public statements and Rule 19, however, Vinson probably meant conflicts of interpretation between various lower courts in independent cases raising the same legal issues. See the excerpt of his remarks before the American Bar Association (chap. 1, n.105).

18. Robert W. Gibbs, "Certiorari: Its Diagnosis and Cure," *Hastings Law Journal* (1955): pp. 131–70.

19. The grant rate for cue-containing cases is determined by assuming that the overall grant rate is reduced by the number of cueless cases whose chances of review approximate zero. Since 40 to 60 percent of the cases fall into this category, the grant rate in cue-containing cases must be significantly higher than the overall rate, or x times $(1 -$ the proportion of cueless cases).

20. Tanenhaus, p. 119.

21. Ibid., p. 118.

22. Sidney Ulmer, William Hintze, and Louise Kirklosky, "The Decision to Grant or Deny Certiorari: Further Consideration of Cue Theory," *Law and Society Review* 7 (1972): 637–43.

23. Wells and Grossman attribute this inattention to the policy variable to the reaction against doctrinal analysis and to the use of analytical tools unsuited to the purpose: Richard S. Wells and Joel B. Grossman, "The Concept of Judicial Policy-Making: A Critique," *Journal of Public Law* [now *Emory Law Review*] 15 (1966): 286–87.

24. Felix Frankfurter and James M. Landis, "The Business of

the Supreme Court at October Term 1929," *Harvard Law Review* 44 (1930): 1.

25. Tanenhaus, p. 122. Harlan, "Manning the Dikes," p. 548.

26. This has always been true. See Frankfurter & Landis, "The Business . . . October Term 1929."

27. Robert Scigliano, *The Supreme Court and the Presidency* (New York: Free Press, 1971), pp. 166–77. See also Robert L. Stern, "The Solicitor General's Office and Administrative Agency Litigation," *American Bar Association Journal* 46 (1960): 154–56.

28. William E. Brigman, "The Office of the Solicitor General of the United States" (Ph.D. diss., University of North Carolina, 1966).

29. Tanenhaus, p. 122.

30. Luther A. Huston, Arthur S. Miller, Samuel Krislov, and Robert Dixon, Jr., *Roles of the Attorney General of the United States* (Washington, D.C.: American Enterprise Institute, 1968), and Scigliano, pp. 175–77.

31. Scigliano, *The Supreme Court,* p. 175.

32. Scigliano (p. 177), reports that in ten recent terms the government participated in 57 percent of all cases argued in the Supreme Court.

33. See the annual reports of the Attorney General of the United States.

34. Baum, "Decisions to Grant," pp. 728–29.

35. Marc Galanter, "Why the 'Haves' Come Out Ahead: Speculations on Limits of Legal Change," *Law and Society Review* 9 (1974): 95–160.

36. Ibid., p. 98.

37. Lawrence E. Rothstein, "The Myth of Sisyphus: Legal Services Efforts on Behalf of the Poor," *University of Michigan Journal of Law Reform* 7 (1974): 501.

38. Corporations sued the NLRB 149 times, as opposed to 36 suits by unions. The probability that their differences in success in gaining review were due to chance is less than .001.

39. *Harris v. Pa. RR.,* 361 U.S. 15 (1959), at 17.

40. For example, Robert G. McCloskey, *The American Supreme Court* (Chicago: University of Chicago Press, 1960), chap. 7; Alpheus T. Mason, *The Supreme Court from Taft to Warren* (Baton Rouge: Louisiana State Univ. Press, 1958), chap. 4; John P. Frank, *Marble Palace: The Supreme Court in American Life* (New York: Knopf, 1958), chaps. 8–11.

41. Tanenhaus does not include these cases either, probably for the same reason (p. 132, n.35).

42. Even though the Tanenhaus definition differs in litigant specificity and in other minor ways from the categorization I have adopted, our findings are comparable because the differences do not involve a large number of cases. Tanenhaus found that when a civil liberties issue was presented, the Court granted review 32.9 percent of the time, whereas my figure (table 3.6) is 37 percent.

43. See table 1.3, above.

44. The literature on the post–1937 shift is enormous. See Robert H. Jackson, *The Struggle for Judicial Supremacy* (New York: Random House, 1941) bibliographic materials in McCloskey, *The American Supreme Court,* pp. 249–50, and in Alfred H. Cope and Fred Krinsky, eds., *Franklin D. Roosevelt and the Supreme Court,* rev. ed. (Lexington, Mass.: Heath, 1969), pp. 114–15.

45. Henry J. Abraham, *Freedom and the Court,* 2d ed. (New York: Oxford University Press, 1972), p. 10.

46. Thurgood Marshall was the attorney of record in sixteen cases between 1947 and 1957 according to *U.S. Law Week.* He was granted review unanimously in five cases, granted review with at least one justice opposing in four cases, denied review with at least one justice approving in six cases, and denied review unanimously only once.

47. In the same period Hayden Covington was attorney of record in thirty-eight cases. His cases were granted review six times unanimously, eight times nonunanimously. Certiorari was denied with at least one justice voting for review twelve times, and with no one voting for review seven times. Five of his cases were special-listed.

48. Frank J. Sorauf, *The Wall of Separation: The Constitutional Politics of Church and State* (Princeton: Princeton University Press, 1976), pp. 126–27.

49. Books on federal-state relations usually include civil rights issues. See John R. Schmidhauser, *The Supreme Court as Final Arbiter in Federal-State Relations: 1789–1957* (Chapel Hill: University of North Carolina Press, 1958) and John D. Sprague, *Voting Patterns of the U.S. Supreme Court: Cases in Federalism, 1889–1959* (Indianapolis: Bobbs-Merrill, 1968), appendix A.

50. See also table 3.5, above.

51. Felix Frankfurter and James Landis, *The Business of the Supreme Court* (New York: Macmillan, 1928), pp. 308, 318.

52. Address before the American Bar Association, September 7, 1949, *St. Louis Daily Record* (September 8, 1949, p. 1).

Four

1. See table 1.4.

2. C. Herman Pritchett, *The Roosevelt Court* (New York: Macmillan, 1948), p. xii, and Pritchett, *Civil Liberties and the Vinson Court* (Chicago: University of Chicago Press, 1954), p. viii.

3. Chief Justice Vinson's address before the American Bar Association, September 7, 1949, *Saint Louis Daily Record* (September 8, 1949, p. 1).

4. See S. Sidney Ulmer, "The Decision to Grant Certiorari as an Indicator to Decision 'On the Merits,'" *Polity* 4 (1972): 429–47, and "Supreme Court Justices as Strict and Not-So-Strict Constructionists: Some Implications," *Law and Society Review* 8 (1973): 13–31. See also Lawrence Baum, "Policy Goals in Judicial Gatekeeping: A Proximity Model of Discretionary Jurisdiction," *American Journal of Political Science* 21 (1977): 13–35; "Decisions to Grant and Deny Hearings on the California Supreme Court: Patterns in Court and Individual Behavior," *Santa Clara Law Review* 16 (1976): 713–44; and "Judicial Demand-Screening and Decisions on the Merits: A Second Look," *American Politics Quarterly* 7 (1979): 109–19. Others who have not used voting data have also concluded that the two stages of decision are not as independent as official statements of review criteria indicate. See Robert W. Gibbs, "Certiorari: Its Diagnosis and Cure," *Hastings Law Journal* 6 (1955): 131, and Glendon Schubert, "Policy Without Law: An Extension of the Certiorari Game," *Stanford Law Review* 14 (1962): 284–327.

5. Ulmer, "Supreme Court Justices."

6. Ulmer, "The Decision to Grant."

7. Ibid., p. 437.

8. Ulmer eliminated four of the Burton-period justices: Murphy, Rutledge, Brennan, and Whittaker from his analysis because his sampling method made their participation level too low. Of the remainder, relationships were not statistically significant at $p < .05$ for Clark, Warren, or Harlan. The statistically significant lambda relationships were: at a $p < .01$ level—Vinson, Black, Jackson, Douglas, Frankfurter; at $p < .05$—Reed, Burton, Minton. Ulmer also divided the cases by whether they raised economic liberties or civil liberties issues and performed the same statistical tests, but this altered his findings only slightly.

9. Baum, "Decisions," "Policy Goals," and "Judicial Demand-Screening."

10. Baum, "Policy Goals."

11. See especially Baum, "Decisions." Brenner also demonstrates a relationship between votes to review and votes to re-

verse. He shows that when four justices who favor affirmance on the merits are the only ones to vote for review, they have an excellent chance of "winning" affirmance on the merits; not so a four-man pro-reversal case-selection group. Although Brenner did not suggest it, the reason appears to be that justices tend not to vote for review when they agree with the lower-court result. It is easier, therefore, for the pro-affirmance group to pick up the fifth vote necessary for a majority on the merits (Saul Brenner, "The New Certiorari Game," *Journal of Politics* 41 (1979): 649–55).

12. Perhaps because Ulmer analyzed unanimous as well as nonunanimous Burton-period cases in which review was granted, the ordering in table 4.1 does not correspond very nearly to Ulmer's lambda findings (see n.8 above).

13. Felix Frankfurter to Harold Burton, December 13, 1946, re #142, *Louisiana v. Resweber,* Box 171.

14. Edwin McElwain, "The Business of the Supreme Court as Conducted by Chief Justice Hughes," *Harvard Law Review* 63 (1949): 13.

15. During the Burton Period, the range of disagreement in civil rights–civil liberties cases was 70.9 percent and the standard deviation was 22.9. In criminal cases the range was 67.5 percent and the standard deviation was 26.1. At the opposite extreme were federalism cases and the Residual Category discussed in chapter 3. The range in both of these categories was around 40 percent and the standard deviation about 10. The justices voted mostly in keeping with their overall ranking in review proneness in civil rights–civil liberties cases and in criminal cases, and to a somewhat lesser extent, in labor cases. The overall voting patterns fit U.S. and federalism cases least well.

16. Hugo Black, Jr., *My Father: A Remembrance* (New York: Random House, 1975), p. 187.

17. Ibid., p. 258.

18. For another view see S. Sidney Ulmer, "Selecting Cases for Supreme Court Review: An Underdog Model," *American Political Science Review* 72 (1978): 902–10.

19. Felix Frankfurter to Chief Justice Warren, January 26, 1956, p. 1, Burton Collection, Box 283.

20. Fowler V. Harper, *Justice Rutledge and the Bright Constellation* (Indianapolis: Bobbs-Merrill, 1965), p. xii.

21. Douglas, "The Supreme Court and its Caseload," pp. 401–14.

22. Sherman Minton to Felix Frankfurter, August 31, 1954,

reprinted in David N. Atkinson, "Justice Sherman Minton and Behavior Patterns inside the Supreme Court," *Northwestern Law Review* 69 (1974): 734.

23. T. O. N. to Justice Burton, #198, 1954 Term, *Silverman v. U.S.*, p. 2, Box 271.

24. W. B. M. to Justice Burton, #219, 1954 Term, *Jason v. Summerfield*, p. 3, Box 271.

25. W. B. M. to Justice Burton, #445, 1954 Term, *Sing v. Barber*, p. 4, Box 271.

26. T. O. N. to Justice Burton, #272, 1954 Term, *Anderson v. McKay*, pp. 2–3, Box 271.

27. W. B. M. to Justice Burton, #244, 1954 Term, *River Cliff Co. v. Linebarger*, pp. 2–3, Box 271.

28. T. O. N. to Justice Burton, #362, 1954 Term, *Cooper v. Maryland*, p. 1, Box 271.

29. A. J. M. to Justice Burton, #92, 1955 Term, *Black v. Cutter Labs.*, p. 9, Box 280 (Argued Cases: 1955 Term).

30. T. O. N. to Justice Burton, #110 Misc., *Williams v. Georgia*, p. 1, Box 280. The issue was the constitutionality of the prosecutor's use of peremptory challenges to achieve a racially segregated jury.

31. R. S. T. to Justice Burton, #88, 1954 Term, Box 271 (Certs. Denied and Appeals Dismissed), p. 2.

32. Unsigned, #763, p. 2, Box 280.

33. Pritchett, *Civil Liberties.*

34. Ibid., p. 198.

35. Ibid., p. 191.

36. Justice Murphy to George Murphy, September 9, 1946, Murphy Collection, p. 2.

37. J. Woodford Howard, "Role Perceptions and Behavior in Three U.S. Courts of Appeals," *Journal of Politics* 39 (1977): 935–36.

38. Ibid., p. 923. See also James L. Gibson, "Judges' Role Orientations, Attitudes, and Decisions," *American Political Science Review* 72 (1978): 911–24.

39. Walter F. Murphy, *Elements of Judicial Strategy* (Chicago: University of Chicago Press, 1964). Murphy defines the subject of his book, the policy-oriented judge or justice as one "who is aware of the impact which judicial decisions can have on public policy, realizes the leeway for discretion which his office permits, and is willing to take advantage of this power and leeway to further particular policy aims" (p. 4).

40. J. Woodford Howard, *Mr. Justice Murphy: A Political Biography* (Princeton: Princeton University Press, 1968), p. 338.

41. Clerk to Justice Murphy, *Enoch Pratt Free Libr. v. Kerr,* #113, 1945 Term, p. 2, Box 67, Murphy Collection, Bentley Historical Library, Ann Arbor, Michigan.

42. "The Supreme Court: Deciding Whether to Decide," *Time,* December 11, 1972, p. 72.

43. Baum, "Policy Goals."

44. Ibid., p. 16.

45. Pritchett, *The Roosevelt Court,* p. 278.

Five

1. Glendon Schubert, "The Certiorari Game," chapter 4 of his *Quantitative Analysis of Judicial Behavior* (New York: Free Press, 1959) and "Policy without Law: An Extension of the Certiorari Game," *Stanford Law Review* 14 (1962): 284–327.

2. Joel Grossman, "Dissenting Blocs on the Warren Court: A Study in Judicial Role Behavior," *Journal of Politics* 30 (1968): 1068–90. The subject of his critical analysis was S. Sidney Ulmer, "Toward a Theory of Sub-Group Formation in the United States Supreme Court," *Journal of Politics* 27 (1965): 133–52.

3. Although Burton joined the Court in 1945, he did not keep very complete records during his first two terms.

4. Pritchett used the term "bloc" but did not imply by that term collusive activity. See C. Herman Pritchett, *The Roosevelt Court* (New York: Macmillan, 1948) pp. 42–43, including table 12. Sprague took the safe route and limited his definition of "bloc" to "a name for a pattern of scores in a summary voting record": John D. Sprague, *Voting Patterns of the U.S. Supreme Court: Cases in Federalism, 1889–1959* (Indianapolis: Bobbs-Merrill, 1968), p. 7. Powell and Murphy discuss the implications of "bloc" behavior as conscious coalition making and reject such behavior as improbable: Lewis F. Powell, Jr., "Myths and Misconceptions about the Supreme Court," *American Bar Association Journal* 61 (1975): 1347; Walter Murphy, *Elements of Judicial Strategy* (Chicago: University of Chicago Press, 1964).

5. Justice Murphy died on July 1, 1949, and Justice Rutledge died in September 1949.

6. On March 30, 1954, Justice Jackson suffered a heart attack and was confined to a hospital. He died seven months later.

7. Harlan was selected to replace Jackson late in 1954, but he did not take his seat until the spring of 1955 because of opposition in the Senate.

8. Sprague, *Voting Patterns,* chapter 2, "Block Analysis Critical Development," pp. 21–50.

9. Jurisdictional dissents, it could be argued, also show stress on the Court and signal a departure from role expectations. See Grossman, "Dissenting Blocs," p. 1072.

10. Justice Frankfurter was more critical than anyone else of the Court's practice of reviewing these cases. See, for example, Frankfurter's dissent in *Ferguson v. Moore-McCormack Lines,* 352 U.S. 521 (1956). Such statements of dissatisfaction caused some justices to defend the grants and others to side publicly with Frankfurter.

11. L. S. Shapley and Martin Shubik, "A Method for Evaluating the Distribution of Power in a Committee System," *American Political Science Review* 48 (1954): 791–92. See also Glendon Schubert, *Quantitative Analysis of Judicial Behavior* (New York: Free Press, 1959), "The Hughberts Game," pp. 192–210. Two articles critical of this approach as it is applied to judicial voting patterns are William B. Schultz and Philip K. Howard, "The Myth of Swing Voting: An Analysis of Voting Patterns on the Supreme Court," *New York University Law Review* 50 (1975): 798–868, and "Mr. Justice Reed—Swing Man or Not?" *Stanford Law Review* 1 (1949): 714–29.

12. Resolutions of the Supreme Court Bar, 14, L. Ed. 2d, xxxviii (1965).

13. Interview with Justice Tom Clark (retired) at the Supreme Court, February 8, 1977.

14. Schubert, "The Certiorari Game."

15. Schubert, *Quantitative Analysis,* pp. 210–11.

16. 35 Stat. 65 (1908), as amended, 45 U.S.C. sections 51–59 (1958).

17. See, for example, Douglas's concurring opinion in *Harris v. Pa. RR.,* 361 U.S. 15 (1959), at 16, and Frankfurter's dissenting opinion in *Ferguson v. Moore-McCormack Lines* 352 U.S. 521 (1956), at 535. Most scholarly comment has been critical of the Court's tendency to take up FELA cases. See James C. Conner, "Supreme Court Certiorari Policy and the Federal Employers' Liability Act," *Cornell Law Quarterly* 43 (1958): 451–68; also, "Supreme Court Certiorari Policy in Cases Arising under the Federal Employers' Liability Act," *Harvard Law Review* 69 (1956): 1441–51. A more favorable view is expressed by William H. De-Parq in "The Supreme Court and the Federal Employers' Liability Act, 1960–1 Term," *Chicago-Kent Law Review* 39 (1962): 127–37.

See also Richard F. Wolfson and Philip B. Kurland, *Robertson and Kirkham: Jurisdiction of the Supreme Court of the United States* (New York: Matthew Bender, 1954), sec. 373 (pp. 741–43) and notes thereto.

18. See statistics in "Supreme Court Certiorari," pp. 1442–44.

19. In recent terms, FELA petitions have become less frequent and their proportion of the now much larger docket has declined. See Gerhard Casper and Richard Posner, "A Study of the Supreme Court's Caseload," *Journal of Legal Studies* 3 (1974): 356 (table 11), and, by the same authors, "The Caseload of the Supreme Court: 1975 and 1976 Terms," *Supreme Court Review* (1977): 87–98, esp. table 7 (p. 94).

20. Felix Frankfurter and James M. Landis, "The Business of the Supreme Court at October Term 1931," *Harvard Law Review* 46 (1932): 260.

21. Ibid., p. 244.

22. See "Supreme Court Certiorari," tables 1 and 4 (pp. 1442, 1444).

23. Schubert, "Policy without Law," table 3, p. 294.

24. See Schubert, "Policy without Law," table 16 (p. 321), and Wolfson and Kurland, *Jurisdiction,* sec. 334 (p. 664).

25. This term is employed in an article by Lawrence Baum, "Decisions to Grant and Deny Hearings in the California Supreme Court: Patterns in Court and Individual Behavior," *Santa Clara Law Review* 16 (1976): 713.

26. Douglas cites the statistics in *Harris v. Pa. RR.,* 361 U.S. 15 (1959), at 17, Douglas concurring.

27. See Brennan's opinion in *Rogers v. Mo. Pac. RR.,* 352 U.S. 500–511 (1957).

28. *Wilkerson v. McCarthy,* 336 U.S. 53 (1948), at 68–69.

29. Ibid., p. 69.

30. Justice Hugo Black, Memorandum for #282, *Schultz v. Pa. RR. Co.,* p. 6. In Box 281 (Argued Cases: 1951 Term).

31. Schubert, *Quantitative Analysis,* p. 216.

32. This is the root of much critical comment about the Court's practice in these cases. See Frankfurter's discussion of this issue in *Wilkerson v. McCarthy,* 336 U.S. 53 (1948), at 66–68.

33. See the discussion of "libertarian activists" in Pritchett, *Vinson Court,* pp. 186–200.

34. Schubert, "Policy without Law," pp. 296 and 319.

35. Schubert, *Quantitative Analysis,* p. 231.

36. Joseph Tanenhaus, Marvin Schick, Matthew Muraskin, and

David Rosen, "The Supreme Court's Certiorari Jurisdiction: Cue Theory," in Glendon Schubert, ed., *Judicial Decision-Making* (New York: Free Press, 1953), pp. 123–24.

37. Schubert, *Quantitative Analysis,* pp. 234–36, and "Policy without Law," pp. 296–97.

38. Schubert, "Policy without Law," pp. 305–6.

39. Ibid., pp. 298–302.

40. *Wilkerson v. McCarthy,* 336 U.S. 53 (1948), at 66.

41. See for example, *Ferguson v. Moore-McCormack Lines,* 352 U.S. 521 (1957), at 535.

42. Schubert, "Policy without Law," p. 318.

43. One of these was unanimous. Frankfurter included only one of the two in his list of relevant cases.

44. Schubert, *Quantitative Analysis,* p. 233, "Policy without Law," pp. 304–5.

45. Reed and Jackson each cast the only vote for review in two cases, and Reed joined Douglas and Rutledge in one.

Conclusion   1. Felix Frankfurter to Chief Justice Warren, January 26, 1956, p. 1.

2. C. Herman Pritchett, "The Development of Judicial Research," in Joel Grossman and Joseph Tanenhaus, eds., *Frontiers of Judicial Research* (New York: Wiley, 1969), pp. 27–42. To the same effect, see Pritchett, *The Roosevelt Court* (New York: Macmillan, 1948), p. 20.

3. S. Sidney Ulmer discusses this problem in "Researching the Supreme Court in a Democratic Pluralist System," *Law and Policy Quarterly* 1 (1979): 53–80.

Index